Back of History

WILLIAM HOWELLS is presently Professor of Anthropology, Curator of Somatology, and a member of the faculty of the Peabody Museum at Harvard University. Born in 1908, he attended St. Paul's School and was graduated from Harvard, where he received his s.b. and ph.d. degrees. He taught at the University of Wisconsin from 1939 to 1954 and was Chairman of the Department of Sociology and Anthropology (1953–54). In 1954, he became Professor of Anthropology at Harvard University and is now Chairman of the Department.

Professor Howells is a past president of the American Anthropological Association (1951). He was a Research Associate at the American Museum of Natural History from 1932 to 1943 and he edited the *American Journal of Physical Anthropology* from 1949 to 1954.

In addition to *Back of History*, Professor Howells is the author of *The Heathens, Mankind So Far*, and *Mankind in the Making*.

BOOKS BY WILLIAM HOWELLS

Mankind in the Making

Back of History

The Heathens

Mankind So Far

BACK OF HISTORY

THE STORY OF OUR OWN ORIGINS

BY
WILLIAM HOWELLS

Revised Edition

Illustrated by Nancy Gahan

PUBLISHED IN CO-OPERATION WITH
THE AMERICAN MUSEUM OF NATURAL HISTORY

THE NATURAL HISTORY LIBRARY
ANCHOR BOOKS
DOUBLEDAY & COMPANY, INC.
GARDEN CITY, NEW YORK

Back of History was originally published
by Doubleday & Company, Inc., in 1954.
The Natural History Library edition
is published by arrangement with
Doubleday & Company, Inc.

Natural History Library revised edition: 1963

Library of Congress Catalog Card Number 63–11257
Foreword copyright © 1963 by
The American Museum of Natural History

Copyright © 1954, 1963 by William Howells

To My Parents

WITH LOVE AND THANKS

Foreword

History for a long time has been taken to begin when written records became available and the actors in the human drama could be identified. Everything before was dismissed as legend and unworthy of serious historical scrutiny because of its obvious unreliability. Thus it came about that by far the greater part of the span of mankind's existence on earth, over ninety-nine percent of it, has remained a realm ignored by conventional history. But for the past one hundred years or so scholars have been discovering meaning in the fossils of men and the relics of their handiwork that belong to this former limbo of history. The detritus of man's progress has become a record that can be read, sometimes more clearly than the written word.

Anthropology has a large stake in this extended history. And anyone familiar with the history *of* anthropology knows that even in its early days one of its formative influences was an interest in how civilization developed from simpler societies. Thus history to the anthropologist has always carried the notion of development or evolution. And because it has dealt with preliterate people mostly and reconstructed their past from fossils, anatomic as well as cultural, it has always had to forgo the glamour of the personality which plays so large a role in conventional history. This in many ways has been an advantage, for this very anonymity instead of deflecting the reader from the main currents of human development by the drama of its actors, focuses his attention where it ought to be.

It might seem that this kind of history or prehistory would be dull, lacking as it does the interplay of personal passions and ambitions. That it need not be is amply proven by this masterly work. The author, Professor William Howells, is an anthropologist who wears his erudition gracefully. He has made *Back of History* an entrancing account of all the long stretch of human striving and painful advance that precedes the beginning of written records and of conventional history. And he goes farther back than most anthropologists who essay this task, for he also includes the biological background of mankind itself. *Back of History* is more than an absorbing story, beautifully told; it has the full weight of critical scholarship to lend it authenticity. It is in many ways more historical than many histories.

Harry L. Shapiro
CHAIRMAN AND CURATOR OF
PHYSICAL ANTHROPOLOGY

October 1962
THE AMERICAN MUSEUM
OF NATURAL HISTORY

Acknowledgments

For permission to use various illustrations or quotations from other publications, I wish to make grateful acknowledgment to the following:

Professor Alfred L. Kroeber and Harcourt, Brace & Company for a quotation (page 164) from Professor Kroeber's *Anthropology*, revised edition, New York, 1948.

Dr. Margaret Mead for the quotations on page 227; William Morrow & Company, New York, for quotation from *Sex and Temperament* (copyright 1935 by Margaret Mead); the American Museum of Natural History, for quotation from *The Mountain Arapesh* (Volume 40, Part 3, Anthropological Papers of the American Museum of Natural History, New York, 1947).

The Tweedsmuir Trustees for a quotation (page 360) from Lord Tweedsmuir's *Pilgrim's Way* (Houghton Mifflin Company, Boston, 1940); A. P. Watt and Son, London, and The Musson Book Company, Ltd., Toronto, for permission to quote from *Memory Hold-the-Door* (original title of *Pilgrim's Way*), published and copyrighted by Hodder & Stoughton, Ltd., London, 1940.

Bureau of American Ethnology, Smithsonian Institution, Washington, D.C., for Figure D, Plate 6, Bulletin 57, "An Introduction to the Study of the Maya Hieroglyphs" (1915), by Sylvanus Griswold Morley (page 304).

Ignacio Marquina, for basing a drawing (page 308) on his model of the central plaza of Tenochtitlan (shown as Plate 37 in *Aztecs of Mexico* by George C. Vaillant, Doubleday & Company, New York, 1941).

Sir John Myres and The Clarendon Press, Oxford, for the figure (page 344) of Tablet 04–05, from *Scripta Minoa*, Volume II, by Arthur J. Evans (1952); Mr. Michael Ventris and Dr. O. G. S. Crawford for translation of this tablet appearing in Volume XXVII, No. 108 (December 1953), of *Antiquity*, the British periodical of archaeology for nonprofessional readers.

Contents

THE NEW WORLD

CITIES AND BRONZE—THE THIRD STEP

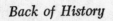

Back of History

Prologue

It's a wise child that knows its own father. And it is a wise father that has more than the faintest idea where we all began, and why we behave as we do. Here we are, frightened in a complicated world of machinery and threats of war, each of us depending on all the rest of us. Somehow we came to be human. And somehow we came to be civilized. But how? We think of ourselves as the creatures the earth was made for—something quite apart from other animals. And then we take a closer look, and are amazed to find ourselves so like the animals, in our bodies and our needs, that we almost pinch ourselves to be sure we are human after all.

History tells us little enough: king reigned before king and then, five or six thousand years ago, no more kings are remembered, and no word comes straight down to us to say how men arranged their affairs in the remoter past. But we may look about or dig for other kinds of information about our whole complicated, untidy existence of today, and perceive something of the outlines of its beginnings, its development and its relations to our own animal nature. For the story of man is a nature story.

This is not an easy thing to understand, and never has been. Many primitive people have some story about a Maker, who simply baked up the first man like a cake, and then showed him what to do. And even our own philosophers have usually tried to explain man's relation to nature in man's own terms, not nature's. We think of Mother Nature without too great respect. She is somebody else's mother, not ours.

Now of course having a life strikingly different from the rest of nature is the essence of being human. That is the obvious part. What is not so obvious is that this difference arose within nature, by natural processes and events; and that humanity, difference and all, is just as much a part of nature as ever it was. We wear clothes, and in other ways, too, we separate ourselves from nature; but we easily fool ourselves, and forget how much clothes make the man. We are apt to let our differences from nature hide our very great connections with nature.

The dilemma is not surprising. A native child growing up in the Australian bush may feel more of the strength of his kinship with nature, and sense more keenly his lack of arts to control it; furthermore the tribal beliefs he will be taught as a young man will tell him that he, the animals, the sky and the wind are all cousins. But one of our own children goes hopefully forth to school and is soon overwhelmed, and usually repelled once and for all, by the sight of so much to learn about what man can do and has already done. We have now made ourselves such a world, and are so completely governed by it, that we do not even know it. It is likely that if your goldfish could think, he would take it for granted that you were in a bowl and he was outside in the water, peering in at you. Actually, we ourselves are a good deal like that goldfish.

Look at a medieval cathedral like Chartres, as Henry Adams did, or at a modern newspaper, and all that lies back of either of them. Things like this measure humanity, the difference between the human species and everything else in nature. How can such a life as ours possibly be a logical, integral part of nature itself? It is a paradox of such staggering proportions that there is little wonder if tribes and nations have simply screened it off with myth. But man and his life consist of paradox, and paradox within paradox. He is the hairy animal without hair, the four-legged animal with only two legs, the dumb animal that talks, the creature who comprehends things he cannot see and believes in things he cannot comprehend. He can only be explained by a lot of oddities, but at the end of all this he can only be understood if the oddities themselves are understood as perfectly natural oddities.

We usually think of history as history, and of biology as biology. Our familiar, written history begins with people already living in cities, an easily imagined life. On the other hand, animal history, or evolution, deals with fossils, and with horses and elephants, fishes and protozoa. But if you are going to study the full history of man, you must be aware that there is no real line here. You begin in a biological world, when man's existence was that of an animal. Then, as man appears, you must shift interest gradually from man himself to what he is doing, since he is beginning to do things no other animal can do. Your clock, which was first ticking in millions of years, then thousands, then hundreds, has slowed down, and man himself changes less and less, until you are considering men all like ourselves, who differ simply in the life they lead. You are now in the preface of history proper.

Remember that this shift of interest is only a transition, for there is a long time when what man does is very much a question of what he is. Slowly he became able to treat ideas in a new way until his ideas in turn became, as they are today, the major part of the world surrounding him. We cannot properly separate the story of his ideas from the story of man himself, any more than we can separate the heartbeat from the heart.

THE NATURE OF HUMAN LIFE

1. *The Coming of Mankind*

Before we could be human we had to be animal, just as each of us must be before he is born and when he is very young. Mankind became able to talk and plan and be mechanical only because a billion years or so of evolution had laid the groundwork. This evolution allowed simple living things to become complex, and later allowed the lower vertebrate animals to provide various structures—eyes, brains, skeleton—which, in higher animals, were capable of being finally developed to the degree that human life demands. We could not call ourselves human, or behave human, if our brains were not quite so large as they are, our hands not quite so useful, and our legs not quite so efficient in holding us upright while we do our work. Yet we would not be here at all if there had not been animals of just this almost-human sort from which we could arise. And indeed we can see something like them in various ways in our cousins the anthropoid apes.

Most of this history we need not inspect at all; certainly not a billion years' worth. The story begins, for practical purposes, about seventy million years ago. This rough date marks the opening of the Cenozoic Era (Tertiary Period) of geological time, or the Age of Mammals. Now of course the human ancestor had already covered important ground, though it is ground we shall take for granted. In his very ancient first stage, as a fish, he had been endowed with his basic form: his backbone and skull, his central brain pattern, his system for the circulation of blood, and even the rudiments of limbs and lungs. Following a shift from sea to land, much-improved "fish" appeared in the ancient amphibians and reptiles. Some of the latter, in fact, carried the possibilities of progress in the design of the skeleton, and such functions as egg protection, to the point where they moved up into a second great stage, that of the mammals.

These new animals bore their young alive, cared for them after birth, and fed them milk; furthermore, they were warm-blooded, with warming fur and cooling sweat glands. They were, in a word, creatures who could grow slowly to a complicated mature form, receiving the utmost in parental nourishment and protection in the most crucial stages, arriving finally at a body organization without a peer in activity, stamina, excellence of senses and nervous and muscular response. And they were able to combine all these things with large size.

When the mammals first arose, however, large size was a monopoly of the dinosaurs. Mammals were still small and simple when the dinosaurs left the scene and Cenozoic time began. Their promise as a type of animal became fulfilled during this period, as they took many forms, which tended severally to become larger in size, to develop larger brains, and to vary themselves in the most astonishing way to fit themselves to the diets and regions offered to them by the continents, and even the sea and the air. This mammal family tree, as we know it from its fossil remains, is something to return to again and again when we study how evolution takes place. Let us look for a moment at a few of the principles of evolution that will have a bearing on our main story.

Evolution at work

Evolution is no simple process, but we may say with Charles R. Darwin that the ruling agent, without which the whole makes no sense, is natural selection. This in itself is not a single, simple thing. Instead, it is the result of the most advantageous fitting together of everything in the environment of an animal breed with everything in the physical nature of the animals themselves. Out of the en-

tire breed, those most favored by their individual heredity in this fitting will be most successful in surviving and
reproducing (and so passing on their inherited features),
and their progeny should become more numerous relative
to that of their brothers and sisters. Thus the breed as a
whole tends to become, or remain, "fitter." ("Survival of
the fittest.") In all this, the interplay between animals and
their environment may be far too intricate for us to analyze
fully, but of course the effective environment is very much
a result of what the animal brings to it. As a crude example, a stream may be a way of life, but quite a different
one, to a fish and to an otter; while it may be only a barrier, but a small or large one, to a buffalo or to a field
mouse. Thus accidental new or modified features (arising
as mutations) in members of an animal breed, or changes
in the environment itself, may affect the total combination
and allow natural selection to pull the breed away from
its existing form. So does a breed evolve, and so may two
breeds, once identical, separate, follow different paths, and
become finally quite unlike.

Such gradual changing and constant adjustment will
give a picture of slow evolution, seemingly smooth but
actually made up of a great many tiny interlocking steps,
which may go a long distance in one general direction in
pursuit of a constant advantage. Among the mammals,
otters, seals and dolphins have all given themselves over
to swimming, to different degrees. Along with this dignified
progress, however, there may occur much more rapid motion at certain junctures, bringing more radical changes.

Suppose some hitherto neutral, unimportant feature,
which the animal type happens to have, or has been using
in one particular way, accidentally develops to a critical
point, or otherwise comes to match some brand-new use
(perhaps the environment changes). Such an event may
open up new territory, which the species could not penetrate before. So on a grand scale the birds, who may have
had feathers to help them keep warm[1] before ever they

_____

[1] Birds are not mammals but arose somewhat later from the
reptiles, and, like the mammals, also developed warm blood.

could fly but who, on using them for flight, found the domain of the air wide open and became a major form of vertebrate life. So, for a better example, some of the ancient horses, whose teeth at one stage became high enough and complex enough in the crowns to chew up the grass of the plains as well as the softer undergrowth of the woods, whereat they came out into the grasslands and spread over nearly the whole world, in great numbers.

Such rapid strides may look deceptively like long jumps, without intervening steps. But it is actually more like the trip from first base to second, on which one does not tarry unless one wants to be tagged out. The fully adapted new form, and the older form from which it sprang, are each better fitted than the ones between, which are off base. It is not, of course, as though the breed concerned knew which evolutionary goal was calling it, and sprinted in that direction. Rather, it is figuratively as though some of the animals, doing well enough on an island home, accidentally wandered down onto a tidal beach and found that it led them to a new uninhabited islet on which this colony could flourish anew. Their stay on the beach would have been short, and the beach itself would be likely to wash out, carrying any laggards with it.

Thus it is that, in the history of evolution, the important transitions sometimes took place rapidly, and left so few of the transitional fossils that such forms may never be known. The early birds did *not* get all the worms; the first birds were rare birds, and we are extremely lucky to have found a few traces of them. They were, so to speak, experimental models. You might compare the total of all the planes ever made by the Wright brothers with the total of all the planes ever made by the Boeing, Douglas and Martin companies. Once across the beach, however, the new territory has generally encouraged the migrants to be fruitful and multiply like the Mayflower descendants, diversifying to meet various possibilities offered. All kinds of new models of the type will arise, until competition establishes a few of them as the most successful, and many of the others become extinct. These phenomena—the occasional rapid transitions, the washouts of the transitional forms, the burgeoning of types among the successful crossers, and their final narrowing down—all have their applications to the ancestry of man.

Primates' progress

Going back to the main story to look for the human forerunner, we shall find him somewhere in the ancient Primates, whose nearest modern descendants are the lemurs and the strange little bug-eyed, skinny-fingered tarsiers of the Philippines and Borneo. At the beginning of the Tertiary the mammals were already busy splitting up into different major lines. They were all, however, on the whole still small and primitive, and thus more alike than the mammals are today; they would be best represented in living animals by the unpretentious insectivores—shrews, moles and the like. From them arose the Primates, not by radical changes or progress but rather by retention and moderate improvement of some ancient traits which, in particular, gave them fairly efficient grasping paws. These traits were nails where most mammals had claws, five well-separated fingers or toes, an ability to rotate the thumb and great toe so as to oppose the other digits, and a good movable arm helped by a good development of the collarbone and the two bones of the forearm.

Otherwise the Primates were quite unprodigal. Generalized as they were, they were well suited to make use of all aspects of forest life and its natural foods, and the Primates ran riot, in North America and Europe especially, during the Paleocene, the first of the five divisions of the Tertiary. A great many fossil forms have been preserved, both of lemurs and of tarsiers. These halcyon days came to an end, however, about the close of the Eocene, the next division. The lower Primates vanished from America, and survived elsewhere only in spotty fashion, in Africa and southern Asia. They had one more, very late evolutionary outburst, but it was in the seclusion of the island of Madagascar, and had no effect on the faunas of the continents.

Shrinking tropical climate probably had much to do with their extinction, but also it is likely that they met serious competition in their way of life from animals whose origin was later than their own. Some of these may have had more specialized capabilities, like rodents. Some of them may have been simply improved versions of themselves, their own descendants, the higher Primates, the monkey-like creatures who make up all the rest of this order of mammals.

A monkey is a better man than a lemur, in every way. He is typically bigger, if that is any reflection of success, although there have been big lemurs. Monkeys have, in general, highly mobile and skillful hands. Their eyes face to the front, and are unsurpassed for all-around usefulness: most mammals pride themselves on their senses of smell, but the higher Primates have taken the primate preference for eyes and evolved both stereoscopic (distance-judging) vision and the greatest sensitivity to colors. High intelligence is evident in many monkey types, and all are perceptive, active animals, well suited for their principal habitat—trees—which furnishes them with flowers, buds, leaves, fruits, seeds and insects. Without having developed any specialized oddities of form (if you will overlook the indecorous behinds of some species), the monkeys represent a high level of organization in the brain- and hand-using kind of existence which is the particular property of the Primate order. It is not hard to suppose that they soon prospered in the tropical forests, which they finally took away from the lemurs and tarsiers.

How did they appear? Unfortunately there is a pretty bad washout here—there are few early fossils of higher Primates, and these are not transitional in type, but already belong to higher forms. However, three strains seem to have developed in different places toward the end of the Eocene or somewhat later.

One lot, which appeared in South America, became the New World monkeys—marmosets, spider monkeys, howling monkeys, cebus or organ-grinder monkeys, and many others. All the monkeys who can swing by their tails belong in the group.

Another lot, which seems to have no connection with the American monkeys, developed in the Old World, and gave rise to all the monkeys of Africa and Asia. The whole fossil picture, bad though it is, indicates that the two lines have always been isolated from one another. And they differ anatomically: both are "higher Primates" in organization but are distinct in many details. For example, the New World monkeys retain three premolar (our bicuspid) teeth, out of the ancestral four, on either side of their jaws, while the Old World monkeys have lost still another, and have only two. These monkeys, typically large, are greatly varied in type and highly successful as a group. Some live partly or wholly on the ground, notably the baboons.

The upright hominoids

Enough of these monkeys. The third line of higher Primates is the one of real concern to us. These are called the hominoids, meaning apes-and-men. The word sounds as though it meant humanlike. However, it is derived not from description but simply from the name of the supergroup in which apes and men must be placed: Hominoidea. It contains our ape cousins and ourselves, and also our remote common ancestors which, as Darwin long ago remarked, would have to be classified as apes.

The history of this group is not as well known as we could wish. Nevertheless there are more and better fossils than in the case of the monkeys—enough at least to show that it was once much larger, and has shrunk today to a mere corporal's guard: gibbons, orangutans, chimpanzees, gorillas and men. There is no doubt that the hominoid line came into being in the Old World, but whether it first arose as part of the same stem as the Old World monkeys is simply not known. Most authorities think not, and consider it an independent development, probably from a similar parent stock of lower Primates. Probably because of this, the hominoids are more like the monkeys of the Old World than those of the New World, in a great many ways, even to having reduced the number of premolar teeth to two.

One fact is paramount: whereas the monkeys of both hemispheres remained quadrupeds, going through the trees on all fours, the apes or hominoids went off on a different tack, which was a tendency to maintain themselves in a more upright position. At any rate, the existing species all show common features of the upper body strongly reflecting this tendency: heads carried partially or fully erect, broad shoulders placed well to the side of the trunk, flat chests with long collarbones and broad breastbones, and vertically suspended internal organs.

They do not all follow the same habits, but have specialized their generally upright attitude into three more or less distinct methods of getting about. One is used by the gibbons, who swing overhand from limb to limb with rapidity, ease and elegance, at something like the tempo of a Viennese waltz; this progression might be called arm-jumping, with some of their leaps covering considerable spaces between handholds. Gibbons are small animals—large ones could not safely be so acrobatic—slender and lithe, with greatly elongated arms and fingers and narrow hands; altogether they have become markedly adapted to their particular style of locomotion.

The great apes are the other three species: the orang of Borneo and Sumatra, and the chimpanzee and gorilla of equatorial Africa. The chimp is smaller than man, the orang has about the same bulk as a man, and the gorilla far more. All of these, and particularly the orang, brachiate, or swing about by the arms, and do it very well and actively. But in this case it is not a succession of jumps, like the gibbon's. It is more deliberate, and their progress includes a lot of other gymnastic clambering around in the trees; the gorilla and chimpanzee, furthermore, spend much of their time on the ground as well. The arms of these apes are relatively long and strong—in a well-grown orang they can be absolutely massive—and in general their tree-clambering life has made its mark upon their bodily designs.

Man, finally, has naught to do with trees. He uses the third method of changing his scenery: he walks about on the ground on his excessively long and strong two legs. He shares the same basic adaptation to uprightness as the tree apes, however, and in fact the hominoids are all basically much alike. All, except of course the gibbon, are now of large size, long-lived, large-brained and, compared to the rest of the animals, extremely intelligent.

It was not always so. The first hominoids must have been small animals, starting from undetermined lower Primate ancestors in Eocene times. One small fragment of a fossil jaw of this date seems to be that of a tiny, primitive ape (Amphipithecus), which still had the ancestral three premolars. Just how the tendency to uprightness arose must for the present be a mystery. It may be extremely ancient, deriving from the parental form itself; or perhaps the early apes were less slavishly arboreal than the monkeys, and shifted more readily between trees and the ground. But there is also good evidence that the marked development of arm-swinging seen in all the living apes is something rather late.

At any rate, one branch of hominoids, the gibbons, early became distinct from the rest, although not at once as lithe and long-armed as they are today. The jaw of what was most likely a small and simplified gibbon is known from the Oligocene, about halfway along in the Cenozoic. It is not until the early Miocene, at perhaps the two-thirds mark, that apes of respectable size are known. The most interesting, Proconsul, was a little monkeylike, being apparently a tree-going quadruped, and unusual in other ways. But by this time, and later, there were other apes already more like the forest-living great apes of today, with their heavy canine teeth and their sharp-cusped molars, all well suited for the coarse fruits and vegetable stalks of the jungle. The hominoids were flourishing all through the tropical Old World.

This gives us, in unsatisfactory outline, the past of the apes you can see in the zoo. It does not, however, give us the background of man, for it does not seem likely (as it once did) that one of these large brachiators, say a species of chimpanzee, simply began to stand completely upright, devaluated his canine teeth and became rapidly converted into a human being. Nevertheless, man is clearly closely related to such animals, and does not go back in a separate line to the early Tertiary. There must have been a fork on the main hominoid path, that of the large apes, at which these apes continued with, or increased, an emphasis on tree life while a special group did the opposite and became fully committed to ground life. Remember that gorillas and chimps are by no means full-time tree climbers, at the present day.

But the fossils show us almost nothing about such a split. All those remaining from the later Tertiary are obvious apes, except Oreopithecus from Italy. This, from the beginning of the Pliocene, ten million years ago, has such human traits in skull and teeth that some authorities make him an early relative, if not a direct ancestor, of man himself. But others, noting his chimplike body and certain marked peculiarities of his teeth, reject the idea firmly, and for the present call him neither human nor ape, but a new, third branch of the hominoids.

The man-apes of South Africa

So we know of our ancestors only that they diverged from their forest-dwelling, shambling and swinging relatives, the apes. They became, in fact, upright walkers like ourselves. They must already have had the basic hominoid form of the upper body, adapted for uprightness, but they underwent some radical changes from the waist down, for what was fundamentally a new set of habits. The spine acquired the "lumbar curve," a backward twist just above the pelvis to hold the upper half of the body erect. The pelvis itself became low and broad, quite different in shape from that of the tree apes, an important change of shape that allows the placing of muscles to guy up the trunk in its upright position above, and also the efficient hitching, below, of the powerful muscles of the human stern, which

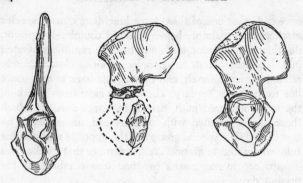

FIG. 1. *Side view of the left hipbone of a chimpanzee, a man-ape, and man.*

pull the leg strongly back as you step strongly forward. The difference in function between this human arrangement and that of the apes can be adequately understood only by seeing a chimpanzee, let us say, walking erect, and noting his difficulties.

Another fundamental change was in the foot. Here the thumblike great toe of the other Primates lost its opposability and lined up fore and aft with the others as the most important toe of all; and this made possible the fitting together of the bones of the mid-foot into a strong arch, with a single hinge joint at the ball. This also is of immense importance for true walking, in the force and length it gives to the stride—imagine running, in our fashion, on the loose-jointed foot of an ape, which can use only the ankle, and not the ball of the foot, as a fulcrum.

The evidence of this history of the ground-apes, apart from the nature of our own anatomy, is provided by an extraordinary and well-preserved group of fossil animals found in recent years in various parts of Africa. These man-apes are known officially as the Australopithecinae. Some of them were of approximately our own size; some were distinctly less, standing perhaps four feet high. They lived in the open country, and apparently on a general, mixed diet, including meat. Their skeletons are incompletely recovered as yet, but the pelvis is known from several of them, and these hipbones, so different in the apes and men of today, unquestionably have the same form as the latter. This says positively that the rest of the body was similarly fitted to the special, two-legged walking gait which distinguishes humanity.

At first glance, a man-ape skull looks like that of an ape. This turns out, however, to be due to its small brain and massive jaws, and the situation will bear a closer look. The brain is well below our own in size, but varies from that of a gorilla to something above any of the other apes. Also, the position of the markings of the neck muscles in the back, as well as the entrance of the spinal cord, shows the head to have been carried definitely more erect than in the living apes, if less so than in ourselves.

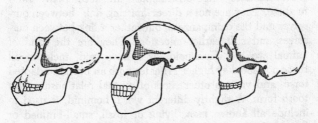

FIG. 2. *Skulls of a chimpanzee, a man-ape, and man.*

The jaws in some of them were enormous, but these, and the tooth rows, are seen to be broad at the back and narrowed to the front. Also they are equipped with smallish incisor teeth, and with canines which, like our own, do not stick up decisively above the others. Now we and all the apes are closely related, and distinct from monkeys, in the details of the crowns of the teeth, especially the molars, and this is in fact a principal way of knowing where to place a fossil fragment. Yet in spite of these main hominoid like-nesses, we and the apes each have our own special charac-teristics of the molar teeth, and here the man-apes, big though their teeth are, side with us.

Finally, careful examination has been made of a lot of

other minor details in the construction of the skull in which we differ from living apes, and here again the man-apes show that their likeness to us in being erect walkers is not a coincidence, but rather that they can only be our very close relatives.

Therefore the australopiths show that the essential piece of evolution for mankind was the walking gait, and the bodily features connected with it, and not anything connected with the brain or the jaws. This shift in function was the signpost that caused a split in the hominoids and gave rise to the line leading eventually to ourselves. And that is how the man-apes have become the most important of the missing links: we can say they are apes that walked like men, or else they are men with brains and jaws the size of apes'.

Nevertheless, these australopiths are not actually intermediate. They are not a direct "missing link" between ourselves and the chimpanzees, but rather a link between ourselves and still earlier ancestors. They are the kind of animal we are. Hominoid, as I have said, includes all those non-monkey higher Primates with an upright-adapted torso, and various other signs of mutual relationship, like tooth form. A slightly different word, hominid, is used to include all known *men,* living or fossil, small-brained or large, as against pongid, which applies to the big anthropoid apes.[2] Obviously the basic evolutionary difference between them is the walking versus tree-climbing commitment, and obviously the man-apes are perfectly good *hominids.*

Unfortunately nothing else is known about hominid history. These particular South African fossils existed very recently, a million years ago, more or less, and are probably a hangover from the very stage through which our own ancestors passed, possibly not long before. When did the whole hominid line actually arise? Possibly fairly recently, meaning late in the Pliocene. However, if the peculiar

[2] The terms come from the families into which the hominoids (Hominoidea) are divided: Pongidae, the apes; and Hominidae, men.

Oreopithecus should on closer acquaintance demand definitely to be recognized as a hominid, then the date would have to be placed earlier, in the Miocene, and over twelve million years ago.

This process of hominid appearance need not have taken a very long time, or have been a gradual process. We may not have great luck in finding the fossils we would like to have. Even though our relationship with the pongids may be close and recent (that is, in the Pliocene), we can expect the fairly rapid emergence of certain radical differences, such as we find in the lower body, when we consider the radical shift from tree-hanging to ground-walking. This actually is one of those tidal-beach situations, in which some rapid evolutionary striding would have taken place, since the beach, or middle ground, would be a poor place to be. The man-apes had already made the crossing. And we would expect a washout here, with very little chance of finding remains of early forms. Time, as usual, will tell.

This is the gist of what we know about when and how we became human. "Human" is a treacherous word. In one important sense, we can say we began to be human when we began to be hominid; that is, when we began to be true walking animals with all the consequences, at some point in the Tertiary. This is perfectly correct. But we generally consider as human only man of today and his way of life, neither of which are at all old. There is a long distance between these two kinds of "human," which we shall be exploring. The man-apes had mastered the business of walking and the use of the crudest tools, and were apparently giving signs of undertaking another vital trend —enlargement of the brain—when they vanished from our view.

We have taken a look so far at only one aspect of being human, the purely evolutionary, structural one. Nevertheless, it is well to grasp the meaning of this physical heritage from our entire past. We have the superb and flexible body organization of the mammals. We have the rather simple, uncontorted forelimbs of the Primates, with their enhanced power of grasp, and also their emphasis on the sense of vision. We have the particularly wonderful eyes of the hominoids and also their modifications for an upright torso. We are now seen, in our own right, to have enormous brains, small jaws, upright heads and a body suited throughout to erect walking, not only in the torso but in the pelvis, legs and feet as well. Above all, along with the brain, we have the primate grasping forepaw freed completely—not partially as in apes or monkeys—from its ancient obligations in locomotion. We have—there is no simpler way of saying it—the brain and hand of man.

2. The Meaning of Society

There is, of course, more to being human than having a human body and a big brain. The side of humanity just considered could be studied as well on a dead man as on a live one—better, in fact. We are not human until we begin to behave human. And here also we have a wide background from nature.

We have, obviously, the same vital needs as other higher animals. We must eat and breathe, with some regularity. We must keep warm, at least above certain limits. We have the urge of sex, so that we shall not get absentminded about reproducing our kind. Now many mammals, and certainly the higher Primates, have found advantages in combining to meet these needs and so forming social groups. Sexual activity, evidently, is a joint undertaking, but this can be casual. Many animals form more definite groups for the help this gives them in rearing the young, getting food, protecting themselves and so on. Monkeys, as we shall see, manage a still more efficient life in this way, and show that their social tendencies are an important evolutionary adjustment, like their hands, eyes or other body structures. And these, his highly social relatives, show how basic is the social nature of man himself. It is much better to observe living monkeys in action than to go in for speculative maunderings about the development of the social instinct in long-dead ancient man.

We have some excellent accounts to turn to. Some years ago, Sir Solly Zuckerman kept an eye on the doings of colonies of baboons in the zoos in London, Paris and Munich, which had been allowed to arrange their own

affairs, and made notes on what he saw. What he saw
was disgusting and brutal, but instructive. He saw, as any
zoo-goer may, that they are large and powerful animals,
the males distinctly larger than the females. He saw that
the males do not hesitate to take advantage of this, and
dominate the females completely. The males also differ
among themselves in size and fierceness, and there is much
fighting. But Zuckerman noted that there was not as much
fighting as might have been expected; not an endless
tournament which would leave only one bleeding survivor.
Instead, he saw a fine example of the famous "pecking
order" of the henyard: everybody is a bully, but every
bully knows a bigger bully on sight, and defers usually
without argument, so that one is dominant and the other
submissive and nonprovoking, and there is actually a sort
of rank order of dominance throughout the group. Thus
there is a *modus vivendi*, or a state of armistice.

The organization of the group itself and the relations
between the sexes express this extravagant development
of dominance. The dominant males hog all the females, so
that while some have one "wife," others have small harems,
and the whole arrangement is semipermanent. One can
almost measure the relative dominance of a male overlord by the size of the sphere of influence he casts about
him. Not only must he constantly dominate his several
females, so that they do not stray more than a few feet
from him and even sit patiently by while he eats his fill;
he must manage all this and still have enough dominance
left over to repel questing males. Fortunately for him, of
course, other males of equal or greater dominance rank
likewise have their hands full. And what about the extra
males, at the low end of the scale? They are bachelors. But
strangely enough, for the sake of company, such a one is
allowed to attach himself to a harem group in the capacity
—strictly—of friend of the family, and as long as his demeanor remains innocent of the romantic spark, serenity
prevails. In fact the status quo is peaceful, and has its
major upsets in case of a death in the group, since a
widower may try to make good his loss at the expense of

somebody else's harem and, on the other hand, if a male overlord dies, the bidding for the hands of his widows will be ferocious in the extreme.

Now it is to be seen in all this that the group has, at any time, a well-defined and well-knit structure, and that it is very "social," if you can allow yourself a little relaxation in your usual appreciation of the word. It is an ugly picture of terrorism rampant, evident to a casual visitor, but it has its uses. I should say that a primary one is this: the factor of dominance allows the group to exist and function as a group, raising the young and getting such other advantages of group living as I mentioned, without destroying itself through the simple savagery of the largest and best-developed members; while at the same time it allows that savagery and fighting power to exist for the purpose of leading and defending the whole group when necessary in its natural life.

But there is more to the meaning of social, here. Zuckerman has pointed out something of importance: he observed that the individual baboons never move at random, but always with relation to the other baboons of the group. Infant to mother, of course, and vice versa. Female to male, always a female keeping close enough to her overlord to preserve her from the appearance of straying, and keying her actions to his. Male to female: the watchful or the lustful eye. Male to male: all the nuances of privilege and of circumspect behavior. Altogether, the action of any animal at any time seems like the complicated sum of all these relations and the animal's own individual personality plus his needs of the moment; it is as if each has his special electric charges and fields, all interacting in common to determine the way the members dispose themselves about.

One may suspect that the harshness of expression of the dominance pattern, and the general ferocity, were exaggerated by the fact that the animals were confined rather than free, but in at least one case careful observation has revealed very much the same thing as Zuckerman described in nature. Sherwood Washburn and Irven DeVore, however, working in East Africa, found less tension and greater co-operation among the males of the bands they studied. At the same time, like Zuckerman, they stress the high co-ordination of activity among all the animals of a troop and point out that—this is in the wild, not an enclosure—"most of a baboon's life is spent within a few feet of other baboons."

The same kind of complicated relationships have been seen in studies of other monkeys, especially the Japanese and rhesus macaques. And, note well, the very same thing has been noted by alert ethnologists studying simple human groups, such as aboriginal Australians, here of course without all the baring of teeth and with much reference to rules and customs relating to sex or age (the cultural side of things). And social psychologists have been showing that, all unsuspected by us, much of our own daily behavior with our fellows follows hidden rules akin to those above.

The mellowed howlers

The baboons may be, present company excepted, the most evil of the Primates. They are at any rate not the model of all the monkeys, though others, like rhesus macaques, are not far behind in mental and physical cruelty. Professor C. R. Carpenter investigated the howling monkeys, and found them less offensive, to us and to each other. They live exclusively in the trees, never coming to the ground, and each band is strongly attached to its own home, a patch of forest less than a mile square, which it ordinarily never leaves. Howling monkeys are among the largest monkeys of the New World, and while they are not unaggressive, they prefer barking to biting. Their Adam's apples are greatly enlarged, and with this abnormal voice box the males can produce a roaring and howling so loud as to be unnerving even to a person who knows what it is.

Carpenter went to the island of Barro Colorado, in Gatun Lake in the Panama Canal, and for several months he painstakingly watched and recorded life in the various

howler bands on the island. Like Zuckerman, he saw the
individual monkeys of a band constantly interacting, moving and behaving with relation to the other individuals
according to their mutual ages, sexes and general social
statuses—the daily calisthenics of social living. But unlike
Zuckerman, he witnessed a calm and harmonious disposition in each group, with co-operation the rule and with
dominance and aggressiveness notable for their absence.

Howlers could be perfectly described as lotus-eaters if
only they ate lotus. They eat everything else of this nature:
flowers, buds and fruit; they spend their days eating, playing, napping and enjoying themselves. Their home is boun-
teous, and they may go from one kind of tree to another
as we go from one course of a meal to another; they
have still other preferred trees for sleeping. All their travel,
of course, is through the branches, and they cross from one
tree to another where the branches intermingle. This is
not always perfectly simple, even to skillful climbers and
jumpers like the howling monkeys, and the way the band
manages is a good illustration of the kind of co-operation
that exists within it.

The group proceeds roughly in file, with the mothers
carrying, herding or otherwise looking out for the youngest. The older males, few in number, fan out ahead when
there is any doubt as to which direction should be taken,
or as to how a crossing may best be made to the next tree,
each of them looking for a pathway. This is not competi-
tive, although the males do exert a degree of control over
the band as a whole. A leader who has found a suitable
path will make a clucking noise, whereat the others break
off their search and all get into line behind him. If, on the
journey, a young monkey tumbles out of the tree into the
terrors of the jungle floor, the males immediately gather
around above the spot and howl in unison, to frighten off
jaguars. One reservation here: I am talking about co-
operation, not gallantry; the males howl lustily, but it is
the mother who is allowed to make the actual descent to
the ground to retrieve her pride and joy.

The collaborative behavior and the lack of elements of

dissonance are evident in ordinary "family" life. The howlers seem to lend themselves to clichés, because we can say that a band is one big happy family. There are, for reasons not clear, more adult females than males, but they do not form harem groups like the baboons; there are no standing associations of this kind, and consorting of males and females for purposes of sex is brief. Thus, practically speaking, all the males are men-around-the-house but none are husbands. None are "fathers"; all are "uncles." So, while sex fulfills its indispensable function, it does not rear its ugly head; as a spur to possible competition, or to the expression of dominance, among either males or females, it has been pushed sternly into the background.

Let us look in on a howler band around midday, as it is coming to the end of a long morning meal. Hunger has been allayed, and the older males are feeling the need of a snooze; they are disposed here and there in comfortable positions on the branches. Mothers are occupied with their younger children, perhaps teaching them what and how to eat; they may be clustered excitedly around a mother with a brand-new baby—an object that seems to have the power of well-nigh deranging any female Primate. Like all monkeys, apes and men, howlers develop slowly; they are carried around by their mothers for about a year after birth, and are not fully independent for about three. The older youths of the band are active, and play together constantly. There is general roughhousing, hanging by tails and scuffling, and chasing one another around. It is typical puppy behavior, and friendly: if it gets too rough, and particularly if there should be a cry of pain from one of them, an older male is likely to give a warning grunt, which will serve to calm things down. This is not simply elderly impatience, however, because otherwise the adult males give a picture of indulgent unclehood, allowing small fry to climb all over them and generally be annoying. When the human male would end this by saying, "Beat it," the howler may extricate himself by playing ostentatiously with the little pest for a moment, which will ordinarily start a general melee of the young, from which he can retire to

keep one eye on the situation while he gets forty winks
with the other. Howler males would seem possessed of a
transcendental affability, but then howler males never have
a hard day at the office.

It might appear from their domestic relations that howling monkeys are by nature gentle to the point of being
effete. This is not so. As the young males approach adulthood, signs of fighting behavior intrude themselves into the
previously good-humored horseplay. The young bucks do
not, however, begin to fight more and more; they simply
play less and less. More important, the peacefulness prevailing within the band is offset by absolute antagonism
between bands, with the males taking the leading role. As
I said, each band has its own home, and guards it jealously
against all other howler bands though not, oddly enough,
against other kinds of animals or monkeys. If invaders
appear, the males of the band get out in front and howl
violently, being answered by the males of the other band.
The battle is fought by howling, not by bloodshed, and
ends with the invaders finally retreating into their own territory, evidently from a feeling of strangeness or weakness
of position at being in unfamiliar trees. Thus the home
band preserves not only its food supply but also its very
integrity, since bands are kept strictly separate by their
mutual antagonism.

How is this anger and aggressiveness, so manifest when
stranger groups come together, suppressed, especially
among the males, within the band itself? Obviously, by the
social education the young ones get as they grow up. In
such a closed band, every member is a completely familiar
object to the rising youth, and particularly his own age-
mates, with whom he has been scuffling intimately and
safely for most of his life. This complicated fitting together
of personalities and smoothing out of relationships inhibits
natural male rivalry and the antipathy between unfamiliar
individuals, such as nevertheless comes promptly into
play when a stranger band shows up. All of howler behavior relates to this pattern of play-school education and
the achievement of harmony: the absence of competitive-

ness over sex, the fostering of play among members of a well-defined group, and the working together of the males in guiding the group, in howl-fighting with other groups, and in howling to save fallen children.

Social life is more than a convenience; it is a necessity. Consider the case of the solitary stranger. Carpenter never saw a lone female, but he did observe an occasional stray male, without being certain how he came to be that way. Such a one was obviously not content in his solitude, since he was generally engaged in trying to join one of the bands. Easier said than done, however, since he is usually howled at and driven off by the males. If he persists, as he is apt to do, for four or five months the resistance to him will finally diminish and end, and he will be allowed to come into the group. He has been adopted: he has gone through a compressed version of what the ordinary howler goes through in growing up, and has become so familiar, through patient hanging around, that he might as well have been born and raised in the group, since he no longer arouses the aggressiveness of any of its members.

This incident puts howler sociability in a nutshell. It demonstrates the need felt by an individual to be in a group. It shows the natural antagonism between howlers, particularly males, and also the countering influence of the cohesiveness of the group, and the existence of "group consciousness" of an unconscious sort, and the process of natural education by which it comes about.

Taking them together, the baboons and the howling monkeys must come near to being the extremes in the matter of higher Primate social organization. But the contrast may actually be more instructive because of the underlying likenesses. More than is apparent, the two kinds of monkey share some important elements of behavior, and differ in the emphasis they have placed on them. We are appalled by the ugly cruelty in which baboon society functions, while we beam benignly on the happy howlers who lead their lives, it would certainly seem, according to all those kindly injunctions that we have honored more in Great-grandmother's samplers than in our own activities.

However, this is reading our own ethics into animal psychology, a popular habit but a sloppy one. Both baboons and howlers have the capacity for aggressiveness and dominance; both have the great primate adjustability, psychologically and temperamentally, to others of their species. The baboons happen, in their biological natures, to emphasize the first, while in howling monkeys the first —the aggressiveness—has been heavily repressed by the second. The "organization" of their social relations follows from this: among baboons each individual is riveted to place in the cast-iron social order, and "marriage" is a sort of polygamy that is only one expression of dominance. Among howlers there is easy cohesiveness of the group, helped by outside pressure (stranger bands), with dominance doing no more to differentiate individuals than to give the adult males some control over the actions of the group; "marriage" is promiscuity. Note the important thing: that each of the two species *has* a very definite organization, and that in each it works efficiently. We do not have to approve either of them, or note that promiscuity works nicely for the howlers. We are neither howling monkeys nor baboons, nor are they human.

The jealous gibbons: no triangles allowed

We are, nonetheless, Primates. We are closer, in physique and lineage, to the apes than to these monkeys and we are, fortunately, beginning to know a good deal about the behavior of some of them. Dr. Carpenter, long our most industrious foreign agent among our kindred species, finished up with the howling monkeys and then betook himself to Siam to study the gibbons. This was no easy task: gibbons, like howlers, live exclusively in the trees, in rugged jungle. However, also like the howlers, gibbons are territorial, meaning that the groups have their own territories or homes, and stay within them. Carpenter was therefore able to build blinds at strategic points, or to spot the same groups day after day and patiently follow them around on the ground below. He discovered that gibbons

live in families, consisting of a permanently mated pair
and such of their children (born on the average about every
two years) as have not yet become adult, of which there
may be as many as four or five. But before we incautiously
conclude that gibbons are monogamous in anything like
our sense—that is to say, by custom—let us have a more
careful look.

Gibbons are rather small, and attractively gentle as a
rule, but they can be savage and, with their spiky canine
teeth, dangerous. The sexes differ little in size or in self-
assertiveness. Dominance is visible to a mild degree in the
family, and more so when two groups come together and
there is a vocal dispute over boundaries. Most important,
there is evidently a strong aversion between any two adults
of the same sex: Carpenter almost never saw an extra
full-fledged male or female in any group, even such as
might be grown sons or daughters. It is evident that, as
with Zuckerman's baboons, the male would drive off any
other male; furthermore, the thing cuts both ways, and the
female would drive off any other females, which leaves us
with a total of two. So it would look as though a gibbon
marriage arose by a process of subtraction, rather than one
of addition as among ourselves. But this is not quite fair,
because Carpenter saw mated or friendly gibbons showing
positive affection and pleasure in each other's company,
and greeting one another, after having been foraging separately for a brief time, by what can only be described
as smiles and hugs (the brachiator's hug is done with one
arm and two legs, but otherwise compares well enough
with our type). Thus there seems to be more to the association than the bond of sex.

Gibbons show us, not quite so clearly, the same elements of interpersonal behavior that we have seen already
in monkeys: on the one hand, aggressiveness or dominance
giving some animals a degree of control of the group, and
the whole group a sort of natural patterning, which helps
it to operate successfully; on the other hand, sociability, or
a strong adjustment and cohesion, or bonding, of the group
itself as distinguished from other groups. These elements

do not get the same emphasis as in the other species—the more equal status of the sexes in size and dominance produces a mating pattern different from that of the baboons —but the gibbon type of grouping is just as rigid, in its way, as the others, and just as clearly an expression of the particular nature of the animal. In the other apes, particularly chimpanzees, we see something of a difference, a sort of loosening up of personal relations, which seems to put them in another, and I should say more advanced, category.

The rambling chimps

Chimpanzees have been studied wild in West Africa at the price of heroic efforts by Dr. Henry W. Nissen. Watching gibbons is not for children, but watching chimpanzees is something else again. They are not territorial: they do not stay in the same area, but are truly nomadic and move rapidly, mostly on the ground, when traveling. A group of them, resting, eating or even moving, will be well spread out in the trees or undergrowth, and most difficult to see individually; the only advantage they give an observer is the constant noise they make, chattering, calling and banging on tree trunks. This advantage goes for naught if they notice they are being spied upon, because they dislike it intensely, and will stop their noise, put on a burst of speed and be over the hill in no time. Nissen was thus quite unable to study any one group systematically and repeatedly, and so could not bring back the kind of voluminous notes, on the day-to-day behavior toward one another of specific members of the same group, which Carpenter obtained. It is remarkable that he got anything of worth at all. The burden of his findings, as far as social behavior goes, is that they move in bands averaging eight or nine, with some larger and smaller; that there was no obvious or striking kind of mating organization, although there were fewer adult males than females, and there might be only one male adult in a group; and that they all acted peaceably and co-operatively. He did not report signs of competition or aversion between different groups, and indeed was convinced that two groups might mingle temporarily and then separate. He did not report signs of dominance among members of a group, though this would have been hard to see under the circumstances. He conveys, in fact, a very strong impression of independence and flexibility of movement of the individuals, wandering around where they felt like it and apparently keeping in touch by means of all the noise.

Fortunately we do not have to rely on such peekaboo evidence to know more of chimpanzee nature. They have been studied intensively in captivity, in a great variety of ways, because their close relationship to ourselves makes them so exceptionally important; the only drawback is that captive apes are, after all, not leading natural lives. They are, as everybody has noted, highly emotional and sensitive animals, and one needs very little experience of chimpanzees to realize the force of their interest in, and reliance on, other chimpanzees or such near-chimps as human beings. It is hard to convey the meaning of this briefly. You might almost say that chimpanzees are like us, but more so, in the degree to which their behavior relates to that of others. Dominance is present, with the larger male tending to dominate a female. This is not invariable, however, and a female can use the advantages of her sex temporarily to dominate a usually dominant male. Furthermore, dominance is less obvious than in the monkeys: one gets the impression that the more forceful and positive individuals are not simply the most blatantly aggressive, and that the interplay of personalities has a complexity that suggests the human. A chimpanzee group, in other words, has, like other primate groups, a definite arrangement of its individuals which rules activity, but which depends on other considerations besides brutishness. It is unsafe to humanize such traits, but they give the appearance of amiability, general vigor, self-confidence and so on. Special friendships and enmities are plain. I might say that Professor Robert M. Yerkes, the great authority on chimps, never hesitated to emphasize the humanness of chimpanzee personality and responsiveness.

The other large apes support this analysis, although orang behavior is very little known and gorillas were never carefully studied before the late 1950s; and both species will be lucky if their extinction is not soon brought about by human behavior. If they survive, the gorillas will have much to tell us, but it appears that their bands have patterns similar to those of chimps. One thing is certain: gorillas lack the ferocity and aggressiveness they have always had a reputation for. Orangutans on the other hand surely do not form troops of the size of the other two, and in fact may be content with solitude on occasion, which if true is certainly extraordinary for Primates.

What is the meaning of all this for us? It lies in the understanding of what a society is, among the higher Primates. They are animals who need to be in a group. As Dr. Wolfgang Köhler has said, a lone chimpanzee is not a real chimpanzee at all; he is more like a prisoner in solitary. Further, they are animals with a high capacity to form groups, to become educated to one another by an actual learning process which leaves strangers strangers but which gradually interlocks and dovetails the personalities of the individuals of that particular group, to make a tightly knit whole. Dominance simplifies things, apparently, and may make the group a more efficient one, like army discipline. But at any rate, such a psychological interweave as this is a true society, and not just a collection of animals.

It is totally different, of course, from the societies, so called, of insects, whose actions are pure instinct and as much a part of them as their heads or legs, and in which there is no such thing as variation or adjustment among the individuals. And although social relations and such phenomena as dominance are widespread in higher animals, they are rudimentary outside the Primates, who are by nature more disposed to make use of them. For one thing, the higher Primates breed at all times of the year, so that the protection of infants is a constant problem. For another thing, they are large-brained and intelligent. Now we are given to thinking that brains and intelligence are for doing arithmetic in the head and for exercising logic.

And so they are, but that is too narrow a view. A large brain signifies, first, a high nervous organization; and a high intelligence, I suggest, means primarily the ability to react successfully on a very broad scale. Thus high intelligence would include the primate characteristic of forming complex adjustments among individual animals, and forming the animals into a society. The monkeys and the gibbons do this but are somewhat rigid in their social patterns, and dominance plays a marked role in many species. Chimpanzees, as I said before, seem to manifest greater fluidity in the individual's position and his relations with others, still with enormous cohesiveness in the social group, and I consider this to be the result of their particularly high intelligence. This, therefore, is the kind of society, and the trend in its development, that points toward our own.

We can hardly understand human social relations until we see that our basic social institutions are imposed over a powerful set of natural inclinations, derived through our *biological* evolution, to act in the very ways we act. The other Primates have shown us what these inclinations are: the need of individuals to be in a society and to establish secure, specific and complex relationships with one another. The institutions we have gradually developed as human beings did not force us to come together in groups, or to take our various kinds of status; rather, they have modulated, channeled and made more effective the kind of life we would go in for anyhow. Like other Primates, we are social, and have societies, because of our nature.

3. *Culture: How We Behave*

It ought to be plain by now that man, in his physical and social nature, is very much at home among the Primates. If he did not do certain other things which mark him off from his relatives, this book would be finished here. But he does: almost every action we take, all day long, is something that apes, the brightest of the other animals, cannot do. For man is a creature with culture.

I am not indulging in a piece of outrageous snobbery, hoping that the gorillas will not find out what I have said. I am not trying to say we have better breeding than they, or more appreciation of the Finer Things; for culture, in this proper sense, is something much broader, and all men live by it, even though some have more than others. It consists, simply, in all the inventions, and all the conventions, ever made by humanity. Culture is what it takes to be human.

Without it, we would simply be another kind of animal, a kind of ape, living like the other kinds in small groups, true societies, but cultureless societies. Every band, or society, of chimpanzees behaves in the same way, in its manner of eating, sleeping in nests, traveling around, and in its noisy social intercourse. This is all characteristic of chimpanzees, and it is determined by their general nature and capabilities. The case of man is different. Every human society has an added stock of behavior, which overlies, and modifies, the other, and it is this added stock that is called culture. Furthermore, this overlay is never identically the same for two different societies. Why? Because it is not inborn and never becomes inbred. It is not in itself biological; it is "inherited," which is important, but it is inherited like property, not like blue eyes. Culture is all those things that are *not* inherited biologically.

Instead, culture consists of everything that has ever been accepted as a way of doing or thinking, and so taught by one person to another. Because that is how it is passed on, and—this is vital—that is how it can change and grow so readily. It is the entire knowledge, and patterning of behavior, which human beings have, and of course it must be taught and learned for the very reason that it is not inborn. The teaching and learning can be perfectly direct, like arithmetic in school, or it can be so subtle, as in adopting attitudes from parents and friends, as to be quite unconscious and unrealized. That does not matter; man is the only animal capable of both teaching and learning this mass of conventional patterns. As any psychologist will tell you, animals react to a stimulus according to their nature and needs, and also according to their experience or conditioning (Pavlov's famous dogs drooled at the dinner bell as well as at dinner). So also do we, but we alone have this extra, socially shared screen between us and our actions. And of course since we alone can teach and learn culture, we alone can invent or create it effectively. Once started, however simply, there is no end to its complexity.

Let us take some simple examples from what would be a very simple human culture. A digging stick of a particular kind, for digging up wild vegetables for food, is culture. So is using a skin for keeping warm. So is the idea of appointing a war chief for the group, or the idea of marriage. Now apes might give the impression of having or using these things. They will use sticks readily in captivity, given sticks and something interesting to use them for. You may have seen a young orang in the zoo rapturously using a gunny sack for a blanket. As you know, many Primates will defer to a dominant animal and take their cue from him. And gibbons pair off permanently for mating. But there is a distinction. Different gibbon societies have no choice in the matter; their kind of mating is all the same because it is entirely controlled by biology instead of biology plus convention; it is in their natures. That is why their monogamy cannot be compared with human monogamy, and why their mating is not marriage. So with dominance and leadership. As for sticks, chimpanzees can use them in ways of their own devising, and even fashion them; in fact, fads of stick-using, particularly for mischief, may sweep through a captive chimp colony. But this actually happens at random. It is not created, maintained, handed on and understood, as a regular prop of chimpanzee life.

To men, however, such things can be handled not only as objects but as ideas. A digging stick is not just a stick you happen to have around. It is a *digging* stick for digging *vegetables*. You are welcome to chastise your wife with it, but if you do, you are beating her with the *digging stick*. Furthermore, the important thing is not so much the stick as the pattern for the stick. It is a pattern of behavior. The social group possesses it; we know one uses a digging stick for vegetables, and we know what the best kind of such stick is. This known pattern, which breeds digging sticks, is the actual culture item. The same for a skin robe, or a war chief, or a form of marriage. Man is able to maintain these ideas, to change them, and to add to them. So I do not feel rash in saying that there is, in a way, less difference between Buckingham Palace and a cave with a fire near the entrance than there is between a cave with a fire near the entrance and a cave in which nobody can make a fire.

Brains and their uses

How does it happen that men can handle culture and apes cannot? Because of greater brain power, certainly. We have brains larger by about three times than the great apes, and that is a huge difference. We all have the same general pattern of the cerebrum, the outer layer, which takes care of the senses, of control of the muscles, and of higher processes. Sight and hearing, an itch in the scalp, a command to the toes to wiggle, each has its special part. Around such special parts there are other areas of the brain, more general, in which things seen and heard in the past are stored up, or special patterns of toe-wiggling kept; in still more general parts of these association areas, wider connections between such specific odds and ends can be handled. It is a little like going from the mail room busily dealing with incoming and outgoing stuff all through office hours, past the executive offices to the quieter research laboratory, which can take the resources of the business and come up with new ideas and ways of doing things. The association areas are already large in the higher Primates, and it is in these parts of the brain that the great human expansion has principally taken place.

Sad to say, this kind of thing is most difficult to study, and we still know all too little about the brain at work and at play. However, chimpanzees at work and at play do give us some idea about the end product, and about the elements of intelligence which underlie our capacity for culture, the chimps in particular showing us where they fall down and where we rise above them. As Yerkes said, we must be grateful for the existence of chimpanzees, who make fine, generally enthusiastic laboratory animals, and who are so like us: we know they hear about the same sounds, and that they see in the same terms, with full color and stereoscopic vision. Like us also, they are poor at smelling and good at handling. Only in apes can we find a usable smaller-brained near-facsimile of humanity.

You can hardly find more delightful reading than what has been written on the doing of chimps, from anecdotes about chimps living in the house to their report cards in the most carefully designed tests. I regretfully leave all this to other books, and confine myself to remarks on the results. Chimps are masterly imitators, both of one another and of human beings, being able to observe and copy whole patterns of action with the greatest of ease. Thus do they learn our own low habits, smoking and spitting. Köhler saw an anthropoid victim of the Tom Sawyer motif: the chimp absorbedly watched a workman painting the enclosure and, when the man temporarily went off and left his paintpot, the chimp at once fell to and painted a large rock in the yard, and did, what is more, a Grade A job.

Therefore they can be trained at all sorts of things, particularly those at which they would be naturally adept, as long as they are interested or can be bribed. The idea occurred to Köhler that the animals might do their own housekeeping, and he set one of them to picking up the banana peels in the yard at close of day. The chimp took a basket and went at it like a demon janitor the first time, but found it all too much like work in the next day or so, and after four or five days he could not be prevailed upon to go from one skin to the next by cajolery, threats or brute force.

Chimpanzees remember well, recognizing people or apes after long periods, and also remembering the solutions to puzzles without difficulty. Because of all this information, Yerkes did not like to have them considered incapable of culture. He noted that when the colony was founded at Orange Park, Florida (now known as Yerkes Laboratories of Primate Biology), the pioneer chimpanzees were shown how to work the drinking fountains, and through the years ape has aped ape, and no further instruction of new generations has been necessary.

But all of the above manifests what chimps can do naturally and well, the sort of thing in which they merely excel various other mammals, who do similar things well also. It does not reveal them at the height of their mental abilities, or show where their shortcomings lie. This is what the more rigorous problems are made to test. Now, typical animal learning is done by trial and error: a rat in a maze tries again and again, gradually having his right moves reinforced by success and his wrong moves checked more and more by failure, until his successful runs become more numerous and at last he makes no mistakes. This is a simple kind of learning and problem-solving, and is practically thinking with the muscles, or with the muscle-controlling part of the brain; it is like the thought, or lack of it, which we use to get us home from the bus stop after ten years of doing the same thing.

But consider a problem, an old one though a good one,

which has repeatedly been put to chimpanzees. The bait, a banana, is hung well out of reach, in fact where the ape can reach it only by bringing over two boxes, which are provided, and by stacking one on the other to climb upon. Now trial-and-error solution would not solve this, without the intervention of earthquakes, since the only approach would be jumping up toward the bait repeatedly from underneath it until exhaustion or frustration ended matters. That is all a dog could or would do. This is a hard problem for chimpanzees, but most can solve it. And it demonstrates, many claim, an advance in mental processes from trial-and-error work to insight, which means fitting possible activities to the situation in the imagination, not in actuality. It means, obviously, using parts of the brain less closely related to muscle activity proper.

See how a chimpanzee would make an ideal solution of this problem. He might begin with a few jumps, for size, which he would at once observe to be unfruitful, or unbananaful. This, rather than sheer muscular failure, would stop his jumping. He might not even try a jump. There might follow evidence of continued attention to the fruit, or there might be a long period before anything else was tried. However, the moment would arrive when the ape's experience with boxes would suggest using one, and he would reveal the fact that this was a truly mental solution by the directness with which he would try to carry it out; there would, in other words, be nothing random about his actions, but rather a perfectly transparent awareness of what he was doing. Discovery that the height was still not enough has been known to cause an immediate tantrum, showing even more positively that the solution was all there in the head, with the picture of success. Going on to the use of the other box would be a repetition of what had already been done, in similar, clear-cut steps.

Abstractions and symbols

This is a sound example of what an ape can do in many such tests, quite unapproached by other animals except

monkeys. The chimpanzee's eyes *see* the situation, just as
a dog's do. (They see it more completely, as to color and
depth, which is certainly important.) But the chimp himself grasps more of it, because his brain is capable of applying more things to it. Notice that he does not respond,
in ordinary mammal fashion, directly to what he sees by
endless jumping, or simply as a result of experience or
training, like going to ring a bell for which he will be given
the food as a reward. Instead, he is also using, with varying degrees of consciousness, some abstract elements of the
situation: the actually unjumpable gap between him and
the banana, and the movability of the box, and the property the box has of serving to fill the gap; he is also at the
same time a little bit conscious of himself at work, so to
speak, so that he hits the ceiling figuratively when he fails
to reach it in reality, contrary to his expectations on using
the first box.

Thus the apes can make and handle abstractions to a
significant degree. They show it in other kinds of tests perhaps more distinctly, as in grasping the principle that the
middle box or door is the right one to choose, no matter
how many there are. They also seem to be superior in
recognizing objects in a photograph, that is to say in a
black-and-white, two-dimensional representation, which
would be meaningless to a cat or a dog.

But it is apparent that ape abstraction is done with the
brakes partly on: their obvious cleverness is the result
largely of their particularly high ability to learn and
memorize through the senses, which is an ordinary mam-
malian mental process. Take this problem: a chimpanzee
is allowed to see food being put into one of a series of different boxes, and then led away, perhaps into another room
where this is done again, or into a series of such rooms.
After a lapse of time he is turned loose to find the food.
This test shows how good chimp memory is, but it also
shows that an ape will depend, whenever he can, on the
position of the right box, rather than on any of its other
properties, and this links him with other animals which
respond similarly (providing, of course, that they are work-

ing from memory, without smelling the food itself). He does very well with his sight and memory, but he is largely doing what a bloodhound does with scent. If the boxes have been shuffled around after he has seen them, the ape is all too likely to try the one standing in the same place in the room, whereas we would immediately see that someone had switched the round box covered with shiny red paper and the square one covered with green baize. It seems obvious to us to remember the color, and also those other somewhat abstract qualities of shape and texture. We can thus promptly learn to solve such tests, if the solution involves any shiny box or any round box. Chimps can too, but with more reluctance compared to using clues of space.

Therefore apes can deal in abstractions, especially if they are closely related to concrete problems. But accumulating abstractions and juggling them around—abstract thinking— is a much harder job, and here we have an advantage. We can keep tabs on our ideas, or abstractions, by using symbols to represent them, especially words. We are adept at using such symbols; the apes are very poor, even if they excel other animals. Without something to stand for an idea or abstraction, it is difficult to carry the idea around and apply it elsewhere, and impossible, of course, to give it to anyone else.

For example, a chimp is able with training to recognize colors, and to use them as clues to a problem, such as this: show him a colored patch, either red or green; red is a signal to press one button, green the other button. This is simple, when the ape can take the color as a direct cue. But make him wait a short while: he sees the red, and he recognizes it, but he must somehow bear in mind the simple fact of a color, and then apply it to something that has nothing to do with color in itself; it must be remembered simply as a fact. This is easy for us: we can just say "red" to ourselves, consciously or unconsciously. But it is a tough problem for a chimp and it is clearly near the limit of his capacity to use symbols at all. Otherwise this capacity is limited to symbols relating to position and space, something of which other animals are also capable.

Frankly, we must remain vague about such important matters at the moment, because our most persevering psychologists are still only in the fringes of the jungle of the brain and how it works. But we have to try to describe man's ability to use culture nonetheless. It is clear that we make and use symbols freely, that apes give signs of being barely able to do this, and that our advantage is our much larger brain. It is also apparent that these things—abstractions, and symbols of them—crowd into the area between something we experience and our reaction to that something, and so govern our behavior, and make it "human" or "unanimal." Only because of our ability in these things are we able to invent, to keep and to be governed by the patterns of behavior that make up culture. Finally, only because we are social animals can culture exist as it does, the property of an integrated group of animals, affecting them in common and being maintained by them generation after generation.

So it is clear that we get our human quality from natural, animal sources. We would be nowhere without the hands and eyes of the higher Primates. We could not have culture, a social thing, unless we were one of the social Primates. Nor could we have culture if we had not expanded the cerebrum of the already large hominoid brain or, in practical terms, become able to deal with abstractions and symbols far beyond that place in the road, which barely points the direction, at which a chimpanzee gives up and turns back. We came by these things through straightforward evolution, in continuous descent from our simpler Primate forebears, but in us their working jointly gives us culture, something new in nature.

Culture is only human

Culture was obviously gradual, not sudden. It had a beginning, perhaps being present even among the higher Primates, depending on how you look at it. I have been emphasizing the lack of culture, in the sense of definite social traditions differing from group to group, in such animals as chimpanzees. Nevertheless Japanese students of the free-living macaque of their own islands have found distinct differences in the pattern of behavior of different bands of monkeys, in such things as the degree of dominance of the females by the males; and they have also observed the spread of a custom, by introducing a new and unfamiliar food to them, and seeing some animals learn to eat it and teach its use to others. Such a structure of social habits looks as though it were waiting only for the more advanced mental capabilities I have been describing—the use of abstractions and symbols—to develop at once the kind of social heritage that constitutes the culture of a particular human group.

As it is, however, there is a great gap between ourselves —living men—and any kind of living ape or monkey, and we can only make suppositions as to the steps in the gradual process of change. We know from their skulls that men living in the remote past were more primitive than we, and that they had more primitive cultures. But we can judge very little from this. We cannot test these men as we can apes, to see what their actual capacity for culture was like.

Culture has continuously grown. From the very beginning, man has used it to solve his problems and make his life easier. This also emphasizes its special nature: it is a new, largely mental way of reacting to the environment. It is radically different from the old system of changing body form, or native abilities, in response to natural selection, and thus remaining closely bound to nature. Culture is a way of departing from nature, of putting a protective layer between man and nature, whether in concrete things like clothes and houses or in less conscious inventions like social customs and religious beliefs, which make for more efficient and happier living. The tip of the wedge was perhaps things like the use of clubs, fire and language. Just what they were in detail it would not be safe to say, but it is certain they had the characteristics of culture, and served to improve the state of man, making him more powerful (weapons), broadening his diet (cooking), and so on.

From such a point as this, of course, culture has expanded enormously, becoming an ever fatter cushion between man and his environment. But now see what happens: the bigger it gets, the more culture itself *becomes* the environment. Culture is not to be thought of as a stock of clever ideas out of which we are continually making selections for our own benefit or delight. On the contrary. Man invented culture, and culture promptly took charge of man. We do what culture tells us to, whether we quite know it or not.

In the first place, people have never been very much aware that there was such a thing as culture. It goes back before history; it has seemingly always been there; they take it for granted. It actually grew up out of the sum of inventions and adjustments they happened to make, and it could not have followed exactly the same course for two different societies. So no two societies have the same culture. And each one thinks its own is the obvious and natural way of doing things. This is not simple preference; it is because human societies, unlike animal societies, are based on their own cultures and cannot continue to exist, as human societies, without those particular cultures that have continuously sustained them.

Why must a society have that particular culture? Because a society has to be a group of individuals, and the individual grows up as the prisoner of his culture. He could not possibly escape it. A human being is no longer born simply as a social animal, like a chimpanzee; he is born into a complicated world he did not make, among a particular set of people he did not choose. Culture is practically his whole environment; culture lets him breathe as he sees fit, but it even tells him what to eat, and how. He becomes a cultured creature of necessity, and of necessity his culture is that of his own society—how could it be that of any other?

I am satisfied you would not be seen dead dressed for

the street as a Hungarian peasant, or a Tibetan monk, or even in the clothes of your own great-grandfather. Why should you object to appearing in such a fashion? You would be as warmly or as comfortably dressed. But do not be confused; you were right the first time. It is not natural, and there are good reasons why. A culture contains far more than any individual could possibly reinvent, or satisfactorily revise, and it forms a consistent whole. An individual needs all of it, not bits and pieces, and he cannot live outside of it in any conspicuous way.

But this is becoming complicated and abstract. There is a great deal to be said about the nature and workings of human culture, but I shall say no more of it here. I shall tackle the history of culture later on; here I have tried to show the relations between culture and society, and above all the place of both of them in the evolution of man.

4. Language: How We Talk

There is one more noticeable difference between men and apes, or other animals. We talk, and they do not; that is to say, we have language. If Siegfried heard the birds talking after he had tasted dragon's blood, the dragon's blood must have been fermented. For language proper is culture, and out of reach of the beasts.

That is not to say that they do not communicate. In the first place, animals readily sense excitement, emotion or shifts in attention on the part of their fellows, and act accordingly. The Primates, as usual, are pre-eminent at this sort of thing and, according to those who know chimpanzees best, the understanding of a situation which can run through a group of them by means of slight attitudes, gestures and facial expressions is a marvel to see. And there is some evidence that this ability helps them considerably to co-operate, as social groups, in their natural surroundings —another manifestation of their high "intelligence." Nissen, for example, tells of being spotted by a single chimpanzee of a group, the others being hidden in the foliage. Chimp number one at once climbed up to where the others were; Nissen did not see what took place, but the whole band came down and trooped off, without trying to see him for themselves.

They have more specific means of communicating. Monkey mothers, for instance, signal their offspring with a gesture to climb aboard when they wish to go elsewhere. But certainly a principal method is actual communication by voice. Howling monkeys not only howl; they cluck to signify that a good pathway has been found, they gurgle if something suspicious makes them apprehensive, they grunt if the young play too roughly; and in each case others respond in the way appropriate to that noise. Carpenter could make out fifteen or more such distinct noises among howlers, each for a given situation, and he found a somewhat smaller number among gibbons. Again chimpanzees, though noisy, do not seem to have their communication so strongly patterned, and probably have more subtle and more fluid resources of expression.

Now all this animal business may be impressive, and useful to the species concerned, but, taken together, it remains distinct from language. These noises and gestures are not words. They are signs, or signals. They do not simply convey information (abstractions). Rather, they fit some specific situation, and pull the trigger for some action connected with it.

Here is an example, again from the hard-working chimpanzees, which shows the breaking point. A box is rigged, and baited with the usual fruit, so that it can be brought within reach (up to the cage bars) only if two apes pull, separately but at the same time, on two different ropes; this was devised to see how well they can co-operate in work. It took a little teaching to get them started pulling, but once over the hump they proved clever at watching one another and timing their pulls together. After this, when the box was set up and shown to one ape, he could fetch a partner who knew the ropes by a little beckoning or making of faces, and a few smart yo-heave-hos would get them a banana.

But let him try to get help from a chimp who was strange to the problem, and no amount of frenzied appeal would convey to the latter what was wanted. The two stood helpless; the gesticulating was empty of symbolic meaning, and only pertained directly to something that was in the experience of one and not of the other; it was even beyond the ability of the first one to try to symbolize his desire in effective pantomime. Yet certainly "I'll pull on one rope and you pull on the other" seems like the easiest sentence one could imagine in the mouth of an early man, being probable in situation and intellectually simple.

Even this might cause us to dismiss the chimpanzees too soon. The more that is known about them, the clearer it is that they have a great many of the prerequisites for talk, in their capacity to perceive, to make associations, to see the need for communicating, and so on. They just do not talk. Viki, the chimp raised from birth by Dr. and Mrs. Keith Hayes at Orange Park, Florida, liked to go for automobile rides. At first the Hayeses always took along an abundant supply of diapers in the car, and Viki promptly adopted the habit, when she felt like asking for a drive, of going and getting an armful of didies and exhibiting them to her foster parents. She employed the same charade when the diapers were no longer taken along. And after they had been disposed of altogether, and she could not find them, she looked around for something similar, discovered some Kleenex, and made her desires clear with that.

Nevertheless, true language depends on symbols, not on signals. Take Professor Melville Herskovits' definition of language as *a system of arbitrary vocal symbols by which members of a social group co-operate and interact*. Speech depends on our ability to make abstractions lavishly, to assign symbols to them and to manipulate the symbols at a great rate of speed.

Let us now take an actual specimen of language in operation. You, an American paterfamilias, wish to break the monotony at dinner with a morsel of idle news, and say, "I saw an overturned truck on the turnpike this afternoon." You yourself have a fresh visual memory, and even such sensations as the heat of the day; you remember what part of the turnpike this was on; it was a green truck and there were squashed grapefruit all over the place, and so on. You cannot convey all this economically; you take the main features, and abstract them from the scene, using only place, time and a general object.

You readily fish up and put into play the symbols that all the people you know attach to these abstractions: for purposes of production, the symbols consist of some very complicated motions of the tongue, jaw and lips made while you vibrate your vocal cords. The product of this, a modulated hooting, resounds in the dining room and impinges on the eardrums of your wife and children, reaching the auditory area of the brain as symbols—this time in the form of sound patterns—which are familiar and easily recognized. They evoke the right abstractions and cause fleeting visual images of overturned trucks on the turnpike, but of different-looking trucks, on different parts of the highway, in the brain of your wife and each child.

The object of all this work is some fairly neutral information, not a stimulus to action. It may result in various responses: "Never hitch rides on trucks, children"; "Was everybody dead, Daddy?"; or the room may revert to the gentle music of knife and fork. You could have used a somewhat amplified set of abstractions from this scene, and you could have used a variety of alternative arrangements of the symbols. Whatever the case, you have given a demonstration of the full process of transferring abstractions from one individual to another by means of vocal symbols. The gulf between this and the parley of a pair of parrots should be apparent.

It is not as though the other Primates were actually mute, or lacked vocal cords or the other instruments of speech. Far from it. Chimpanzees, above all, constantly use their voices in the wild, in a wide variety of calls and mutterings, though these are mostly simple vowel sounds. Moreover, several young chimps at Orange Park have lately been taught to say and use a few words (the same had been done years before with an orang), especially Viki. The standard vocabulary is "papa," "mama" and "cup." The apes have no trouble in understanding what these words (and many others) refer to, or in applying them properly. This still does not mean, of course, that the words are anything more than signals.

Now I should hasten to say that this teaching is not done with the notion of introducing speech to the chimpanzee tribe, or of promoting chimp-human relations, or with the crasser motive, which seems to have occurred to Köhler, of helping out with the servant problem. It has been done to study the basis of human language mechanism by probing and pushing chimp abilities as much as possible, to see what keeps them from talking. And the result shows that the actual speaking, the production of disciplined sounds even so simple as "cup" (as distinct from a yell of pleasure or excitement), is a severe nervous effort. The word is spoken in a toilsome stage whisper, and at least one chimp developed a marked tic with his talk. Chimpanzees, for all their love of noise, do *not* take to language like ducks to water; instead of having the natural impulse and facility to expand and enjoy their vocabularies, it takes continued coaching to make them retain the use of their first two or three arduously learned words.

There is no doubt that the muscular patterns of forming words are difficult, but it hardly seems likely that this would be such a check to a chimpanzee who could find any facility and need in the use of words. It is this last, the use proper, which seems to be too taxing. It seems strange in view of their ready conveyance of simple notions by other means; but it may be just this, that using words is a harder way of doing what they already do more easily by other means. We seem in any event to be up against a chimpanzee's limits; up against his refusal to use these unnatural and conventionalized signals (words) such as might carry over and become mental symbols, as we use them.

All this looking up at language from the animal plane emphasizes its nature as a structure of abstractions and symbols, and the fact that it is essentially like the rest of culture. Indeed, in trying to analyze and define culture scientifically, you cannot find a better illustration than language. It has all the main characteristics of culture and shows them more clearly than any other aspect. It certainly consists of patterns of agreed-on behavior, which is what I have used to define culture. It would not exist without society; nobody ever had a language all his own, which could only be a code, not a language. It is inherited by a society, not by individuals; it is non-biological. And it differs from group to group, although it does the same things for all. Just as there is no one culture, but a lot of them, so there is no one language, but a lot of them. Finally, a language can and does change, much more quickly than any biological evolution, and by different rules.

The sounds, the grammar and the sense

To the unthinking it has been easy to suppose that there was indeed something inherited about a person's speech, because all Indians say "Ugh," and because it is so much easier for Frenchmen to speak French than for English or Americans to do so. The first notion, of course, is nonsense. As to the second, we simply do not give ourselves enough credit for what we have learned in pronouncing our native tongue. We speak, not with things that were put in our mouths to speak with, but with our teeth, which are for grinding up food, and our tongue and lips, which are for shoving it around during the grinding. The wonder is, with all the energetic palaver, that the latter do not get bitten by the former more often than they do. A little contemplation of the hazards should do more to stop you from talking with your mouth full than all the lectures Mother ever gave you.

Now this whole curious engine can make literally hundreds of distinct sounds. That is far more than any one language could possibly use, if the language is going to have any kind of consistency itself. In fact, something in the neighborhood of thirty or forty sounds, a minute fraction, is what most languages make out with, and it is with those particular sounds of your own language that you become exceedingly adept, while you never practice the hundreds of other possible ones. But another language—say French—is now using a different set of sounds, and little French children have been practicing all day every day with a group of rather squashed-down vowels, while neglecting to study the "th" sound which serves us through thick and thin. No wonder you would think their mouths were actually shaped differently.

But sounds are the least of the differences between languages. The words may have no likenesses at all: the same abstraction may be represented by an infinity of different symbols, which emphasizes the symbolic and cultural nature of language. Grammar has more limits: any language has to have a kind of ordering and grouping of its words, since some words have to refer to things, some to actions, some to qualities, and so on. But grammars have an astonishing diversity as well. You have probably studied Latin, at least enough to know that the different forms of a word —which make up its inflections: *amo, amas, amat*—have a lot to do with its meaning. If you have, you are probably extra happy to speak English, which is greatly simplified in this respect, and from which inflections have nearly disappeared. We can still tell the nature of many words from their forms, particularly endings (-ed, -ing, -ly), but on the whole we have to a very great extent given up changing the form of a word because of its sense. However, in Greek, Latin, French, German, Russian and so on, the verbs are energetically conjugated according to person, tense and mood, so that if you say *"Ich verschnipfele,"* it means that the verschnipfeling is being done in the first person singular, present indicative. You have to change the word itself to fit other situations, so that it has about forty different forms that you must know and use.

We have jettisoned practically all of this in English. Skipping the present participle and the verb "I am," we have four different forms of the word in some of our remaining strong verbs—"I write, he writes, I wrote, I have written"—three in most: "I look, he looks, I looked, I have looked"; and two only in many: "I hit, he hits, I hit, I have hit." (It is estimated, from past rates of change, that in less than a thousand years, and without any help from World War III, all English verbs will have the typical form: "I write, I writed, I have writed." Which do you say: "I dreamt" or "I dreamed"?) The "s" of the third person singular present is a vestige, and quite unnecessary: we say "he fights" but not "he foughts," and we do not say "he cans" or "he musts."

English has become strongly isolating, throwing separate items of sense onto separate words, such as person involved (I), tense (have), mood (should), and depending on auxiliaries. All this is a blessing for children in school and other reluctant grammarians, but it puts an extra burden on syntax, or the proper arrangement of words, and on the sense of what is being said as a whole. If, for example, I speak the lone word "flee," without spelling it, you are baffled. You do not know whether it refers to a flight or a bite; you do not know whether it is a verb or a noun, whether it is subject or object, masculine, feminine or neuter. But you probably do not care; at any rate, the English grammar does not.

English is not unique in this general way; Chinese and others are also isolating. But if English is uninflected compared to Latin, there are languages in the Southwest Pacific that make Latin look poor indeed. Some of the natives of Australia, or of New Guinea, have verb tenses—not just past tenses, but a tense for a little while ago and a tense for a long while ago, a tense for pretty soon and a tense for not for a while yet; such variations of tense, mood and so forth may run over seventy, with infinitives, presents, imperfects, present habituals, perfectives, indefinites, subjunctives, progressives, etc., etc. They have not just singular and plural numbers, but singular (I), dual (we, two of us), trial (we, three of us) and plural (we, all of us). And they may incorporate in the verb not only the subject, like Latin (*amo*, I love), but also the object so that, all in all, it is possible to produce a battleship of a verb meaning "you three men killed her." This is fancy inflection, and different from agglutination, another tendency that is also foreign to English: the agglutinating Eskimos, for example, simply paste up most of a sentence into a single word.

English no longer has genders. In Latin or German, nouns are masculine, feminine or neuter, and adjectives have to agree with them. In English, nouns do not fall into such classes. French has distinct forms for masculine and feminine (e.g., *le lion, la lionne*), but it is not fair to say that our similar distinctions are grammatical forms. Lioness is simply a specific word for female lion, or actress for female actor, just as mare is a specific word for female horse, the distinction getting no recognition from the rest of the language, like the French *le* or *la* for "the." But in African Bantu languages there are a number of genders, or classes of nouns, with most of the words in the sentence taking their cue from the noun; and the same usage becomes outrageous on Bougainville, in the Solomons, where a language may have no less than twenty genders to keep straight. In this same misguided part of the world (Australia again) there are native tongues that even conjugate adverbs as if they were verbs. Be thankful, reader, that this book is written in English.

Histories and changes

So languages have a wide choice of grammatical tricks, as they have of sounds. And, as is also true of their sounds, their grammars are clear-cut, and rule the language with an iron hand. I think I have shown that they can be complicated, and that English has a simple one. English has every reason to be unusual among its relatives, for it has undergone an extraordinary manhandling during its history. Starting as a Germanic tongue, it was imported to Britain before 500 A.D. by the Anglo-Saxons and thrust upon the Keltic-speaking natives (not all of whom have accepted it yet), who had already become literate at the hands of the Romans, and were able to write it as time went on. The Danes in their turn arrived and tried to speak it, for they gave us some of our common words. Old English was now a literary language and its inflections were starting to go. Then it suffered the onslaught of the conquering Normans and practically went underground. Nobody wrote it any more, because French was spoken and written by anyone who mattered.

But English won out, bedecked with a vast number of

French words, and with its onetime grammatical structure in advanced decay, so that by Shakespeare's time its vocabulary was enormous and gaudy and its grammar what we use today. Even so, changes have gone steadily on. "Thou" has departed, and the questioning inversion "Have you?" is just now going the way of "think you?," driven hard by the gum-chewing ninety-day wonder "Do you have?" Perhaps this last has a sort of precedent in the English quaintness, "I do be the gardener." Perhaps it got an assist from the other use of "have": "Do you *haff* to make that noise?" But it is certain that "Do you have a match?" is victorious; perhaps we may start scanning the horizon for signs of "Do you can spare a dime?"

Thus fresh mouths taking up English have doubtless been important, pulling and hauling at it, pidginizing it, making it glib and streamlined, particularly when there was a great body of such new mouths, who could take it and use it among themselves. (My own recipe for speaking foreign languages is to take the present tense and stick to it, but the effect on those languages so far has been slight.) Perhaps the latest such body was the slaves from Africa, stripped of their own different tribal languages by being mixed up, and given no formal instruction in the new one. At any rate, one can see signs of still further English simplification in Negro areas of the New World, for example in calypsos. And at a Southern shoot I have heard a Negro helper ask, "That lady, where she gun?"— a triumph of isolationism, since it refuses the chances of "inflection" offered by each " 's " in the normal "Where's that lady's gun?" A preview of future English? In any event, when you look at the exposed position of the "s" in "he says," and realize how often in this country you can hear "he say," you can make out a pretty good defense even for "he don't" or "ain't."

The above doodling should show that English, like any language in fact, is always in a fluid state, which is true of culture in general. English has gone through some particularly striking changes, and we happen to know a good deal about its past. But even if we did not have the written evidence, we could still make out much of what had happened, and where English came from, by studying its structure and rules, and noting that while it obviously had received a terrific infusion from French, particularly of more fancy words, its bedrock vocabulary of names for everyday things is Germanic in nature.

The same sort of thing can be done with any language, written or not, and the more easily if its grammar has not had all the vicissitudes of English. Languages are continually drifting, so that Latin, settling in different places, became French, Spanish, Italian, Rumanian. But languages —all languages—change neatly and consistently as they change. They drift, but they also have a powerful tendency always to regularize themselves. This is especially true of sounds. You do not find that one sound has changed in one word; instead, that sound will have made the same change in all words using it, and certain other sounds which are linked to it in the way the mouth forms them will very likely have made a similar shift.

So whole lists of differing words will be found to differ simply because the people have made a slight cultural change in where they put their tongues or use their breath in pronunciation. German *Teufel* is English "devil," *Taube* is "dove," and all "t's" of the same type are replaced in English by "d's," while the "d's" in turn are replaced by "th's" (*Donner*, "thunder"). This is a general phenomenon; for a single non-European example, Samoan "t" becomes Hawaiian "k," along with other shifts.

In this way it is possible to find true likenesses and put languages into families. If the changes have been slight, they are closely related—have not long been separate. If the differences are very great, so that vocabularies cannot be matched at all, it may be that some general rules of grammar, of ways of classifying and using their words, show a distant, almost lost kinship. This is where doubt comes in. The great Indo-European group, to which English belongs, hangs together easily, since plenty of words can be traced throughout its members, including Sanskrit, one of its oldest, fully fledged forms. But that is as far as one can go; there are only the dimmest hints as to how this massive family might be related to some of the other languages of the Old World, such as Ural-Altaic, if at all. At the other end of the scale, the speech of the Basques in the Pyrénées stands entirely by itself, still not linked to anything else, an orphan remnant of the unknown languages of the time before Indo-European spread out of the East to blanket western Europe. More of an intermediate situation exists among the Indians of the New World. Here are some widespread families, like Algonquian or the homogeneous Eskimo, together with a large number of isolated minor stocks or single languages which offer some vague possible interrelationships to keep the scholars arguing.

Now this should not offer the hope that, if only there were better records, or if more subtle ways of recognizing relationships could be found, it would be possible finally to tie all languages together and arrive at last at a reconstruction of the original language of man. Undoubtedly better ways of analysis will carry the family lines further back and, in cases, closer together. But the fact remains that languages change, and change so quickly that to go all the way back would be like trying to save a ship's wake. Indo-European is estimated to have first come into being about six thousand years ago only, and language is many, many times older than that. Languages, families and patterns probably formed and re-formed several times over before the period when there existed anything that could be recognized by direct comparison as a parent of a living language.

That, at any rate, is what I should read in the demonstrated changes and the great diversity which have been found in the tongues of our own time. I think this even though some other aspects of culture, like tools, are known to have been more sluggish; language is not bound by a hunk of flint but, like supernatural beliefs, may twist and slip from one generation to another, quite without allowing the speakers to be aware. And, in any case, all we shall ever know about languages is limited to the kind of men who inhabit the world today.

Here we have one more interesting and not-to-be-forgotten thing about languages. We know that some of the people who have survived are "savages," having a simple culture and leading a primitive life, and seeming as though they might themselves be primitive men, living fossils. But a careful study of physique shows that we are all the same kind of man, Homo sapiens. And language shows rather well that we all have the same kind of capacity for culture, since we all use language in about the same way. You cannot go hopefully to the poor Bushman, to find him speaking something more rudimentary than yourself, which will point back toward the early days of languages. There are no primitive languages now. Languages of people in primitive cultures may be complicated in form or not, but the average is more complicated than English and they are all equally rigid in their obedience to grammar, and all able to express what is demanded of them, concrete or abstract. They may not have words, of course, for things that do not exist in their cultures. Our inventors have swelled our dictionary enormously. But, at the same time, Eskimo has twenty or more precise words for conditions of snow; and the Tokelau Islanders, in northwestern Polynesia, had nine names for distinct stages of ripeness in a coconut, their main food. In any case, the number of words is not a real character of the language itself.

There must have been a time when language was different, more limited or simpler, just as we know there was a time when men had smaller brains. We cannot dig up languages like skeletons, and we can never do anything but guess about beginnings. It seems only logical that very primitive men—hominids of the man-ape variety—made a good deal of constant expressive noise, just as chimpanzees do, and that, little by little, more symbolic content entered into this noise as the animals making it became mentally more capable of symbolizing. We cannot tell when this happened. We do not know what kind of brain would have been necessary, and so we cannot look at a fossil skull and say, "He talked." (Obviously the jaw will not tell us.)

But true speech must have put in its appearance along with the earliest signs of culture in general, because language and culture are so much the same thing. In fact, since culture is a social thing, and since language is necessary to transmit anything in the least abstract, it is hard to see how culture could have gone beyond the rawest imitation and standardizing of simple actions—the very next stage above the chimps—without language marching by its side.

THE OLD HUNTERS—THE FIRST STEP

5. *Early Tools: the Lower Paleolithic*

We stand no chance of finding out anything about early language. We are not going to know much more about the earliest rudiments of the rest of culture. But there is this difference: the economic or material side of culture does leave actual objects behind, and so we can begin to study its history with these.

It will be only a fragmentary history at best, as common sense will tell you. Imagine yourself as a toothy, not too clever hominid, bent on becoming human. You are a more natural tool-user than is a chimpanzee: your hands are better proportioned, with shorter fingers, and freer and more nimble. Furthermore, your arms are less strong and your canine teeth do not protrude, so that a little something held in the hand will be a distinct help in attacking ape-man or beast or in opening the tough rind of a wild fruit.

The things you would use, back there toward the end of the Pliocene, would be more or less random to begin with: a stick for this and a stone for that. But you and your descendants might begin to keep a stick which seemed to have just the right heft, instead of dropping it and forgetting it after it had been used. Finally your ten thousandth great-grandson not only might be trimming a new stick with a sharp rock to make it do, but also might be appreciating the stick's form and uses so clearly that he and his fellows were making the same thing repeatedly.

This would not accord with the notion of Ug the Caveman whacking a bear on the head with a stick for the first time and then, astonished at his cleverness, rushing around to apprise all other cavemen of what can be done with clubs. On the contrary, the process of the adoption of culture among very early "men" must have been gradual in the extreme, and devoid of such jumps forward, or yet of any clear awareness of the benefits being gathered, even though these benefits were a great spur to the continuing of the process itself. I have pictured the beginning of language as natural chatter gradually taking on meaning. It is fair to think of culture as implements used (as apes sometimes use them) gradually taking on fuller meaning to the user, and with this meaning, taking on pattern, at which point something exists that can belong to a group of people. Apes have been seen to trim branches by pulling off twigs, and to bite sticks to point them, but always in meeting a special problem, and not to fit a pre-existing pattern.

But to return to you in your most ancient days. What sort of things would you find useful? Pieces of wood, or of antler and bone; sharp stones for cutting, and also shells; thorns, animals' claws and the like; doubtless twine, from vines or sinews or hide. Pride of purpose would not compel you to make a neat or fancy job of your utensils if something good enough was at hand, like a natural horn point, or a coconut shell cup. What I am getting at is this: there must have been a good deal of simple culture, in the sense of behavior patterns of use, before anything was made so complicated as to be strikingly distinct from natural objects in its shape. So, even if we should find such very early utensils—and most would be perishable—we would not necessarily be able to recognize them. Primitive people today, along with their best tools, also use things straight out of nature when it suits them: clamshells to cut hair, stones for throwing or for slings, and so forth.

This means that the period of culture beginnings is a shadowy one, and probably a long one. We can know very little about it, and can only speculate, as we have done above. The critical point is looked on as that in which tool-*users* gave way to tool-*makers*, a difference that should be clear in the light of what I have been saying about cultures as social patterns of how to make things. This change may have taken place among the man-apes themselves. The gathering evidence seems to say so, but it is still not clear.

Man-apes have now been found in various places, in Asia (Java and Palestine) but principally in Africa: Lake Chad, Tanganyika in East Africa, and above all in old filled caves in South Africa. These remains go back from about half a million to a million years ago, and just possibly a good deal more. And the man-apes differed somewhat among themselves in type, some being meat-eaters and others more purely vegetarian, like the anthropoids. Finally, the latest of them probably overlapped with more advanced hominids (that is, with "true" men, though this is an uncomfortable phrase). Considering their variety, their widespread and apparently long existence, we might expect some differing cultural behavior among them and, on the face of it, this is what we find.

The first man-ape was brought to light in 1924 by Dr. Raymond A. Dart, who has continued to expose and study them for almost forty years. He has painstakingly extracted great quantities of fossils from their hard matrix from one cave, at Makapansgat, and this is what he found. Along with the rare man-ape fossils, he exposed a number of bones of baboons and large numbers of other animals, mostly antelopes. The baboon skulls almost all showed signs of having been opened to extract the brains, or else simply of crushing blows. Some of the fractures consisted of peculiar paired dents. Evidently the baboons were killed by blows from a club or a weapon, not by wild beasts. And these paired dents are matched by the paired ridges of the bottom, or elbow portion, of the humerus of the forelimb of a largish animal, usually a wildebeest. Just such portions of this bone were found, showing battering and chipping of the ridges in question. Furthermore, says Dr. Dart, the high proportion of half jawbones, of limb bones, and of horns of antelopes in the debris means that the man-apes were collecting and bringing in just those parts of killed animals that could be used as clubs, saws, knives

and points. Since they were consciously saving and preparing these tools (for example, breaking the limb bone to
the right length), they had, claims Dart, a true bone, tooth
and horn culture, which he delights in calling osteodonto-
keratic. In a word, he pushes the man-ape inhabitants of
this cave over the border into tool-making.

A few people have dismissed this as an illusion created
by bone-collecting hyenas, but others regard such an explanation as still more dubious. The middle ground is found
by those who can see no positive sign of use of all the
bones, and view them as the remains of the man-apes'
meals rather than of their tools. This would not entirely
disallow the use of some bones as clubs, but it would
leave the man-apes themselves principally in the zone of
tool-users (and, of course, meat-eaters).

There is another side to it. No stone tools whatever were
found in this cave. But perfectly recognizable stone tools
did occur in two other such man-ape deposits in South
Africa, as well as at least one definite bone tool. And at
Olduvai in Tanganyika Dr. L. S. B. Leakey found similar
tools in the same level as his large-jawed australopithecine called Zinjanthropus. So possibly the man-apes *made*
tools in some places, or among some tribes, but not in
others. Or they made stone tools in some places, or at
some times, and bone tools in others. And there is a better
possibility: there are signs that more advanced early men
were in the region at the time the stone tools were made
(though in only one case have such remains been found
in the same deposit as the man-apes). So there might have
been such "men," who were making the tools and perhaps
hunting the man-apes into the bargain.

Dr. Kenneth P. Oakley gets out of the difficulty by sup-
posing that the man-apes *could* make tools, but that in
some places, especially in the earliest of the groups
known, they simply had not invented them or been shown
how to make them. This answer is not satisfying, since
their hominid physical form, with hands and small front
teeth, would make the use of tools highly natural and
desirable for all of them. In such a light the contrast be-

tween those making good stone tools and those making
none at all, perhaps not even of bone, seems astonishingly
and implausibly sharp. At the same time their brains, while
essentially not larger than those of apes, were little smaller
than those of the men who followed them. Since the latter
were clearly tool-makers we cannot assume that tool-making did not in fact begin with the man-apes themselves.

The Pleistocene backdrop

If we cannot decide who made the first known tools, we
can at least note that there was apparently a period when
there existed man-apes, tools and later men (they, and we,
are properly called hominines), all contemporaneously.
Now time becomes important: the time of the first tools,
and also the time of later tool developments, since only by
having correct sequences can we know how history really
ran.

The man-apes, all other men, and all the tools, fall
within the Ice Age or Pleistocene. Almost as soon as one
goes beyond this simple statement the arguments begin.
For in spite of a great deal of information there is much
disagreement on details of date, or of interpretation of the
evidence, or of relating what was happening in Africa to
what was happening in Europe or in Asia. And different
experts divide the Pleistocene differently and even give
different meanings to the same terms. This is not scientific
crankiness, but only a reflection of how hard it is to inter-
pret the evidence from the ground. Nevertheless, an outline of the Pleistocene can be given.

Something like a million and a half or two million years
ago (possibly a good deal more), world temperatures fell
somewhat and certain new forms of large mammals appeared and spread widely. These include the modern one-
toed horse, which originated in America but crossed via
Alaska into Asia; modern elephants with their special
teeth; and certain others, such as camels and cattle, differing from their parental genera. These make an animal as-
semblage called the Villafranchian. It marks the beginning

of the Pleistocene geological period; and the long early
Pleistocene, during which it was dominant, is also referred
to as Villafranchian times. After this, further climatic
changes are apparent. A number of definite small cold intervals occurred, even causing traceable expansion of
glaciers in Switzerland, but amounting to little more than
thermal hiccups. These were followed by four major cold
phases, beginning about 600,000 years ago. In Europe
these are generally known (after small rivers in southern
Germany) as the Günz, Mindel, Riss and Würm glaciations, and each of them had two or three (the Würm
perhaps four) peaks of cold, with more moderate stages
between.

These glaciations were not worldwide, but they did
have worldwide effects. Vast sheets of ice spread out of
the highlands and out of the north latitudes, covering varying but respectable portions of Europe, Asia and North
America until, for causes not yet clear, the process reversed
and the ice melted and shrank during interglacial times.
The process was not exactly like the tide rising and falling;
it was more like a tide which came up, hesitated, fell back
a little, became high again, went out uncertainly, and remained out longer than would be expected of a tide, especially on the second retreat, the long Second Interglacial.

Naturally, as the glaciers spread they pushed the zones
of temperature and climate ahead of them, and also
robbed the oceans of water so that sea levels fell while
the glaciers grew. Near the ice there was barren ground
and tundra, something like the present-day Far North of
Canada and Siberia. Then came spruce and fir forests, then
temperate forests or grasslands. All these were displaced
to the south in the glacial phases, moving the animals with
them and bringing them northward again in warmer times.
So fossil elephants and lions are dug up in England, or
walrus in Georgia and musk oxen in Arkansas. Thus the
animals betray the climate, and as those of the Villafranchian gave way to newer species in the Middle Pleistocene,
the groups of fossils changed in this way also, making

estimates of date possible from the group of animals found. Successive ice sheets caused the laying down of sands and gravels in river valleys, as well as changing shorelines, and this also is important in assessing date, or in suggesting at least which part of the Pleistocene is in question.

Still, there is generally plenty of room for uncertainty and differing opinions, especially in the tropics, where changes were less drastic. Thus, unfortunately, the man-apes are especially difficult to place: in spite of the magnificent beds, with their long series of strata, investigated at Olduvai by Dr. Leakey, the relations of this with South Africa are still hard to establish, let alone with Europe. So the important fact of what came first is not settled. Two great aids that are not geological in nature can now be used, however. These, which give dates in absolute years, are radioactive carbon and radioactive potassium. The latter, in particular, is beginning to set times for the important early part of the Pleistocene.

Simple tools, slow change

Now as to the stonework. The earliest we have already mentioned; in age it is late Villafranchian, or Lower Pleistocene, and all from Africa. This means anything from half a million years to considerably more. (Many authorities make it post-Villafranchian entirely.) The tools are pebbles that have been crudely chipped to give a sharp edge; some are round in form, some have a little trimming at one end, and some have been flaked along both sides of one edge, so that the cutting edge, coarse though it is, begins to take more definite form and position. This last is the Oldowan type, which has been found at man-ape sites both in East Africa (with Zinjanthropus at Olduvai) and in South Africa.

Following these pebble tools, early in the Middle Pleistocene (approximately at the Second or Mindel Glacial of Europe), there begins the long hand-axe tradition. This probably flows from a development of the Oldowan pebble into a recognizably two-faced and pointed tool. Imagine

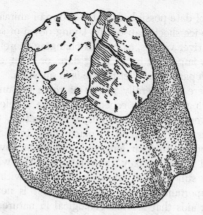

FIG. 3. A "pebble tool" from Olduvai Gorge, possibly one of man's earliest attempts at toolmaking.

an old-fashioned pendant or eardrop of amethyst or topaz, pear-shaped and slightly flattened so that it has a detectable edge running around its outline; imagine the facets of this being very crude and irregular, and the whole thing about seven inches long from fat end to thin end, and made of flint, and you have a hand axe. This name is an old one, and does not mean that its use is known, or that it was held in the hand. It certainly does not mean that the men who made it had bigger and stronger hands, such as would have been needed to use it as a one-hand weapon, because we are sure they did not. It is too heavy to have been swung like a true axe, with a handle. It may have been used in both hands to grub up wild roots and vegetables; it might have served to open fruit rinds or coconuts, taking up work that our ancestors' unobtrusive canine teeth refused. Almost certainly it was used for butchering meat, and it is found in such large numbers as to suggest strongly that the men of the time did not carry them around, but simply made one quickly when it was needed, as when sitting down to carve up a large animal. This earliest form is known as the Abbevillian, abounding in Europe and all of Africa.

Fig. 4. *An Abbevillian hand axe.*

At the same time very crude flakes of flint were in use for cutting or scraping, undoubtedly accompanied also by other stone implements of forms so vague as to make the archaeologists argue, or too casual to be recognized at all. These tools were shaped in the simplest possible ways, principally by striking the object rock with another or, in the case of the hand axe, getting a slightly more controlled flaking process by holding the tool in both hands and bringing it down on another rock serving as an anvil, and striking off good-sized chips in this way. This is how you today, with all your intellect, might begin to do such work yourself, but I think you would not practice for many years before better methods would occur to you. Such improvements, however, took place then and for long after with tantalizing slowness, over hundreds of thousands of years.

After the second glacial phase, the hand axes of Europe and Africa did manifest a somewhat advanced form,

FIG. 5. *An Acheulian hand axe.*

known as the Acheulian industry. They were flatter, lighter, more oval generally and more neatly worked, with straighter and more efficient edges, the result of their being shaped with a wooden or bone striker. This, because it is lighter, more resilient and less shattering in its effect than a stone hammer, and since it always neatly strikes the tool's edge, produces lighter, flatter and more even chips. The common type of flake tool in Europe, known as Clactonian (from Clacton-on-Sea, England) remained crude.

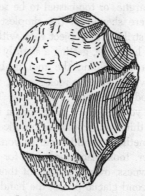

FIG. 6. *A chopping tool from the Pekin cave.*

Tools appeared in the Far East about the same time as the Abbevillian of the West, but not in the form of a hand axe, in China, Burma, Malaya and Java. The earliest are Chinese (those of Pekin Man), in the form of a largish pebble tool. The general type of implement from the whole Far East is related to this, being a fair-sized chopper having one edge flaked along one side and constituting something quite distinct from the two-faced hand axe of the West. There were some local variations on this, owing in part to the kind of stone used (in Burma the choppers or cleavers were made of petrified wood). There were also some flake tools. But the whole area stands independent of the West, with a boundary in India. Furthermore, it seems to have taken a late start, and to have lagged behind in developments, as did South Africa from this time on.

New ideas in flaking

Toward the end of this period, the Middle Pleistocene, still another advance took place in the method of making flakes, the Levalloisian technique. A flake tool, unlike a pebble tool or a hand axe, is made from a flat flake that has itself been struck off from a core. The Levalloisian technique made the shape of this surer by advance preparation: first the core piece was flaked to a turtle-shell shape, and then a flat place made, as if you had chopped off the turtle's head and chopped off some of the shell in doing so. Then a careful blow against this special platform neatly takes off the crown of the turtle's shell, giving you a well-formed flake, smooth on one side and preflaked on the other. It is practically a prefabricated spear point, or knife, or scraper, as you wish. In this method the basic form of a tool had been brought under a considerable degree of control, and for that reason it was an idea important for the future of stoneworking.

Still later, similar flakes for tools were made in another fashion by the Mousterians. A core of the same general kind was used, but the flakes were made directly, by strik-

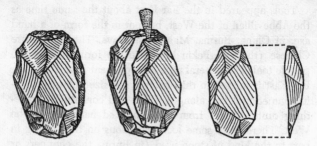

FIG. 7. *The making of a Levallois flake.*

ing from the edge toward the dome, and taken for use instead of being discarded as a mere step in preparing the dome for the striking off of a flake of the Levalloisian type. And, as another new technique, the edges of the flakes were trimmed around by knocking off small secondary chips.

This brings us into the last and highest phase of the long Lower Paleolithic period of human culture, in the third interglacial and the early part of the last glacial. Over more than half a million years stone tools had lost much of their early crudity and had shapes that were both definite and efficient, though nothing as fine as an American Indian arrowhead had ever yet been made. The Levalloisian technique prevailed widely. So also did the Acheulian tradition, now producing relatively small hand axes of a more special nature.

With the progress of time, and as the Würm or Fourth Glacial Phase of the North came on, further advances and varieties manifested themselves. In Europe, along with the Levalloisian and Acheulian traditions, there had already grown up a new industry, the Mousterian, related somewhat to both of them, and possibly also to the older, simple flake industry, now marked by good secondary flaking. In Western Europe the Mousterian was identified with the Neanderthal men, but it was more varied in its tools and techniques, from place to place and time to time, than its name might imply. Actually in this phase, which is some-

FIG. 8. A *Mousterian point*.

times and properly set off as the Middle Paleolithic, tools
had become distinctly smaller and more varied, though
appealing largely to familiar and ancient techniques. In
Africa other cultures of this nature appeared, differing
from the Mousterian and from each other, being suited to
forest (Sangoan) or open country (Fauresmith), but exhibiting a reduction in size of tools, and more specific
forms, while harking back to the same basic techniques.
These techniques still spread over enormous areas, covering Europe and most of Africa and extending into Central Asia and India. The Far East stuck to its ancient
choppers, however, and neither the hand axe nor the
Levalloisian flake technique ever appeared there.

So, from the beginning right up to the end of the Lower
Paleolithic, practically all we know about culture is stonework; at least this is all that can be studied systematically.
It is a rather surprising thing that bone or antler does not
seem to have been used to any degree. It might have decayed entirely in all the oldest deposits, but this is not the
complete answer, because it would have survived in the
Pekin caves dating from the Second (Mindel) Glacial,
since unworked antler and bone is there in profusion.
(Some of this was used by man, but it is doubtful whether
any of it was shaped intentionally.) Also, the Mousterian

people used bone anvils for their stoneworking, and a few crude split-bone skinning tools, and that seems to be all.

The rest of what we can tell is made up of random bits of information and guesses. At first man's culture did not separate him very far from nature. His economy was not really different from that of the apes: he gathered the goods of nature to eat, and spent his time at this. Probably, however, his gathering included meat, at least as far back as the man-ape stage, and not vegetable matter only. A little further along we can make out his actual bill of fare somewhat, in such a place as the Pekin caves where quantities of animal bones are found along with berry seeds. Something more important is found too: charcoal. So we know that the Pekin men, in the Second Glacial, were already using fire, and cooking is a great aid to digestion. This is culture with a vengeance.

These people probably used caves for shelter only casually, like the man-apes. Whether they dressed themselves we do not know. But life probably had become this formal much later on, among the Mousterians, because they lived close to the glacier, and because their implements suggest skin-working. Other touches of formality appear. The Mousterians were without art, but they must have had religious ideas. In Swiss caves they left what look like shrines made up of the skulls of bears they had killed. And they buried their dead, which the Pekin men did not do. The Pekin men had, alas, different ideas of sepulture: they ate each other, cracking open shinbones and skulls, and strewing the grisly remnants around the cave, to be found in our own century. In this they were apparently like the man-apes, some of whose skulls seem to have the same kinds of wounds from a bone billy as did the skulls of baboons they used for food.

Whatever we may find out, or not find out, about culture in this long dawn phase, the striking thing is the pitiable slowness with which it changed and went forward. In this chapter, describing the Lower Paleolithic, I have covered very nearly all the Ice Age. And the clumsiness of the most ancient tools, persisting so long after the benefit of tools must have already strongly affected human life, is surprising. But perhaps after you have seen the men of the time you will be less confounded.

6. Early Men

We have a far broader view of the tools of the Lower Paleolithic than we have of the men who were making them. Early human fossils are all too scarce, and we still have a lot of puzzles on our hands as to just how humanity was developing in the Pleistocene, even as to who our own proper ancestors were.

We start, of course, with the australopithecine stage. The man-apes now known may be mostly or all too late to be our direct ancestors, since other men—hominines—were apparently on the scene along with them. This is not the point: we certainly arose from this kind of animal, even if the event must be pushed back a little or a lot in time. They are precisely the springboard humanity needed. And there are enough differences among them to suggest that evolutionary experimenting was going on; again, this is the sort of promising brew from which advancing kinds of men could emerge.

We have seen that they were all erect walkers: the pelvis shows it, and fragments of the spine, limbs and feet confirm it. So does the skull, which was hinged to the spine in a generally upright position. But there was work to be done. The hipbones, though basically like ours, showed minor differences; and fragments of the hand suggest that it was shorter in the thumb and less suited for fine work than ours. Above all, the man-apes were still decidedly ape-headed in general appearance. Jaws were large and deep, if not greatly jutting forward, even in the smaller types. In the largest, the lower jaw was astonishingly broad at the corners, with massive molar teeth and really huge chewing muscles. Thus the jaws were ape-size, but distinctly not ape-shape, being wide behind but not long, and not having the broad and protruding front teeth that mark a great ape. The brains were also ape-size, though possibly with relation to body size, the man-apes were a little better off in this respect. With about 500–600 cubic centimeters of room inside the skull, they had made no significant start toward the figure of about 1450 cubic centimeters for the average American male of today.

As we have seen, the man-apes come out of the haze of the earliest Pleistocene during Villafranchian time, or in the early Middle Pleistocene following the First Glaciation—some say exclusively in the latter period. They are now known from several places in South and East Africa, from Lake Chad, and from Palestine and Java; obviously by this time they were spread throughout the tropical Old World. Whatever the precise time was—let the geologists dispute this—they were being pressed by the first wave of hominines, or early men, whose fossil remains have been found in the same deposits as the man-apes both in Africa (Swartkrans, South Africa) and in Java (Sangiran).

Ancient men

We can represent these new hominids by describing the famous Java Man, named Pithecanthropus by his discoverer. His thighbone is perfectly modern, and of modern size, leading us to suppose that the same may be said of the rest of his skeleton when it comes to light. But his head was a brutal affair. It represents a distinct step up from the australopiths: like them, the region of the mouth is protruding because of a large jaw and teeth (in an ape the whole face is simply one long slant), but the jaw and the protrusion are relatively less. And he had a slightly larger brain, though so slightly that we can make little of it: males probably had a brain volume of about 900 cubic centimeters. The whole appearance of his skull is unmistakably more human, to use the word charitably, than that of a man-ape. And yet some features of it seem actually to be more primitive. The braincase is low and entirely without a forehead, and exceedingly thick—more so than that of any man, ape or australopith. His front teeth were relatively large and spread out, and there was a gap in the upper tooth row at the corner, to receive the tip of the lower canine tooth. This is an apelike trait not seen in any other human or australopith fossil, which emphasizes the broadened, rather apelike nature of the front of the mouth.

The remains of the Java men consist of several leg bones, major parts of five skulls (one a baby), and various odd teeth and other fragments. They came from riverbanks at

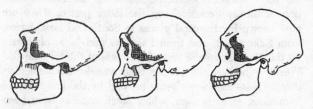

FIG. 9. *Skulls of the Java, Pekin, and Solo men.*

different places in central Java, and are believed to belong to levels corresponding to the First Interglacial and Second Glacial phases, or possibly two periods of the Second Glacial; at any rate, a respectable period of time. In the island of Java, the Villafranchian fauna is immediately succeeded by a new group of animals, opening the Middle Pleistocene, known as the Djetis fauna, followed by another, the Trinil fauna. Java Man's remains occur in both of these last. His age therefore would be on the order of 500,000 years and less, though I dislike to deal in figures; the geological relationships remain the same, but new methods of dating may at any time change considerably the actual number of years involved. Let us just remember that Java Man is a very early man, perhaps the oldest, living there with his more primitive man-ape cousin (known since its discovery as Meganthropus), and that the time of both of them is the very beginning of the Middle Pleistocene, marked by the first new animal group (Djetis) to succeed the Villafranchian. Quite possibly the whole lot, Java Man among them, walked into Java when it was hitched to mainland Asia as a result of the fall of the sea in the Günz, or First, cold phase. No sign of a tool has come to light in any of the deposits containing Java Man, but the crudest of choppers do occur in the upper Trinil zone—just after—and we may judge that they were made by the immediate descendants of the men whose bones we have.

The men of the Pekin caves (*Sinanthropus*) lived just after the known Java men, during the late Second Interglacial. There is no question about their tools, found in a large filled cave along with their own bones: they are one form of the same general Far Eastern chopper type. The human bones were fairly plentiful, as such things go, and pieces, large or small, were recovered of about forty different individuals. A few fragments of thighbones assure us that they were entirely modern in shape, as in the case of Java Man, though a little heavy in construction.

As to the skull, a look at it reveals at once that it is basically like Java Man's. It is simply an improved version. The bony brows are just as massive. The outline is much like the Javanese form. But the brain volume of males was something not far from 1150 cubic centimeters, or about what an unusually small normal brain of today might be. The skull itself was thinner, with signs of a less massive set of neck muscles to hold it up at the back, and it had in outline a distinct if modest angle at the front, the merest suggestion of a forehead. The face has a general resemblance to Java Man's, but the whole mouth has receded and become smaller. The smaller teeth make a more human arch, and the shorter jaw is not so sloping at the front. It has no real chin, to be sure, but it has at least an angle where a chin ought to be, and is not so arrogantly retreating as is the Javanese jaw. Pekin Man had about as much of a chin as he had of a forehead, and this was very little of either.

Away at the other end of the Old World, near Oran, in

Algeria, a French paleontologist, Professor Camille Aram-
bourg, discovered several human jaws and part of a skullcap, in an ancient filled lake at a place called Ternifine. He
pointed out, and everyone agrees, that these jaws are
strikingly like those of Pekin Man, and the teeth as well,
though the teeth are actually as large as Java Man's. The
animal bones proclaim an age that is probably early Middle
Pleistocene and late in the Second Glacial or just after,
which should correspond well with the time of Pekin Man
in China. The men of Ternifine were making hand axes of
an early form.

So was the Chellean Man found at Olduvai Gorge in
Tanganyika by the Leakeys. This appears to be the skull
that goes with the Ternifine jaws, and it also resembles in
form and size the skulls of the Far East, although its brows
are more swollen and projecting. It lacks a face, so that a
tight fit with the Ternifine jaws cannot be made. The fossil
lay in the now well-known Bed II at Olduvai, some distance above the man-ape Zinjanthropus, and it has the
provisional designation of Chellean, an older synonym for
Abbevillian, because it was accompanied by hand axes of
early form. While it cannot be proved that the skull
matches the Ternifine jaws, this is certainly the conservative conclusion to draw at the moment, by the rule that one
must not multiply kinds of fossil men without clear reason.

This seems also to be the way to deal with Telanthropus,
whose two lower jaws and facial fragment were found at
the man-ape site of Swartkrans in South Africa, along with
plentiful remains of man-apes themselves. The parts quite
clearly belong to a primitive hominine, being distinct in
bone and tooth from the man-apes of Swartkrans, and the
only safe place to put this hominine for the time being is
with the same general type found in the four regions we
have visited. The time is tentatively Second Glacial, or
about the same as the *later* Java men. The tools found in
man-ape sites are Chellean (including early hand axes)
according to Drs. R. Mason and J. T. Robinson, who as-
cribe them to Telanthropus, not to the man-apes.

Thus, and only in recent years, we are beginning to get

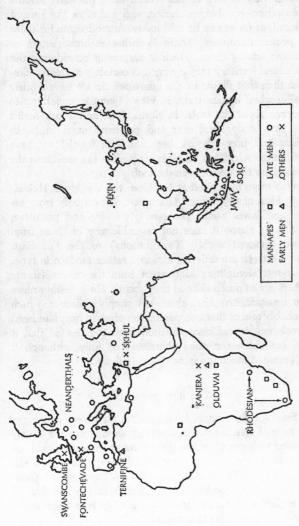

FIG. 10. *Where fossil men have been found.*

a clear view of men of this crucial time, the early Middle Pleistocene—just before, during, and just after the Second Glacial, as far as can be said today. A good name for them is pithecanthropines. There is rather a high degree of likeness among them, which is surprising considering the enormous territory they cover; it is certainly a greater likeness than that shown by the man-apes. So we have a fairly well-marked human stage in view. There is something to observe about the tools: in North, East and South Africa we have early hand axes and pre-hand axes; in North China and Java (though here not with fossils) we have chopping tools. Thus, one cannot decide the tool from the maker, nor the maker from the tool.

One more man lived at the time, the European Heidelberg Man of the Second Glaciation, known only from his jaw and lower teeth. The jaw is massive and primitive, but in its shape it does not resemble any of those from Africa (except slightly Telanthropus) or the Far East, and the teeth are different also and rather modern in type. This sets Heidelberg Man apart from the others (if the others are as much alike as they seem). He is neither more nor less primitive than they, but simply different, which probably means that one population of early men had been developing in sufficient isolation from the rest so that it did not share the same characters so fully, although it represented much the same stage of advance.

The next steps up

Surprisingly enough, from here on, for a very long time, remains of man become distressingly skimpy and are largely limited to lower jaws in a poor state of preservation. I am now talking about the later Middle Pleistocene and the early Upper Pleistocene, a period of hundreds of thousands of years and running roughly from the late Second Interglacial of Europe over the Third or Riss Glacial and into the early Third Interglacial.

First, the jaws, from Morocco (Casablanca, Rabat, Temara), from East Africa (Kanam) and from South

Africa (Cave of Hearths, in the Makapan Valley). They say very little, and if we can speak in their behalf it is to remark that they seem to be descendants of the general African-Far East (pithecanthropine) lot of primitive men we have just reviewed. In general, the jaws are chinless and robust, but they have become definitely lighter, shorter and smaller. They tend simply to confirm the persistence, and gradual progress (as we see progress) of this ancient stock, at least on the continent of Africa.

However, other populations were not waiting on such a gradual pace. For the long interval, our prime evidence is four important skulls, or sets of skulls, and they show us a much more rapid move in the direction of our own kind. Let us look at them in their probable order of appearance.

The first two are alike in time and type: Steinheim and Swanscombe. These are the localities of gravel pits in West Germany and southern England, respectively, and the gravel of the pits can, by the animals contained, be firmly dated to the late Second Interglacial. Both pits yielded the skulls, or partial skulls, of young women of this time, and at Swanscombe the skull layer contained Middle Acheulian hand axes, which are appropriate for such a date.

The Steinheim girl had a skull with a good forehead, flattish sides, a moderately high vault and a gently rounded descending profile in back, as well as a vertical face. All these are the special marks of modern humanity, of Homo sapiens in the strict sense. But above her face there bulged forward a large and primitive brow ridge such as no modern man would ever have, and her nose and mouth were also fairly large and spacious. Her back teeth, however, all that remain, are generally modern in size and form.

Of the Swanscombe girl only the two sidewalls (parietals) and the back and base (occipital bone) came to light. A particular interest of this fossil is that the three bones were recovered over a period of twenty years at short distances from one another but all in exactly the same thin seam of gravel in the long series of such gravel deposits laid down by the Thames during the Second Interglacial as it was silting up. Thus the genuineness of the skull's origin in the gravel was perfectly demonstrated; this may not seem so exciting a matter as it once did, but in former years the arguments over the antiquity of various specimens—and I am not referring to the Piltdown fraud—were long and bitter, and usually turned on this matter of exact derivation. Fortunately such ambiguities of finding are now almost always avoided.

The skull has the same general kind of vault as the Steinheim specimen, and since it lacks forehead and face the impression of modernity it gives is striking. Nonetheless it is somewhat low and, most important, one can only assume that it resembled the Steinheim skull in having large and primitive brows as well; at least it would be more adventurous to assume the contrary. These brows, let us say, are not as large and heavy as those of the earlier men, nor yet of some much later men; and the brains of the two girls were smallish to medium by modern standards. What they really demonstrate is that the kind of high and rounded braincase, with a fairly good forehead and flat sides, which graces our own head, had taken shape by the end of the Second Interglacial in Europe.

We should ask ourselves whether these people really differed from those whose still-crude jaws from Africa I have mentioned above. We have skulls without jaws in Europe, and jaws without skulls in Africa. Could they be put together? From their nature it seems most unlikely, the jaws being too crude and heavy. Perhaps the next case sheds a little light.

At Kanjera, near Lake Victoria in Kenya, Dr. L. S. B. Leakey in 1932 picked up and dug up shattered fragments of at least four skulls, and of a few skeleton bones. Their date has been much disputed, but all the positive evidence has continuously pointed to something as early as Steinheim and Swanscombe, and at least not later than the succeeding Third Glacial. The dispute has been stimulated by the thoroughgoing sapiens or modern features of the skulls: though robust (and densely fossilized) the parts are quite

sufficient to show that the braincase was of modern form
and that the brows were of modern size, not bulging as in
Steinheim or in any of the other known fossil men of almost
the whole Pleistocene. The rest of their structure also seems
fully modern. The Kanjera men were therefore one more
and final step beyond the two European girls in the evolution of modern man. The vital question of their date has
not been resolved fully, but the evidence in the case is such
as to keep these skulls in the forefront of consideration.

In any case, the final set of skulls tells the same story.
These are once again from Europe, and from the first part
of the Third Interglacial. They consist only of the skullcap
of one individual and a patch of the forehead of another,
from the Fontéchevade cave in the Charente, France.
Along with them were found the bones of warm weather,
Third Interglacial animals, and implements of a particular
industry, the Tayacian. This is earlier than the Mousterian;
and Mousterian material (everywhere associated with Neanderthal Man) lay above these skulls at Fontéchevade,
and is thus definitely later. In spite of being so fragmentary,
the skulls show quite clearly that their owners had brain-
cases and foreheads of modern type, without large and
protruding brows or slanting foreheads. They finish this
slender trail of evidence to the effect that the skull type of
modern man had been taking shape in the later Middle
Pleistocene, and had essentially finished the process in the
Third Interglacial. Simply for a general idea, we might
say this was about 150,000 years ago.

The last lowbrows

This is not the end of the story. Paradoxically, the stage
was now taken over in the next period, the later Third Interglacial and early Fourth Glacial, by a cruder group of
men. Their brains had indeed reached modern size (in
some cases rather less), but their skulls were low and flattened, bedecked in front with heavy, continuous bars of
bone forming projecting brows, and their faces were similarly large, with big tooth rows and, as far as we know

them, longish jaws without projecting chins. Taken generally, these were markedly advanced over the old pithecanthropines while they lacked the delicate vertical face
and high rounded skull of modern man.

Consider first Solo Man, so named because he was
found, under dismaying circumstances, at Ngandong on
the Solo River, only a few miles from Trinil, also on the
Solo, where the first specimen of Java Man was found long
ago. A remnant of an older bank of the river yielded two
shinbones and eleven skulls, and nothing else; furthermore
the skulls lacked every vestige of face and jaw—not a tooth
was found—and all had their bases broken in, most being
discovered lying upside down in the gravel. Another case of
cannabalism is indicated. Such specimens of stonework as
were recovered from the deposit seem to have disappeared
during the wartime Japanese occupation of Java, but what
is known from them and from geology points to a late
date, that is, during the Fourth Glacial phase.

The leg bones are modern, though robust. The skulls
are also robust, remarkably so, and larger in every way
than the older Java Man's; the brain, however, was not as
large as the appearance of the skulls suggests, and was only
a little larger than those of the Pekin men. The crania
have massive brows, thick walls, fleeting and nearly absent
foreheads, and low ridged roofs. They look on the whole
like a later and expanded version of the Java Man, and
general opinion takes them as just that. In other words,
they are probably direct descendants, hundreds of thousands of years later, of the original Java Man, having undergone a modest degree of cerebral evolution from that general stage.

The Mapa skull, from South China, is incomplete but
evidently represents this stage of humanity on the Asiatic
mainland. Its date is not well known as yet, but seems to
fall in this time range, and in itself it has not been fully
described. From its appearance it has a resemblance to
the Neanderthal men, whom we shall come to soon.

Southern Africa was occupied during the time in question by Rhodesian Man. His first skull, in good shape but

minus its lower jaw, was found in 1921 during mining operations far down the sloping back part of an old cave at Broken Hill, Northern Rhodesia, where some other Rhodesian man may well have tossed it. He certainly was not buried. Nearby were other human bones, from at least two people: hipbones, a sacrum, leg bones and an upper jaw. The jaw is related to that on the skull; the limb bones do not differ from our own. The top part of a second skull, broken into more than two dozen parts, was found in 1953, naturally exposed on the surface by the wind, at Hopefield, on Saldanha Bay, north of Cape Town and a long distance from Broken Hill. Thus Rhodesian Man evidently occupied most or all of South Africa, at a time from the middle of the Fourth or last Glacial Phase of Europe (about 40,000 years ago) back for an unknown period. The Broken Hill skull belongs to the end of the period, and the Hopefield skull cannot be very much earlier.

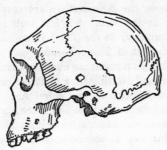

FIG. 11. *The skull of Rhodesian Man, from Broken Hill.*

The two skulls are generally alike, and suggest slightly the Solo skulls in their form. Over the eyes is a tremendous straight bar of bone, the largest known in man. Behind this the braincase, as in Solo Man, is low and somewhat ridged, and the forehead is hardly present; at the back of the head there is a sharp crest of bone for the neck muscles. Beyond this, however, the skull is far less heavy, and is deeper than in the Solo skulls, with a brain volume of some 1300 cubic centimeters. Whether the face was any-

thing like Solo Man's of course cannot be told, but the
Rhodesian face is very large, and not projecting, though
primitive in form. The teeth form a short, round arch of
modern type, contrasting with the Java and Pekin men.
The teeth themselves are large, but badly worn and very
badly decayed. Viewed from the back, the skull does not
appear so primitive, having the vertical sides of Homo
sapiens. So, in various ways, Rhodesian Man suggests that
he may be, like Solo Man, a late African descendant of
the old pithecanthropine stratum; at the same time he resembles modern man in his teeth and palate (the second
upper jaw is smaller and less primitive-seeming) and in the
back of his skull.

The Neanderthals

The last of the human types of this time period and stage
of development is Neanderthal Man. Unlike the Rhodesian
and Solo people, the Neanderthals are very well known.
They appear in the form of a few scattered specimens
(Italy and Germany) in the Third Interglacial, at a time
subsequent to that of Fontéchevade; but in the Fourth
Glacial their known remains are numerous, from Spain right
across Europe and North Africa to Palestine and Iraq on
the south and Uzbekistan in Central Asia in the north.
This whole distribution in time and space agrees, as I have
said, with that of the Mousterian culture. Now we cannot
prove that this was a monopoly either way and it may
not even be a safe assumption to make, but the fact is that
neither has been found in some other association as yet.

The Mousterian culture, in fact, is not as uniform as the
single name implies, and seems to be an amalgam of various
predecessors. The Neanderthals also exhibit some physical
variety, perhaps of a tribal or racial nature. Nonetheless
they have a well-marked character of their own, readily
distinguishable from modern man's as well as from that
of their contemporaries, just described, the men of their
own "stage." Heads were long and low, and brow ridges
were sizable and continuous, but unlike Solo or Rhodesian

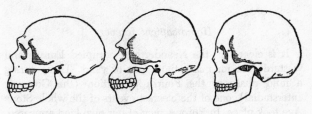

FIG. 12. *Skulls of one of the later Western Neanderthals, of Mount Carmel Man, and of modern man.*

man the brows formed rounded arches over the eyes, not bars, and the skull was flat, not ridged, on top, and the sides bulged out over the ears in a curve. And instead of a sharp ridge across the back, typical Neanderthalers had a smooth though prominent mound. The whole face jutted particularly far forward, so that the cheekbones were not high at the corners, but ran back in a smooth curve from the large and prominent nose. The face was long, the teeth formed a generous U-shaped arch, and the large lower jaw receded without any chin prominence. (Rhodesian Man, or course, shared a face of this size though details are different.)

Strangest of all, the bones of the skeleton, which seem to have been quite modern in all other human types back to Java Man (admittedly little is known), had in the Neanderthals an extraordinary character, perhaps more marked in some cases, but in any case unique to this population and found throughout it. The bones were relatively short, bowed and thick-jointed, with various special features of proportion and of muscle attachment, often exaggerated in the telling but unmistakable all the same. In the pelvis Dr. T. Dale Stewart of the U. S. National Museum has detected a minor peculiarity of conformation, in the only two complete hipbones, which is not seen in modern man at all.

Homo sapiens forever

It is clear that the Neanderthals occupied Europe and western Asia for many thousands of years. Then, during a mild phase of the Fourth Glaciation (the Göttweig Interstadial), one of the clearest events of the whole Stone Age took place. In Europe, men of our own kind appeared, and the Neanderthals vanished. Bones of the newcomers, and their tools, lie directly above those of the Neanderthals in the western caves. There cannot have been a simple transition, in a few thousand years, from one population to the other—a sudden evolution from Neanderthal to the later form. Just what took place we do not know, but a triumph of the new people in the competition for game would explain things. There need not have been actual warfare, and no signs have ever been found suggesting it.

I have referred to "modern man" and to Homo sapiens as being suggested or represented by Steinheim, Swanscombe, Kanjera and Fontéchevade. Except for these, he now appears for the first time as a new kind of physical type, though there is no reason to think he was actually more intelligent, as his traditional name implies, than the Neanderthals. What distinguishes modern man from all the others I have described is a final refinement of the head. This is neatly held fully erect on a slender neck, a neck that does not fasten its muscles over a large area, or on a prominent ridge, at the back of the skull. The skull itself is high, well curved over the crown and well filled out, and its walls are thin. The brain overhangs the whole face, so that the forehead is nearly vertical. If there are brow ridges they are not heavy or, so to speak, structural, acting to finish off the top of the face; instead they are essentially vestigial, being bumps on either side of the midline. The face is small and more delicate than in other types, so pulled in below the forehead as to give the nose a bridge, and actually producing hollows in the cheekbones on either side of the nose. In the mouth there is some racial variation in the general amount of projection and size of the teeth, but the retraction of the mouth is extreme and the shrinking lower jaw has developed a chin as a new kind of stiffening for its arch.

This is a well-defined form of head and face, which characterizes all living men and is easily distinguished from other types of known hominids. We assume that it is more advanced in an evolutionary sense without knowing exactly why. It does of course represent the furtherance of the trend seen from the man-apes through the pithecanthropines of the Middle Pleistocene and the more recent lowbrows. Its braincase must have emerged as the brain increased, by natural selection, in connection with the making of tools and the development of culture generally, and as the brain's housing, also by selection, tended to become more efficient and economical. Similarly the face possibly responded to the evolution of human language: with the needs for strong jaws and teeth out of the way, the mouth could become more of a squarish box well suited to forming difficult sounds with the teeth and tongue.

Such is the kind of man, then, who came into Europe about 35,000 B.C. at the opening of the Upper Paleolithic culture stage. These people, in Europe, are spoken of broadly as the Cro-Magnons, and many of their skeletons have been found in the caves. They are simply robust versions of the Europeans of later times—they are already White in racial nature, that is to say—so that the population of Europe, North Africa and the Near East is a continuous one from this point on. Also, as far as we know, no other kind of man—no non-sapiens populations—survived beyond the same point in other parts of the world, though the evidence is far poorer. In South Africa, the Florisbad Man lived even earlier—about the same time as Rhodesian Man, perhaps 40,000 B.C.—and his skull and face were also of the sapiens type, though with exceptionally large brow ridges. His racial nature is not clear. Also uncertain in racial nature is a skull that may be of the same age from the Niah Cave in Borneo; this one lacks brow development and contrasts with Florisbad. Men had entered Australia by at least 15,000 B.C. and were clearly of the racial type of the living Australian aboriginals. And the American Indians had crossed into America ten thousand years earlier or more; the indications from later remains is that they were of the general type of later Indians.

Thus we see Homo sapiens, as we have defined him, appearing literally all over the world before the end of the Pleistocene, with indications that his basic racial distinctions already existed in 35,000 B.C. But all the evidence is still most unsatisfactory and we are left with a major puzzle: where did he come from? Or, put in more scientific terms, what was the process of his evolution?

He clearly did not come from Europe, but that is about all one can say. In the Near East an Upper Paleolithic type of culture succeeds a Mousterian one as it does in Europe, but also occurs in lower levels as well. Does this mean that, although this was Neanderthal territory, modern man was hovering in the vicinity? (I do not like, as I have indicated, to diagnose physical types from tools.) In caves at Mount Carmel in Palestine, regular Neanderthals are succeeded after a few thousand years by the Skhul men, who are essentially modern but for enlarged brows and some Neanderthal traits of the face (they are quite unlike their contemporary, Florisbad Man). Some believe this demonstrates mixture of moderns and Neanderthals. Some anthropologists believe it shows modern man evolving directly from the Neanderthal population here, but this is an explanation that neglects the rest of the world, and ignores the much earlier Fontéchevade and Kanjera men, as well as others.

What is the pattern? Dr. Franz Weidenreich, who did much work on Pekin Man, believed that each local type of earlier man had gone straight forward to evolve into one of the modern races: Pekin into the Mongoloids, Solo into the Australian aboriginals, Rhodesian into the Africans, etc. But modern races are all actually very similar physically, certainly in the skeleton, and not likely to have come from markedly differing parent stocks. Others believe that, from the early pithecanthropine stage, several lines began to diverge, all tending to evolve in brain size, with one—our own—evolving also in head form. This would give Solo, Rhodesian, Neanderthal, Homo sapiens and perhaps others.

Some think, in fact, that the Steinheim-Swanscombe people were ancestors both of ourselves and of the Neanderthals, by one line which continued to progress and another which slid off into a special and peculiar form, both of course in different parts of the world. But the solution of these most interesting problems remains in the future. All we really know is that, late in the Pleistocene, Homo sapiens prevailed, and we find him in possession of Upper Paleolithic tools and a hunting culture that was clearly superior to what had gone before.

7. The End of the Stone Age

If you go to the town of Montignac in southwestern France, cross the bridge over the Vézère River, and follow the road around the shoulder and up to the crest of the hill, you find yourself before the entrance of the Lascaux cave. You can walk down into it by concrete steps and view it with ease: the floor has been deepened and it is dramatically lighted for you. Things were less easy for the hunters who by torchlight, some twenty thousand years ago, painted on the walls pictures of the animals they hunted. But they painted well and you will never—if you have as much soul as a microbe—forget what you have seen.

Huge spotted bulls face you. In a line, little red or yellowish horses, rather Chinese-looking, prance down a corridor. All around the main cave and in galleries leading off are other animals, painted on a natural white background in shades of red, brown, yellow and purple, and in black: a row of antlered deer heads, small antelopes, a rhinoceros, a wounded bison with its entrails dragging below. They are painted with verve, and not by children or doodlers, but by men who knew how to portray what they had seen, using only natural earths and charcoal, made into paint with animal fat.

These were the people of the middle of the western European Upper Paleolithic. When you have finished with Lascaux and walk away, you are facing down a valley that was the Fifth Avenue of the late Pleistocene, thronged then with large game. It is still lined with the caves and shelters used by the hunters, and a number of these other caves are also painted, engraved or sculptured. We meet at last the cavemen you have heard so much about. The late Neanderthals used caves, and many of the same caves at that, but it was the men of the Upper Paleolithic who decorated them so spectacularly.

However, the "caveman" label is a little unfortunate. Generations of school children have heard that "our ancestors lived in caves" and the whole thing has become a frayed item of humor like a banana peel or a mother-in-law. Certainly the Cro-Magnons and their confreres used caves and gladly; that is where we find their skeletons and their household rubbish. So also have other men used the caves, for various reasons, down to the present; and if the archaeologists of our own century had only left things alone the archaeologists of the next would doubtless find a layer of Coca-Cola bottles and beer cans overlying everything else in the cave floors. But if the Paleolithic people had depended wholly on caves for shelter there would have been a fearful housing shortage. They are known to have made tents and underground houses and, if some of the cave paintings can be so understood, summer wickiups of sticks and brush.

It is difficult indeed to conjure up, from their skulls and their meager tools, any kind of a convincing mental picture of the hunting and daily life of the lowbrows of the old Lower Paleolithic. Not so for the later Stone Age, whose denizens stand out nearly in the round, and have not entirely vanished yet. They are the kind of "savages" we can recognize. These people were from the beginning "modern" men, as I have said, and also "modern" hunters, with a bigger bag of tricks and a richer inventory of items of culture than the Neanderthals or any others.

They were certainly skillful hunters and, in these glacial times, may have been especially dependent on meat as opposed to vegetables. For meat in those days went around in very large packages, from mammoth-size down through woolly rhino (in earlier phases and colder zones) and bison and large wild cattle, to the reindeer and the rela-

tively small horse of the time. But this might be an unbalanced picture of diet, because most of what we know
comes from Europe and North America (since this includes the time of the arrival of the American Indians),
where climates were much affected by the glaciers. The
rest of the world has been insufficiently studied, and in any
case all Africa, and southern and eastern Asia, were somewhat behind in culture development.

This whole new phase, the appearance everywhere of
advanced hunters, belongs to the tail end of the Pleistocene
and the beginning of postglacial times. Open tundra covered only by moss and low shrubs, or grassy steppe, held
sway while the ice sheets remained and retreated, giving
way at last to forests in the newly temperate zone. The
period runs from about 35,000 B.C. to about 8000 B.C.
Both dates are loose, the first because it is not known at all
exactly, and the second because it marks the end of the
true hunting phase in just one place (the Middle East),
when farming began. It has been ending in other places
ever since, and has never ended at all in a few. It is the
period of the Upper Paleolithic and the Mesolithic. These
are old names, meaning (upper) Old Stone Age and
Middle Stone Age respectively; the distinctions are now
almost meaningless, but the names have remained in good
use for other reasons.

During the Lower Paleolithic the basic industries or
stone-working techniques were apt, as in the case of the
Acheulian and Levalloisian traditions at least, to be of the
same general style over enormous areas for vast lengths of
time. The shorter Upper Paleolithic contained more variety
in stone tools and other objects, and there was a larger
number of distinct cultures, looking like the work of specific
major culture groups. To call these groups "tribal" might
be cutting it too fine, but that is the rough idea. In the
old days, archaeologists used to talk about "periods" of
the European Upper Paleolithic, and you may have heard
of them: Aurignacian, Solutrean and Magdalenian. Nowadays they think instead of somewhat different populations
(you might compare them with some of the main Ameri-

can Indian types, like the Plains versus the Pueblos) with different cultures, partly existing at the same time and partly succeeding one another in Europe or parts of Europe, as new immigrants or influences arrived, or as changes took place on the spot. The main series of events is the same, and the old terms still have some meaning. But the archaeologists today see much more complicated groupings, as they work out finer distinctions of stonework, and as they plot these all on the map, observing how they are related to one another in layers in the ground at a great many different ancient living sites.

As things now stand, there were two early traditions, one called Perigordian (comprising the Châtelperronian and Gravettian) and the other Aurignacian, each of these made up of rather complicated successions in themselves. The former Solutrean "period" seems to have been instead a relatively short florescence of some older ideas, perhaps of African derivation, which were especially developed both in eastern Europe and in Spain; this outburst of striking stonework was relatively short. The latest phase in the west of Europe was the Magdalenian; but if you are considering the final stages of Europe as a whole, the picture is more varied, with several related or legatee local cultures to the north and east, all running on to the end of the Paleolithic.

Virtuosity in stone

The manufacture of stone tools was more of an art than ever before, and involved some new inventions. And, instead of a few kinds of tools only, these cultures had literally dozens of forms. But they all began in the same way, being made from a parallel-sided flake called a blade. In the Levallois school, a core was prepared to look like the back of a tortoise, and one flake knocked off for a tool. By this new method, a core was made to look like a medium artillery shell, and a strip flake was knocked off, from the edge of the butt end, running down the side toward the point, giving in its most perfect form a long knife with two razor edges and a slightly curved-in point. This process probably involved wrapping the core in a skin to get the right distribution of pressure, and using a bone punch along with a stone hammer in order to direct the critical blow to exactly the right point on the butt end, from exactly the right direction. A large number of such blades could be struck off a good core, one after another like the leaves of an artichoke, until there was almost nothing left of the core itself.

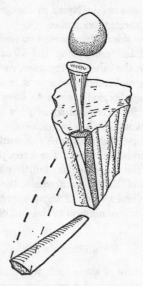

FIG. 13. *The making of flake blades.*

This achievement in forming a blade was complemented by an achievement in finishing up the tool, known as pressure flaking. Instead of a small chip being struck off the flake by a blow, it was pressed off with a small bone tool in some way, which would produce no shattering effect and made it possible to apply just the same pressure for every chip at exactly the place wanted. So, for giving final shape to an implement, it was something like using a penknife for whittling in place of trying to whittle with an axehead.

The raw flakes struck from the core were used like a key maker's blanks to make all the other kinds of tools needed, by this pressure retouching. You might want a knife; you could hardly use the sharp untrimmed blade because you would be as likely to cut your fingers as your chop. So you would dull one edge simply by bruising and blunting it. The working edge, also, would be too sharp, being likely to nick and break down, to say nothing of leaving little chips in the food. So you strengthened it by working it back with pressure retouching, which thickened the edge while still leaving it quite sharp enough to be efficient. A deliberately duller and steeper edge gave a scraping tool, for cleaning the flesh away from the inside of an animal's hide with less danger of accidentally cutting through the hide itself, and so spoiling it. An easier scraper to use was an end scraper, from a flake with blunted sides and a rounded, steeply flaked end. A spearpoint was made by retouching both edges and bringing them to a point, reshaping the tool as much as necessary.

These are basic tools, and efficient ones. But the Upper Paleolithic brings into prominence whole new sets of sec-

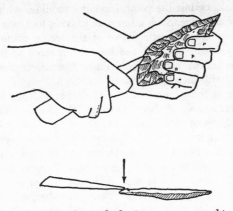

FIG. 14. *A simple method of pressure retouching.*

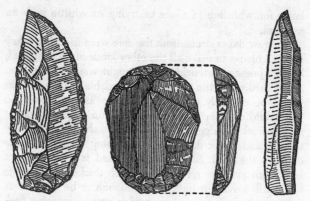

Fig. 15. *Upper Paleolithic flake tools. Left, a flake-blade knife. Middle, a double-ended scraper. Right, a flake-blade burin or graving tool.*

ondary stone tools, made for working wood and bone into the actual tools wanted. Concave scrapers are found, for shaving down the shafts of spears or darts. Awls were made, for drilling holes in either bone or wood. And for all kinds of work with these materials there existed a number of different types of small chisels or engraving tools, made by striking a flake from the blade the wrong way, so to speak, against the point, leaving a shoulder with a narrow, sharp edge. Such a burin, or graving tool, was in fact the most characteristic object of the whole culture. Perhaps you can begin to see how much more at home in nature human beings could make themselves than ever before, with such a kit of tools.

This is the general picture of Upper Paleolithic stone implements, all of them showing skill and ease in workmanship, even to the point of apparent carelessness in some of the Magdalenian work. The opposite extreme, very great skill and symmetry, characterizes the Solutrean culture, which spread across Europe for a brief time. Its best work, from France, includes such things as "laurel leaf" spearpoints with ripple flaking. These terms bespeak the perfection of shape of these points, and also the incredible expertness of technique, by which long shallow chips were pressed off from the edge toward the midline, each chip being parallel and practically identical with its neighbors, and making a surface effect like ripples in water or sand. The Solutreans obviously loved stoneworking as an art,

FIG. 16. *A Solutrean point.*

and their work has been paralleled only in a few places, in Neolithic Europe and Egypt, and among some of the American Indians.

FIG. 17. *A Magdalenian bone harpoon head.*

Not only did the Upper Paleolithic hunters thus equip themselves handsomely with stone tools; they also made plentiful use of bone, ivory and antler, which the Lower Paleolithic people had been too foolish to try to work into useful forms. They began modestly with simple points for spears or javelins, and also with beads, awls, pins and needles. Later on, among the Magdalenians, bone or antler tools rose markedly in importance, especially with the appearance of harpoon heads having a set of barbs running down one or both edges.

The harpoon shows what advances had now been made in weapons. A spear tipped with flint was probably the first and most efficient weapon, but this was improved on by the end of the Upper Paleolithic. A barbed bone or antler point, called a harpoon head (and this is what the

Magdalenian points seem to be), is meant to come off its spear shaft on striking into an animal, and to be attached and held (perhaps to a drag) by a line. This is how it is used by Eskimos for seals, and by Norwegians for whales. Probably the Magdalenians used it for reindeer. At any rate they had another weapon of importance: the spear thrower. This is a shaft which you hold in your hand at one end, while you also clasp the shaft of the spear harpoon or javelin. The end of the spear thrower has a peg or a stop, against the butt of the spear. As you throw the spear, the thrower lengthens your arm and the whiplike motion adds a great deal of force to the throw—if you have ever thrown green apples off the end of a pointed stick you will know what this means. It is not an easy weapon to aim, and beginners would have trouble hitting the side of a barn. It adds force rather than distance, and helps to make a spear penetrate a large animal like a bison or a walrus, and inflict a serious wound, where an arm-thrown spear might be successful much less often.

The Paleolithic people doubtless also used pit traps and such things, but if they had traps of any more complicated kind the parts have not been found. As to bows and arrows, it is not certain they were invented at all before the end of the Paleolithic; if so, they were not widely used. Some small amount of fishing may have been done in streams with lines, not with true hooks but with simple double-pointed gorges having the line fastened at the middle. Fish were also taken with multipronged small spears.

So the European of the Upper Paleolithic was pretty well off. He had supplied himself with good tools and weapons. Meat was plentiful providing he did not let timidity stand in his way, for there were copious quantities of large animals at first and reindeer at the end, all in open country. Along with his weapons he doubtless had special hunting tricks like driving the game over cliffs or through defiles. And he was obviously good at birding and at catching smaller animals: quantities of bones of the arctic grouse and of rabbits are found in different places used by him.

What he did for vegetables, especially in this frigid climate, we do not know, but he probably did without to a great extent, or ate the contents of the stomachs of the reindeers he killed.

At any rate he seldom starved. We know all too little about his housing arrangements. About his clothes we can tell only that he had some, because of all the needles, and because it was cold. His social life is a mystery. But he has left us one impressive legacy, his art.

The art of the caves

One form, related to the Gravettian culture, consists of little carved stone or ivory female figurines. They have been called, sardonically I think, Venuses, which does not signify that they are beautiful, but gives an idea all the same. They may not have been done in the spirit of the Louvre, and they were positively not done in the spirit of Sunday school. Their heads are uninteresting blobs, as a rule, and everything between the neck and the knees is unpardonably exaggerated. "Voluptuous" might be the word. "Fat" would be better. Some writers have supposed that they were fertility charms or something of the sort, but hunters are not as a rule anxious to increase their families—on the contrary. They may have been nothing more than harmless Paleolithic indelicacies. Some of them are certainly ably done in the artistic sense.

The paintings, quite a different thing, began by being drawings in black, with the use of color and the height of achievement coming in the Magdalenian. Perhaps the finest work of all is that in the Altamira cave on the north coast of Spain, showing bison, horse and boar and evidently having a date somewhat later than the Lascaux cave. But there is little to choose between these two (though there are differences of style), or among many other French and Spanish caves. The artists also did sculpture in fairly deep relief in the walls of some rock shelters, and engravings on the wall surfaces of others. Finally, the Magdalenian culture saw much engraving and sculpture of

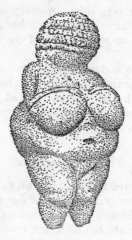

FIG. 18. *The Venus of Willendorf.*

small objects of bone, ivory or antler. Some of it lay in the shaping of utensils such as handles or the ends of spear throwers, which might be worked into the form of an animal or bird, and some of it was seemingly done just for art's sake.

The surprising thing is the average excellence of the work, by any standards. There are, certainly, examples of incompetence. But you would expect to find whole caves spoiled by beginners, or irresponsible back-fence artists, and you do not. Nor do you find much practice sketchbook material among the engraved small pieces, although Dr. Hallam L. Movius, Jr., discovered a large pebble covered with animal forms carved one over the other, which he believes is actually an artist's sketch pad. From the beginning a great part of the work is the work of masters, men whose artistic and aesthetic senses were as powerful as the best of our own, and who shame a hack artist of the present just as surely as a good artist of the present does. Given the knowledge that the Magdalenians were, after all, just like ourselves, it is still hard to understand how they could have rung the bell so decisively and consistently

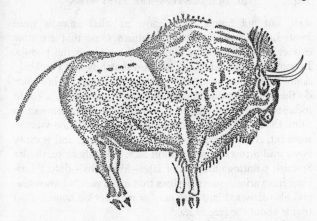

FIG. 19. *A bison from the ceiling of the Altamira cave in Spain. The original is painted in red, yellow and black.*

without leaving more of a litter of their trials and mistakes.

The paintings, in particular, were serious business, and it is at least possible to make out what they were for. The purpose was hunting magic, not picture galleries. Quite obviously they were done to give the hunters some degree of religious hold over the hunted, by directing or "injuring" the animals through spells, or making them breed and be plentiful. It is the game animals that dominate as subjects, and they are often drawn with spears actually thrust into them. Other objects of any kind, such as plants or human beings, are rare, and even these human beings are sometimes shown engaged in hunting or stalking (one man, or possibly a woman, in Spain is climbing a tree to steal honey from bees). Finally, the paintings are usually found far back in the darker recesses of a cave, not in parts that could be used for living quarters, and so they must have had some special purpose. This interpretation is not simple guessing, because primitive hunters of our own times are known to have used hunting magic akin to this.

The paintings are a wonderful sight, and we can get great satisfaction from them. We can get information as

well, but not much. They show us what animals were
hunted, and show as living creatures some that are now
extinct. But they tell us almost nothing about the people.
In contrast to the animals, men are sketchily and carelessly
done. They give no useful information about clothes (nor
do the Venus figurines) although some pictures do seem to
indicate very hairy men. But it may be no more correct to
think that all the men were hairy than that all the women
were fat. A few Spanish scenes show hunting, and portray
bows and arrows, a very useful fact. (But these particular
Spanish paintings may be of later—Mesolithic—date.) Lascaux has various queer designs that make no obvious sense,
and also shows things that may or may not be houses. And
that is about the size of it.

All this time the ice sheet had been retreating from
northern Europe and, after a last stand on the Scandi-
navian peninsula, it expired altogether sometime not long
after 8000 B.C. Some of the Pleistocene mammals, such as
the mammoth, had expired much earlier; others, like the
bison or the Asiatic horse, died out in Europe, while the
king of Magdalenian times, the reindeer, followed the
glacier north to his present home. Open country gave way
to forests housing the red stag and wild boar. Hunting became more difficult all around, both because of the cover
and because of the smaller number of large meat-bearing
animals. To this extent the people of Europe fell on hard
times.

Mesolithic masters of the hunt

At any rate Upper Paleolithic culture came to an end
and was succeeded by the so-called Mesolithic, which developed partly from what had existed and may have been
influenced partly by the late-starting Upper Paleolithic cultures of North Africa. The Mesolithic is looked on by some,
distastefully, as a degeneration from the straight-out big
game hunting of the end of the Paleolithic. But the Mesolithic hunters actually have more in common with primitive
hunters of our own time. That is, they were forced to

balance both their diets and their habits: to use new inventions—which is certainly to their credit—and to fall back on a variety of comestibles their ancestors had disdained.

First of all they took up new aids to hunting. One was the bow and arrow, which may have existed in Paleolithic times but, if so, was not much used. The bow is a wonderful device. It solves the problem of finding great striking force to inflict a wound, both accurately and from a distance, a problem at which the spear thrower fails. When you pull a bow, you store up all the force of your arms and shoulders in it, to release instantly, in the fashion of a gun, instead of more slowly, as when you throw a spear, on which you cannot concentrate as much strength anyhow. Thus the arrow has a high muzzle velocity, something like a bullet.

So in Mesolithic times the bow became the major weapon, using not only the familiar pointed arrows but also chisel-headed arrowpoints, and blunt-headed wooden arrows for stunning birds or small game without ruining skin or pelt. Another "invention" for hunting was the dog, whose parentage is not exactly known. Nor is it known whether people invented dogs or dogs invented people— who struck up the friendship first. Dogs are affable beings, and the chances are good that they took to hanging around the human camps hoping for scraps, and were tolerated in this way and later allowed to come along and make themselves useful in the hunt, long before they were actually domesticated and bred. They have had, in fact, this very status in some recent hunting cultures.

Secondly, the poorer returns from land hunting made for more appreciation of what the water had to offer. Shellfish had been eaten for a long time, but now they were depended on by shore dwellers to such an extent that thick layers of shells were piled up where the people came to eat, especially in Portugal and in Scandinavia. Pike, speared in the rivers, also were widely eaten, instead of rarely as formerly. True fishhooks are found in Mesolithic remains, showing that line fishing was important. Furthermore, the canoe came into existence, which made possible not only marine fishing but also the hunting of seals, in the North, with harpoon and line. Nets and fish traps were used, and their remains have been recovered. Finally, stranded whales gave the Mesolithic people an occasional windfall (Mesolithic implements have been found with the skeletons of several of them). Now this is certainly a thumbnail sketch of Mesolithic sea food, but that should not diminish its significance or that of the various inventions and devices connected with it.

Added to all this, the Mesolithic people must have filled out their diet with a good deal of "gathering" as distinguished from hunting, but this is hard to learn about; we do know that they ate hazelnuts and wild pears, because some of these got charred enough to last to the present in the remains of Mesolithic homes.

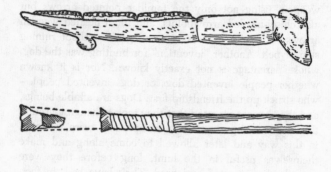

FIG. 20. *Blades or microliths of Mesolithic times, as used in tools. Top, Natufian sickle, Palestine. Middle, transverse arrow, Denmark. Bottom, Maglemosian spearhead.*

What about the remainder of Mesolithic culture? There were certainly tents and huts for living in, doubtless of a variety of kinds in different regions. The Paleolithic people had been forced, in places, by the shortage of wood to make use of mammoth ribs to cover their underground lodges, and even to burn bones for fuel. But the new forests provided wood in plenty now, and in fact one of the type tools of the Mesolithic was a stone axe for wood-working. This was not like the old hand axe, but rather a true axe like ours, for hafting on a handle, and with a cutting edge usually skillfully made by striking off a large flake across the end. The other characteristic of Mesolithic stonework was a dependence on microliths or pygmy flints of different shapes, which could be used for points or barbs of arrows, or for hafting into a piece of bone to make a composite knife blade or a pointed tool.

This general kind of culture shows us artful and able hunter-gatherers succeeding to the rather extraordinary world of the late glacial period and coming to terms with a world of the kind we know. Now almost the whole earth was occupied, and by cultures of this general type. The interminably long advance of human hunters from the baboon-bashing stage of the australopiths to the tricks and skills of the postglacial day was coming to an end. As elsewhere, there were actually different varieties of Meso-lithic culture in Europe. The early and spotty Azilian, which may have been simply a gone-to-seed Magdalenian, had badly made harpoons, and pebbles painted with mys-terious lines and designs. The Tardenoisian culture was the most widespread. The Maglemosian was a bog culture of northern Europe, making the most of a water life and also working wood with axes, which included felling trees to furnish support for their living sites on the soggy ground at the bog's edge.

There were other local cultures. In some of the latest, remains of badly made pottery are found. But it is not clear whether pottery was a really Mesolithic invention as far as Europe is concerned, for by this time it was already being made and used by farmers in the Near East, and we can only assume that it found its way to the backwoods of Europe like glass beads to the Indians. For the fact is that

Europe was not the scene of civilization or of higher culture. It received them in due course, and sooner than some parts of the world. But in the Mesolithic, which here lasted until after 4000 B.C., the Europeans were just natives.

8. The Last Living Hunters

As farming, followed later by civilization, began to spread like ripples from a splash, the Mesolithic peoples all over the earth gave way before it or adopted it. This went on for thousands of years, in different places, up to the time when European culture underwent its renaissance in the Middle Ages and burst out of its own domain all over the world. Then the Europeans, with their "world market," absorbed or upset existing societies in many parts, especially America. But even at the time of their first venturing forth—let us say 1492—they found the Mesolithic survivors already pushed to the wall by other "primitive" peoples. So far, in fact, that they had been shoved nearly out of harm's way for the time being, and have hung on better than many others. It is only in our own day that they and their way of life are at last disappearing for good, as we ourselves find ways and reasons for going into every cranny left on the earth.

That is to say, they were by 1492 already marginal in all senses of the word. Some were marginal in being remote and isolated, literally at the world's ends: the Bushmen of South Africa, the natives of Australia, of the Andaman Islands in the Bay of Bengal, and of Tierra del Fuego at the bottom of South America. Most have been marginal in their resources and territory, and have survived to this day because what they had no one else wanted, and their kind of rude gathering culture was the only way to make a living in these places, such as the last Bushman stronghold in the Kalahari Desert, or the barren ground and arctic parts of Siberia and America. Now, nobody could get more out of the Arctic than the hearty, brainy Eskimos, with their extraordinary inventions to defeat the cold and the ice, and so nobody has disputed it with them. But the Indians in New England, culturally more advanced, had good land on which to grow the corn they gave the Pilgrims. And where are Massasoit's villages now?

The Bushmen, ancient hunters of South Africa

Such survivors as I have mentioned, especially those who were living in a reasonably good environment, can put flesh on the bones of the Mesolithic, and show us what a hunting-gathering culture was and is, and what it means. The nearly vanished Bushmen of South Africa, in fact, run right back into the archaeological past, though some of the connections are not as clear as they might be. For they certainly once occupied all of South Africa, and probably extended far up into East Africa as well. The Bushmen made cave and wall paintings, both recently and long ago, which are like the European ones; they may not have the qualities of the finest of the latter, but on the other hand they are much like those of eastern Spain, with lively animals and human beings in action scenes, done in several colors. And, under the stone- and bonework left by the recent Bushmen lie other stone cultures going back in a sequence to the beginning of the Lower Paleolithic.

But it is not known for certain how far back in this sequence the Bushmen go, or whether the earliest as well as the latest paintings are theirs. Nor do we know anything about the ultimate origin of the Bushmen, and their odd physique. The Rhodesian Man was there long before, and in Upper Paleolithic times there were other, modern men of larger size than the Bushmen, though not entirely different in skull features.

The Bushmen are strange little yellowish-brown people; they are almost as small as the Pygmies of the Congo, and they have hair that forms tight screw curls. But they seem

different from the Negroes, having triangular, rather flat
faces and mongoloid-looking eyes and, of course, the
famous and astonishing ability, shared with the Hottentots,
of some of the women to lay up fat on the buttocks until
they project rearward as does no other human being. This
goes on while they are eating well, and goes down again
when they are not. Such a camellike peculiarity suggests
that the ancestors of the Bushmen evolved it as a special
response to hard times during a long isolation from the
rest of mankind in South Africa, but there is no positive
explanation for it. Nevertheless, the probability is that the
Bushmen are a fairly old branch of Homo sapiens, allied
to the Negroes.

Not so long ago the Hottentots came down into the old
Bushman territory, driving cattle. The Hottentots themselves apparently arose from a Bushman-Negro mixture,
and had got their cattle from the north. They took up
pasturage in the hunting lands of the Bushmen, and the
Bushmen retaliated by hunting both cattle and Hottentots.
Then came the Bantu Negroes with much more solid villages than the Hottentots, displacing both of the other
peoples and reducing the Bushmen even further. The
Bushmen found a final enemy in the Dutch, who moved
up from the Cape with cattle and sheep, losing these to the
Bushmen and killing the Bushmen and their game in return. It was not long before there was little left to the
Bushmen except the inhospitable northern area, with the
Kalahari Desert, and this is where their remnants live today.

They go about[1] in small bands, or even families, looking

[1] I shall be describing native peoples all over the world in the
next parts of this book, as they were in the time after they had
been seen by Europeans who could make records of them but
before this European contact had greatly altered the lives they
were living. Some are still in that state, some have departed
from it only since 1900, and some have had hardly a vestige of
it for generations. Yet, taken all together, these tribes are the
living past, something different from the archaeological past, on
the one hand, and the people of history—the fixed phases, the
Caesars or the Incas—on the other. Since they are to be com-

for game or shifting localities as the game migrates for the season. Practically speaking, all they think about is food, especially in their present poor home, and life is a hunt for it.

They broaden their diet by not being choosy about what they eat, which means just about anything they can digest: not only the preferred game, the larger species of the antelope tribe, but also lions, hyenas, rats, poisonous snakes, lizards, scorpions, frogs, insects, grubs, and any kinds of seeds, berries and roots.

They broaden their diet once again by not being too particular about the state of the food, for they are able to eat putrid meat, or an overdue ostrich egg that smells, Europeans have said, as you would not believe an egg could smell. This has dumbfounded many observers; the Bushmen take real pleasure in eating things you might think would annihilate them.

They broaden their diet in a third way by eating prodigiously whenever they can, and, contrariwise, managing to put up with short rations when obliged to, or to go absolutely hungry for considerable periods. Many people have seen two Bushmen eat up a whole sheep, or comparable amounts of wild game, in half a day; and here a whole sheep does not mean just the parts we choose, but intestines and all. (This kind of voracity and indiscriminate eating up of everything edible is seen among other such wandering hunters in all parts of the world.) It is certainly a real accomplishment, and not something we could man-

---

pared with one another, I shall use the present tense except where it is an absurdity. This has been called the "ethnographic present" by my colleagues Eliot D. Chapple and Carleton S. Coon; it is a literary license, and a way of meeting an embarrassment, like the editorial "we." This present is not a literal one: it may be now, or fifty or three hundred years ago. But it is an attempt to treat these important peoples and cultures as though they were all available for our inspection as we would want to see them, in their pristine condition. But I cannot always avoid the past tense, when a tribe *used* to drink blood, and I hope that occasional tense changes for this reason will be understood and forgiven by the reader.

age without training, to say the least. This is apparently when the women develop their bumptious behinds. Now you will remember that the Upper Paleolithic Venus figurines are all very fat little women. Some students have seen signs of the same trait (called steatopygia) in them, although their appearance is more one of general plumpness (which would in fact have been better suited to a cold climate than would one big lump). In any event, it may well be that they are Paleolithic pinup girls, and that the ideal healthy beauty of that icy day was a grossly overfed one, reflecting in one way their hopes and prayers about food.

Taken altogether, you can see that the Bushmen have accommodated themselves, by their dietary elasticity, to the uncertainties of their food supply more completely than you would have thought possible. How have they organized themselves in positive fashion so as to obtain their food? While they will eat anything, they prefer wild vegetables and the flesh of typical game animals, and they hunt these both individually and communally, and always share a kill regardless of who made it (this is another trait typically found in such primitive hunting groups). It is the business of the women to go out from the camp daily to forage for berries, wild plums, wild melons, wild veld cabbage and many bulbs, roots and other such, often using a weighted digging stick to root them up. They take the children of all ages along, and the older of these help in the gathering. The men have charge of the serious business of hunting, and go farther afield in it.

Their hunting weapons are several. They use spears to some extent, for larger game such as a giraffe. They also have a throwing club, or knobkerrie, a fat-headed stick two or three feet long with which they expertly bring down birds and small game. But their main standby is the bow, a small one, by which they shoot poisoned arrows. The arrows are usually light, and made with a separate hardwood point as long as your hand (so that the shaft falls off when the point sticks into the prey, and can be picked up again) but some have stone-tipped points (or glass or iron, recently). Such light bows and arrows are seldom deadly in themselves, but the poison is effective. The Bushmen compound it from the venom sacs of snakes, a poisonous caterpillar, and various poisonous bushes and roots, cooking the whole thing down into a waxy jelly into which the arrowheads, of whatever kind, are dipped. The poison does not work immediately, but acts according to the size of the animal and the nature of the wound. It may kill off a small antelope promptly but take a number of hours for a large one, which might have to be chased a long distance by the hunter.

Now we come to a difference between our idea of hunting and a Bushman's. We are ridiculously poor woodsmen. Here at home a hunter goes crashing through the woods until he blunders onto some animal or bird that did not realize that the hunting season had started, and opens fire, either killing the game dead, or wounding it and losing it, or frightening it into the next county; if he kills it he usually has to ask a dog to find the body for him. Our more fortunate nimrod may go on an African safari: practiced resident hunters locate an animal for him, which he dispatches with a rifle almost good enough to stop a tank. But a Bushman's weapons, poison and all, are far less lethal, both for distance and for striking power, and along with his weapons he has to throw into the scales his own vast training and skill, which are impressive.

In the first place, he is highly educated. He knows all about the animals he is dealing with, and how they will act, and how to overcome them. And he has learned how to get the last scrap of information from everything around him, in a way to make Sherlock Holmes seem purblind. We look about the empty landscape and see nothing; to him it is as full of signs as the subway. Not having gone through the same lifelong training, it is probable that we cannot even conceive how differently the same things look to him. He simply sees through the camouflage of nature. He points off to nothing on the horizon and says, "There is a zebra." We look in the same direction, expecting perhaps to see a tiny version of what we know a zebra looks like, and do not see it. Nor does he; he has seen something that does not look like a zebra at all, but he knows it is a zebra, or was caused by a zebra, far away. Nearer at hand, he can follow a given animal from its tracks, or from lesser indications, and tell if it is wounded and how badly, and keep on this particular track for any distance, no matter how great a tangle of other tracks it may pass through.

Such abilities, though verging on the incredible for us, are nevertheless commonplace, and turn up among other peoples dependent on hunting. The natives of Australia are equally well known for such feats. And here is a story from Tierra del Fuego. Lucas Bridges, born and raised on Beagle Channel himself, recommended a sixteen-year-old Ona Indian to the Argentine governor of the town of Ushuaia to help track a convict escaped from the prison there. Since a major activity of the place was cutting firewood and timber in the woods all around, and dragging it by oxen, the state of the ground about the town can be imagined, with the tramplings of oxen and hundreds of convicts, soldiers and civilians. The Ona boy was shown a picture of the fugitive and a pair of his shoes (obviously not the ones he had escaped in), given a few details of height and weight, and set to work. Little was seen of the Ona except at mealtimes for a number of days, and nothing learned from him, as he hardly spoke Spanish anyhow. Just as the governor, suspicious from the first, had decided that his detective was goldbricking and getting fat on army food, the boy seemed to confirm this by disappearing altogether. But he came back in a week and made his full report, very positively, as follows: "He didn't escape at all." And the prisoner was accidentally found that same evening hiding in the woodpile just outside the prison itself. The Ona had made his examination not only of the environs of the town but also of the trails to two settlements fifteen miles to the east and west, and he had satisfied himself that none of the myriad tracks had been made by one particular man whom he had never even seen.

To go back to South Africa. The Bushman hunter's great problem is to make contact with his quarry and keep it, while he does what he can to end its life with his venomous but rather puny bow. He must discover it. He must approach it, using every possible advantage and infinite, wary patience to avoid being noticed, by trying either to keep out of sight and smell entirely or to seem like some harmless fellow beast idly moving about in the vicinity. He tries finally to shoot as quietly as he can: the wound may not even make the animal bolt and the hunter, like a good billiard player, may keep things set up for another shot, at the same animal or a different one, leaving them in doubt as to which direction to run off in or whether to run at all. He may actually disguise himself as an animal, crouching under a rig that shows only his two legs and makes him look like an ostrich. (One of the Magdalenian paintings shows a man wearing antlers, who may have been doing the same kind of stalking.) In any case it pays him well to get as close as he can before shooting.

A wounded animal is apt to make off, at a speed, of course, far beyond a man's. Now the Bushman must track it and keep up with it, even if this takes two days and forty miles. For the Bushman hunter can outlast his game whether it is badly wounded, and affected by poison, or not. And to show how important are plain human skill and endurance in this kind of hunting: a Bushman can actually chase down and kill an unwounded springbok, keeping on its trail, giving it no rest, in the heat particularly, until traveling on the hot sand makes its hoofs give out and it is too exhausted to move.

This is the spectacular side of hunting, but the Bushmen have many other resources. They use dogs in the hunt as well. They have traps, pitfalls, deadfalls and snares. They spear fish in rivers, or poison them. And they may cleverly conceal a waterhole with branches, leading off water in a channel to make a false hole, which they poison so as to kill animals who come to drink.

If you look at the rest of Bushman culture you will not see a great deal. Dress may start with a headband which is most likely to be a decoration for women and something to stick small objects and arrowpoints in for men. Then there is a long gap, to a pair of small fore-and-aft aprons for women, or a leather loincloth for men. Bushmen also wear skin capes, if the weather is cool, or to carry the baby. Their houses, when they use them at all (instead of a rock shelter or a windbreak), are temporary little huts made of branches stuck in the ground and covered with grass, grass mats or skins.

For the Bushmen are not settled, and when they move they take everything with them: the man takes his weapons and the woman everything else—baby, extra skins, fire sticks, ostrich-eggshell bottles of water, and perhaps some poor pottery. Their food would keep only a day or so even if they wanted to store it, and we have seen their idea of the proper place for food: in the stomach.

So personal property is not a matter of moment to them. But they have one clear notion of property, which is their territory and the resources in it. Infringement of this is a direct threat to life, and so they are fiercely territorial, like the howling monkeys; the wanderings of each band take place in its own private region, which it would fight to preserve. And they are careful, in the desert, to keep their springs of water their own secret.

Bushman social life is simple. Bands consist of a few families only, which might not always stick together within their territory. And, except for the head of the family, there is hardly anyone to call a chief. For a wedding, there might be a feast but there might, as is usual among hunting peoples, be not the slightest formality. Boy and girl may simply start keeping house and raising children, and if a man can manage more than one wife, and wants to, he may. However, this is lack of ceremony rather than lack of meaning, for kin relationships are clearly denoted and, as in every human society, incestuous unions are unthinkable. And a man and his mother-in-law most carefully avoid any recognition of one another. But, though members of different bands might marry, and so have relationships outside, the social universe of a Bushman is his own small group, which lives and hunts in its own land, and keeps itself happy with dancing, singing and storytelling at night. Religion? Almost non-existent: they reverence the moon and the praying mantis in particular, believe in omens and other "superstitions," use hunting magic, and think diseases are caused by little yellow evil spirits entering the body. But in ceremonies of any consequence they are lacking.

Complicated relatives in Australia

The native blackfellows of Australia, off in another end of the world's land, live a life similar to the Bushmen's, on similar resources. That is to say, their contacts with nature and their cultural defenses are much the same, and they wander in small bands within definite hunting territories. But the African Bushmen, like most such primitive hunters, have no social organization to speak of except a family and a group of families, while the Australian natives have developed some social ideas—it must be admitted that they are exceptionally complicated—which serve them both as a diplomatic structure and as a sort of philosophy.

This is the Australian kinship system. Compare our relatives. "Mother" and "Father" are each a single person. But "Brother" or "Grandmother" can be one of two or more people; "Uncle" can be any brother or brother-in-law of either parent, and in practice does not even have to be related; "Cousin" has less meaning yet. The Australians are more specific: they will have a name which means "Father's Sister's Daughter" as distinct from "Mother's Brother's Daughter" (both are "Cousin" to us), or even "Father's Father's Sister's Son's Daughter." They are also more general: Father's Brother is accepted, socially, as another Father, not simply an uncle, and so this "Father's" sons and daughters are your "Brothers" and "Sisters," not just cousins. And so Father (real Father) himself has a lot of "Brothers" by this rule (who are not real brothers to him), who are therefore also your "Fathers," and whose sons and daughters are also your "Brothers" and "Sisters," until you think you must be in the Hall of Mirrors. Does it sound complicated? It is, and more so, though we will pause here. You can make out a whole chart, showing how these kinship terms are linked together, and where they repeat themselves. This does not mean the Australian natives post such charts to keep themselves straight, or even that they conceive of such a chart. It only means that they know what names to call anyone by, and it also means that this kind of relationship can be carried far afield into other bands, or even tribal groups, if necessary.

For their marriages are enmeshed in this system. A man does not marry his sister, naturally, and in fact in many tribes he must use the most profoundly correct behavior and language when they are together. And of course it would also be incestuous to marry any of his other "Sisters," no matter how distant in actual cousinship they may be. On the other hand, there is in fact a preferred marriage for him: his Mother's Brother's Daughter who, though his true first cousin on this side, is not classed as his sister, but rather as "Expected Wife." His Mother's Brother is *not* "Father," but "Father-in-law." Actually, of course, it is likely that there is no Mother's Brother's Daughter available for him, because the whole system cannot be expected to have the right numbers of people in every pigeonhole. But there will nevertheless be girls who would be the Expected Wife's "Sisters" if she existed, and by the system of classification they are therefore "Expected Wives," by extension, to the man in question. If he should marry more than once, his wives would always have this kind of relation to him. The practical result of all this is that people fall into classes which determine whom they can and cannot marry, and whom their children can and cannot marry. (The system I have described is not the universal one in Australia; some are more complicated. And such systems of kinship and preferred marriage have existed elsewhere, perhaps among the very early Greeks.)

Actually, regulation of marriage is only one side of this. After all, such an overgrown blueprint would be an odd development if it existed only as a guide to betrothals.

Instead, it places everyone in some kind of stated relation to yourself, and tells you how to act toward them, and what to expect from them in return. You know perfectly well which are your true parents, brothers, and so on, but your behavior toward other, distant "Fathers" is a dilution of what you use toward your own father or his real brothers. This is how the system stretches beyond the horizon, so that you can safely go among other bands—a great consideration—establishing your relationships with people who are strangers, by finding some link or, if necessary, assuming one. That is what I mean by speaking about a diplomatic structure. Extensive relationships and channels for contact exist which make travel, trade and intermarriage all easier, countering the natural isolation of separate bands. So it is a matter of lives and security, not etiquette alone.

The Australians take a like view of nature in general, and thus make themselves kindred to the universe as well as to one another. They are the world's great totemists. Ancestor-heroes lived in the dreamtime when everything was being laid out the way it is today; these legends are the black-fellows' Bible, and their rituals are dance-dramas which bring the dreamtime once more to life, revivifying both nature and man. From the ancestors sprang both men and animals, so that kangaroo totem spirits may be born today either as kangaroos or as men of the kangaroo totem, who must never eat the flesh of a kangaroo. Not only this, but marriage classes and other groupings also have totems, and totems run throughout nature, so that the Australians in effect class things by totems. The very features of the landscape were made by the heroes: a certain rock may be the bones of one, a red ochre deposit be blood shed by another, and they know all the sacred trails by which the ancestors traveled.

So the barren bush country is not only the band's vital hunting preserve, practically speaking aloud to the natives (as it does to the South African Bushmen): it is also a landscape of the spirit, of which they are a part, body and soul. It is their ancestral home, where their particular totem spirits are lodged. Here, they are in accord with nature, and by their religious rites they know how to stay that way, causing the animal spirits to be born and so make the game plentiful. Away from home they feel literally uprooted, unhappy and unsafe.

Except for this social (and religious) organization, Australian life is simple. Bands number something like forty people—a handful of families—and if there is anything to be decided, the older men get together and decide it. Occasionally a number of related bands meet for a ceremony; these larger groups could be called "tribes" only in the sense of having a common language and more or less identical customs.

Such a ceremony might be an initiation of the boys, meaning that they are being initiated to manhood. This is an almost universal item of culture, and is particularly noticeable among the simplest people of all. It consists, typically, of making the youths live by themselves in the bush, under certain strict prohibitions, especially as to food; of wounding, hazing or frightening them; and of teaching them moral precepts and (usually) religious secrets, with the adult males of the group performing ceremonies or dressing up as supernatural beings. The Bushmen of South Africa do much the same things. In Australia this is the time when the boys learn the lore of the totem ancestors, kept strictly secret from them before, and never known to the women at all. At this time, too, they undergo circumcision or some other mutilation, such as having a tooth or so knocked out. Now, whether or not these customs of initiation have been thought up with malicious intent (which is not likely), they serve as a drastic education for adulthood, shocking the youth into respect for lore and custom, and into an appreciation of the responsibilities of being a man. At the same time, he becomes aware of the responsibilities of being a hunter, since among the hunting peoples being deprived of food is a painfully obvious part of the whole ritual.

The outlines of Australian economy are precisely like those of the South African Bushmen. Small groups move from camp to camp, looking for game. Shelter and dress are skimpy, except in the south of the continent, where the cold encouraged them to make log huts or to wear a skin instead of simply an opossum fur string around the waist or the head. They hunt, principally, marsupials like the kangaroo tribe and the opossum (there were in prediscovery times no typical mammals except the wild dingo dog, used in hunting, which may first have arrived with the natives themselves), but, like the Bushmen, they have a long list of things for food. The women dig up wild yams and other natural vegetables while the men hunt. Their goods, such as they are, make up a Paleolithic-Mesolithic inventory. Spears and spear throwers (no bows and arrows). Boomerangs (the great Australian throwing club, not meant to return, but to stun or kill game—the returning kind was for fun only). Nets for birding and fishing. String bags and cords. Canoes in some regions where there was water. Their stonework contains many of the styles and techniques of the whole Paleolithic. The natives came from Asia not less than 15,000 years ago, and probably a good deal more; and they have certainly been isolated in Australia for most or all of that time.

Hunting culture and hunting society

The Australians then, like the Bushmen, are simple foragers, supplementing their limited weapons with enormous skill in hunting, and making an accomplishment out of eating or not eating. Now we could review other hunting-gathering peoples of the world, but we would soon see many of the main aspects of their existence beginning to duplicate themselves in our account. This does not mean that their cultures are all alike, or on one level. We have seen the difference between Bushman and Australian social organization, and the difference in their weapons. The weak bows of the Bushmen also contrast with long bows, some of them over nine feet in length, and the complicated manufacture of arrows, of the Siriono Indians of eastern Bolivia; or with the S-shaped bows of the Andaman Islands; or with the blowguns of the Sakai of the Malay

Peninsula. All of these involve a lot of special inventions in their construction, and they are not simple tools at all.

Furthermore, while the Bushmen and the Australians live in climates not too disparate in nature, other hunters may have strikingly different environments and ways of coping with them. Some have a wide variety of opportunity, as in Tierra del Fuego, where the Ona Indians hunt on land with the bow and arrow while their next-door neighbors, the Yahgan, prefer spears and live on the shore and in canoes, depending largely on mussels, fish and birds. Some are highly special in their pursuits, like the caribou-hunting Indians of northern Canada. Some are more gatherers than hunters, like certain of the Indians of the western United States and Lower California, where nuts and vegetables of various kinds were staple foods.

But the behavior of the hunters has similarities everywhere. I have given examples already: the common obligation to give others part of your kill (the same obligation to share food that falls on people in a lifeboat); the gluttonous eating when food is plentiful; and the great sharpening up of hunting skill. Social life as well has such similarities. Now nothing is a greater mistake than to jump in and find general "rules" in culture or in history, fascinating though it is. The next minute you are talking about "stages" in the "evolution" of "marriage," as though marriage were a species of rabbit. Nevertheless, it is not hard to see that the very circumstances of hunting life must logically mold societies to certain main patterns.

Perhaps you once had a picture of all these savages as ferocious, lustful, unrestrained, undiscriminatingly filthy, grunting gutturally, near to animals in their senses and desires and near to children in their emotions and intelligence. This is entirely unjust, both to them and to a sensible understanding of humanity and culture. The savages are profoundly uncivilized, make no mistake, and they are the lowest in the scale of known societies. But do not forget that they represent the end of the Stone Age, not the beginning.

Of course there is much in their visible life to support a

poor opinion. If cleanliness is next to godliness, let us not think what they are next to; and you are certainly not obliged to like the sight of them gobbling rotten meat or kangaroo intestines. You will also be excused for taking umbrage if you should suddenly perceive an arrow shaft protruding from your front and back when you thought you were minding your own business. For they put little stock in strangers, or anyone outside their own group as they define it.

But let this not create an impression of wanton bestiality, brutality and stupidity. Our hunters are perfectly clear about right and wrong within their own bands, and are just as responsive to the restraints and regulations of their own cultures as we are to ours. They are not natural-born killers. Cannibalism is practically unheard of among these hungriest of men (except for instances of magical nibbling), and the Bushmen will not even eat the baboon, because he is so like a man. Headhunting is also unknown, both this and cannibalism being ornaments of higher cultures (although some of our own Mesolithic ancestors in Europe did hunt heads and Pekin Man, of course, ate Pekin men). Marriage regulations are carefully observed, and the rule of avoidance between a woman's husband and her mother (a kind of etiquette which emphasizes the importance of relationships and forestalls dangerous frictions) is widespread. Orgies of sexual license, which may take place periodically at large gatherings, are understood as just that, and approved for the occasion only. And the harsh discipline of initiation rites is not sadism on the part of the elders. On the contrary, it exists to enhance personal restraint and responsibility, traits which we consider civilized.

Nor are such people merely one step away from apes in their general existence. I have said that their economy—simple gathering—is essentially that of apes, and so it is. But human hunters are an aeon away from apes, because they are human and have culture. The poverty of the culture makes the human abilities stand out, such as the endurance, the variegated feeding, and the intelligence required by the incredible feats of tracking. These abilities show us what a dangerous, resourceful animal a man can be, standing alone with his bare hands. But all the lore and skill (which is not mere "animal cunning") is actually culture in itself, just as are the weapons, or the co-operation in hunting and in eating. Bad as it is, this little culture allowed Mesolithic man to conquer the whole world; there is no other large animal that can live in all the same places as man, and even his dog sometimes depends on him utterly.

Also, the social culture of hunters is not really rudimentary, any more than their languages. It may be simple. But the point is that it constitutes true, fully fledged cultural behavior, and that the hunters are capable of using more complicated techniques and institutions if they need to. Hark back to the howling monkeys. They learn to do various things like riding on a mother's back, and above all to live peaceably with the members of the same band, but the rest of their actions are largely instinctive. At any rate the hostility between bands is unvarying, and their isolation from one another is complete. Human bands may be similarly territorial, and jealous of their hunting grounds. The Ona Indians, for example, are not good mixers, being too willing to shoot down men of other groups and steal their wives from them (though this is not the ordinary means of getting wives). But the Australians have a kinship scheme for regulating relations between bands, establishing a kind of communication they would not develop from their everyday pursuits. So cultural means of this kind are available, which the Australians use and the Onas do not. And all societies subscribe to the rule against incest, and this, too, widens social contacts. If a man marries his sister he loses the chance to ally himself with a new family, and the band loses an important element in the interweaving of its members. These considerations are much more important in higher societies, but of no small consequence even here.

So the last of the hunting peoples are an extraordinary object lesson. Certainly they are more to be pitied than scorned. We see them struggling against the limits of a purely natural environment and the necessary isolation of small groups. They show us man—modern man—caught in the toils of a way of life far inferior to what his brain and his psychological nature have long since made him capable of.

THE NEW FARMERS—THE
SECOND STEP

9. *The First Food Growers: the Neolithic*

With the end of the Ice Age the hunting peoples were pressing into every part of the habitable world, except the outer islands of the Pacific and perhaps such poor places as Greenland and Baffin Land. For a time they even roamed the plain between Britain and Denmark which now lies under the North Sea. Making the most of nature, they discovered every kind of available food, including those that have to be specially treated to be edible, like acorns. And in different places they gave themselves the benefit of many fairly intricate inventions, whether weapons or hunting tricks, even though typically they could carry their entire cultures around as they traveled, in their heads or on top of them.

Then, about 8000 B.C., and somewhere in the Near East (as far as we know), the Neolithic way of life began. It is still called "Neolithic" (New Stone Age, as Mesolithic means Middle, and Paleolithic means Old Stone Age), because the older anthropologists saw everything in the light of stonework, and thought of this "period" as the age of polished stone axes. But it means, rather, a state of culture in which food is planted and bred, not hunted and gathered—in which food is domesticated, not wild. If we had to choose the greatest single change in human history right up to the present, this would be it. I mean, of course, a change by cultural evolution, as distinct from a biological change like standing erect, or gradually becoming able to use culture and language in the first place. And I do not mean that the change was sudden, or dramatic to those who were changing, as though a light were being switched on. It was dramatic, but long after, in its consequences, because everything else we have achieved flowed out of this as a beginning.

By shortly after 5000 B.C. there were farming villages spread widely in the Near East, all the way from the Fayum Basin in Egypt (just up the Nile from Cairo and the Pyramids), through Palestine and Syria, over to Iraq and Iran. They were not all the same, by any means, but a summary picture of their culture was something like this. The people lived in houses, of mud brick or mud and brush walls. They grew wheat and barley; they cut the grain with straight sickles made by setting flint blades in a row in a piece of wood or bone; they stored it (in some places) in granaries or pits lined with basketry; and they ground it for bread on rotary hand mills of stone, or in some other kind of grindstone or mortar. They raised cattle, sheep, goats and pigs (and dogs, although remember that a dog is a Mesolithic contraption used for hunting, and not a barnyard animal). But they also hunted wild animals, and took birds and fish, especially in the Fayum, to fill out their diets. They made bowls and jars of pottery. And they wove linen cloth out of flax.

This is a culture which, emphatically, you would not try to carry around on your head, even forgetting the houses and granaries. Its origins are gradually being pinpointed, as more is being learned about the climate of the Near East just after the Pleistocene, and about the foods that were domesticated. The center seems to be the hill country of northern Iraq.

From about 10,000 B.C. to about 8000 B.C. there were Mesolithic hunters and gatherers in the Palestine region, known as the Natufians. They used caves, but more and more made settlements in the open, and, as primitive farming developed, these settlements became permanent. The simplest domestication took place around 8000 B.C., and by 7000 B.C. such a settlement had been made at Jericho, so substantial that the town was enclosed by a high wall of rough stone. The wall still stands, not thrown down by the trumpets and the Lord; it was uncovered far below the remains of the later Jericho that Joshua fit the battle of.

Another village, probably equally early according to radiocarbon dates,[1] called Jarmo, lies in the hills of Iraq, above the Tigris-Euphrates Valley. It was made up of simple houses of packed mud walls, and lasted long enough so that a number of different levels could be made out by the investigators. Grains of wheat and barley were found, along with the household tools for making flour, especially hand mills; this is one of the best signs for the use of cereal grains, here and elsewhere. And there were bones of cattle, sheep, pigs, and dogs.

Now it might be hard to prove just what was the state of domestication of these animals, but here at any rate was the basic domestic livestock in a group; and all wild animal bones—i.e., those that were clearly products of the hunt—amounted to only five percent of the total. One feature of the houses was burning basins of clay (hearths?), but aside from the remains of these there were no signs of pottery until the highest levels, at the end of the settlement, when some fragments of poor-grade stuff appear. (At Jericho, also, pottery appeared some centuries after the first settle-

[1] These dates can be determined from surviving vegetable matter or charcoal, and to some extent from animal remains like shell. They depend on Carbon 14, a radioactive isotope of carbon having a half-life of 5568 years, meaning that it decays at a known rate like other radioactive elements. It exists in the atmosphere in a definite proportion of all carbon, and so becomes part of all living tissues in the same ratio. When the tissue is dead, the Carbon 14 begins to decay, until in about forty thousand years there is too little of it left to measure accurately. So the remaining proportion of radiocarbon in a fragment of wood or in grains of wheat tells approximately when those objects ceased to live. It is a little like this: a tumbler under a running faucet stays full; turn off the faucet and the water in the tumbler begins to evaporate until it is gone. While it was evaporating, you could tell about how long ago the faucet was turned off; afterward you would only know that at least the time needed for evaporation had elapsed. For this reason radiocarbon dates can be worked out only within the last forty thousand years or so, and are presently none too precise beyond the last twenty-five thousand.

ment.) And there were no signs of weaving at all. So here was a group of very early farmers, lacking even the two typical arts of "Neolithic" peoples, pottery and weaving, but with the domesticated grains and animals well in hand.

The beginnings of planting

None of this tells us how the business of domestication came about, and here we have to fall back on a little imagination. But let it be the right kind of imagination, and not one that sees a Mesolithic genius waking up in a hut, exclaiming, "Why didn't I think of that before?" and smartly laying out a garden and planting it full of good things. On the contrary, rapidly though it happened by Paleolithic standards, the deliberate sowing of grain must have come about by accidental steps, at the hands of gatherers.

There is impressive proof that the Mesolithic hunters had come to know and eat every possible kind of natural food, and in this part of the world they surely made use of edible seeds, as in all other parts. Many such people must have anticipated the ripening of wild crops, and perhaps come early to places where they grew, possibly even to pull up weeds or chase birds away. Here in the Near East, the Natufian people of Palestine had a Mesolithic culture, yet they had sickles, which is thought to show that they harvested wild grasses and grains on an important scale. Realize also that these cereals, wheat, barley, the millets (grass-like grains including sorghum, very ancient in use), will keep well if they are stored in a proper cache, and you have something which emphasizes the importance of that crop and exerts a steady pull back to the place where it grows well, or where an otherwise wandering group keeps its stores of the grain. And suppose that little by little the people find other ways of helping the crop, and camp near it, or carry ripe grain home to one of their main camps, and accidentally spill it around so that it grows there. Then the final purposeful growing of this kind of food is probably inevitable. Now the whole process might

be very slow, or too difficult entirely, for many wild vegetable types, and it is probable that the particular qualities
of these grains, like their yearly growth (as opposed to
a tree-borne fruit), their high food value, and above all
their storability, would have helped the incipient farmers
along in their unconscious process of domestication.[2]

It may prove difficult to find the precise home of all
this, since the natural grains grow fairly widely. If northern
Iraq seems likely, on the other hand the Natufians farther
west look as though they might have been going through
the actual process of domesticating grains. The animals
also pose problems. This is especially true because, once
the idea of domesticating them had been clearly established and herds had been introduced into new territories,
then some of the local wild forms in these new territories
may have been brought under domestication, as a way of
enlarging the flocks. This seems to have happened with
cattle and pigs in Europe, for example. That would tend
to make it look as though the original domestication had
taken place all over creation, instead of in one principal
place. The chances are strong, however, that cattle domestication, like that of wheat and barley and other early
plants like flax, happened in the Near East.

It is actually surprising that the main animals—cattle,
sheep, goats and pigs—all show up together in the lowest
archaeological levels of the oldest village, Jarmo. This is
the kind of thing that suggests Neolithic beginnings must
have gone back well before Jarmo's founding about 7000
B.C. But in any event it is likely that the grains were domesticated before the animals.

For the essence of village farming life is building a village and farming; that is, staying in one place. And it is
plants that stay in one place, and so ask the people to do
the same, while the animals may wander. If the people are

[2] Professor Carl O. Sauer has quite a different hypothesis:
that sedentary shore- and stream-living fisher people learned to
propagate roots and cuttings—to duplicate already growing
plants—rather than seeds, partly out of need for fibers for nets,
or for fish poison. See p. 189.

wandering, and living by hunting, they cannot afford the
time to care for livestock. Sometimes hunters bring live
animals to camp as a way of having the next day's food at
hand. But these animals never survive more than a day or
so. And a hunter's real reaction to a food animal is to shoot
it; this was the Bushman's approach to Hottentot or Dutch
cattle, and the Sioux Indians did the same thing when the
Great White Father was trying to make them settle down
and gave them some cows.

But domesticating cattle is not simply stockading them,
or even taming them; it means rather causing them to
breed successfully while they are dependent on human beings. And this means living on something else while waiting for the animals to reproduce and grow and give milk.
Now if you are a hunter, not a farmer, it would seem
preposterous to be hunting rabbits or gazelles if you have
oxen and sheep at hand, all ready to be killed. Of course
we do not know what actually was happening before
7000 B.C., and there may have been special circumstances.
And also there are the reindeer nomads of Siberia, who
give the impression that they are in the very act of bringing
the reindeer to heel; but the circumstances are peculiar.
On the face of it, it would seem that the domestication of
wild cattle would be slow enough and hard enough to suggest strongly that it was done by homesteaders, not
hunters.

Now let us look at pottery and weaving, because they
both appeared in the Neolithic villages fairly soon, and because they tell us a little about the nature of Neolithic life.

Pots and looms

Pottery was the first plastic. It has to be made from
carefully selected clay, which is made into a paste with
water. Before it is shaped, it must be given a temper, in
the form of some kind of sand or grit (unless these are
present naturally) or even of other things, for two reasons:
to keep it from being too gooey to work with at all, and to
make it a little porous so that water may leave it in drying

or firing without breaking it. When it has been completely dried, it is still only a patty-cake of mud, and must be fired to change its chemical nature. This drives out the water that is still chemically part of the clay, removes animal or vegetable material, and changes the clay itself.

Now it is usable, and completely resistant to water and to ordinary fire. Pottery can be decorated in a number of ways: by shaping; by all sorts of surface markings with sticks, stamps or cords while it is wet; by cutting or scratching after it is dry; by painting or glazing or slipping (giving a special finer coating) before it is fired; and various other means. Pots are easy to break, but the pieces last indefinitely, and so the archaeologists love pottery beyond anything else, because they can trace tribes and cultures and periods by styles of potmaking and decoration.

But the people themselves love pottery because it is so useful for storing food, and especially for cooking. Boiling is an important way of making vegetables and grains edible in larger quantities. However, trying to boil in a wooden or bamboo container, or by dropping hot rocks into water in a skin-lined hole in the ground, is something less than perfect. One such substitute is a basket daubed with clay, and it may be that pottery was first invented through the accidental burning of these.

Pottery is by no means simple to make. Like the bow and arrow, it actually consists of a complex of inventions, and so does the weaving of true textiles. Basketry, matting and netting were present in Mesolithic (and Paleolithic?) times, and these, even when fairly complicated, can be made by hand or with the aid of simple tools like net gauges. Actually, if you want to tie a cord between two uprights, and hang the warp threads from the cord, you can do the in-and-out weaving of the weft threads with your fingers. You can also do long division with your fingers, but there are better ways.

You can suspend the warp threads from a stiff bar, and hang weights to the bottom of groups of them, which will give you some tension on the threads and ease the threading of the weft into them. You can have bars top and bot-

tom, making a real frame and enabling you to roll up the
finished cloth as you work. You can use a comb to push
the last weft thread tight against the previous one. You can
tie every other warp thread to a stick, called a heddle, so
that when you lift the stick in one motion you create a
shed between the right warp threads, and can throw the
bobbin through in a single stroke instead of having to
weave the weft thread painfully over or under one warp
thread at a time. Here you have a fully developed hand
loom, out of which we today have simply made a machine;
Neolithic peoples carried things up to this point. In fact,
just as all our edible plants and animals were domesticated
in Neolithic times, so were all the basic techniques of weaving discovered.

Weaving needs fibers, of course, which were found in
flax, and later in cotton and wool (the hairy coat of wild
sheep is much less suitable for spinning into thread, and
the woollier coat developed under domestication). Thus it
depends to no small extent on Neolithic resources, while it
furnishes a superior replacement for the skins used by most
of the hunters. But more than that, weaving, like pottery,
marks the accumulation of new kinds of household gear of
a non-portable kind. Looms are not for traveling, nor are
pots. Instead, they signal the establishment of sedentary
life, which is a central fact of the Neolithic achievement.[3]

[3] There are important reservations here. I am saying that pottery is a prominent feature of Neolithic cultures, but not that
it was invented at the hearths of the Neolithic peoples I have
described. Some hunters, like the Bushmen of South Africa,
make or buy pots, and pottery was used by Mesolithic people
in Europe, Central Africa, eastern Asia and North America.
Some of these might have received the idea from regions already in a Neolithic stage. But pottery seems actually indigenous in others, and according to apparently reliable radiocarbon dates may occur so early (before 7000 B.C. in Japan and
Mongolia) as to show that it was definitely invented first by
Mesolithic peoples. At any rate, at present we have, in some
areas, evidence of pre-pottery Neolithic remains, and in others
of pre-Neolithic pottery.

The meaning of farming

This brings us, in short, to the meaning of the so-called Neolithic revolution. If you generalize, and take the typical effects on culture of hunting life on the one hand and of farming life on the other, you can see that something stupendous took place. As in the case of the appearance of culture itself, it was a breaking of one of nature's bonds, the freeing of man from the limits of the natural supply of food.

You have seen simple hunter-gatherers at work. They have a few crude ideas about conservation and some, like the Australians and the Magdalenians, exerted themselves in pious rites to make the game more plentiful. But that is wishful thinking; nature is in control, not they. Nature goads them about from spot to spot like howling monkeys, and there is nothing they can do about it. They cannot stockpile their food: when they have eaten, it is high time to start thinking about the next meal. Around any camp there are only so many wild animals and so many edible plants, because of the balance of nature. When these have been hunted or picked beyond a given point, the supply becomes too short and cannot recover, perhaps, for that season. What do the people in the camp do? They pick up and move on, to a place where the game is untouched. So this band must have enough territory to keep rebuilding the supply, it must preserve the supply against poachers, and it must move, move, move.

What about the numbers of people? Since they are actually part of the balance of nature themselves, they will be limited to a number which their territory can support in its worst (not its best) years. So the whole human population must be relatively sparse and spread out.

And the size of the band? Actually the simplest family can carry on this kind of a life, the man to hunt and the woman to collect vegetables, insects, water and firewood and to tend to odd jobs. But this leaves them with no help if they have need of it, while larger groups may not only protect themselves better but hunt more effectively, whether by co-operating in a rabbit drive or by multiplying the chances of finding and killing a large animal on which all can feed. However, the size of the band soon reaches a point at which it presses too hard on the food supply. There will simply not be enough food within their radius of action around the camp, or the band itself will not be able to move fast enough and far enough to tap the resources it needs. Only once in a while can bands come together in tribal meetings, and then perhaps when a natural crop—a prickly pear or a kind of grub—comes into season, and for a while creates plenty for everybody. The rest of the time the bands must keep their distance, and the number of each will be something like fifty souls, more or less.

These laws of nature have teeth in them: many such peoples accept the necessity of killing some of their infants at birth because the mother already has all the young children she can cope with on the march; and most of them ruthlessly abandon the sick or the helplessly old to freeze or starve. If, rarely, they put forth efforts on the aged one's behalf, these efforts are visibly at great cost. Such action is not subhuman callousness. Even though they may appear to take it calmly, the people have no choice at all in what they do, or even the face they put upon it.

We see, in fact, human beings like ourselves trapped, without knowing it, in a life that prevents them from having higher material inventions and social combinations. Small nomadic bands can hardly become civilized if they cannot even set up substantial households. They must find some escape from nomadism first, and from isolation and the limits of small numbers. They must find some escape from the treadmill of food-getting, which has them almost always either hunting or getting ready to hunt, and so keeps them from having any specialization of their energies, and makes the only division of labor that between the animal-hunting man and the plant-hunting woman. This escape was found with domestication, when the ordinary balance of nature was broken and food was made to grow not by nature but by man. Camps changed to villages, and dozens of people to hundreds.

But the millennium did not arrive with a rush. This was the basic change, ideally, but it was gradual, and there has always been a lot of overlapping. The Siriono Indians, nomadic hunters of eastern Bolivia, are normally so hungry that their conversation is largely about food, or squabbling over food, or begging one another for food (they are perhaps the least honorable of the hunters, and will eat in the middle of the night to avoid sharing). And yet they plant small plots of corn and other vegetables around the house or at some place near which they expect to be hunting; still the corn patch fails to rescue them from their hard lot. Many Neolithic peoples hunt and fish avidly and, as we shall soon see, the more primitive ones cannot even remain long in one place because of the inefficiency of their methods of farming. Even in archaeology we can see the gradual nature of the development.

Peasants on the Danube

In a few thousand years, Neolithic farming villages were established all over the Near East. Gradually, as the new ideas seeped westward into the European forests, the Mesolithic people there began to practice the new arts. Very bad pottery makes its appearance in the shell heaps of Scandinavia (in the mainly Mesolithic Ertebølle culture), and then in the French Campignian are found occasionally the bones of the domestic animals. These Neolithic-influenced settlements more and more began making stone axes, of the Mesolithic type, but with polished rather than chipped cutting edges. Such polished axes are considerably more effective in cutting wood, because they break less easily and have a cleaner, deeper bite; and they show that woodworking was coming into its own, for clearing land and for making houses. The polishing of stone tools, and indeed the skillful chipping also, later became a striking feature of the European Neolithic.

But this was in country where Mesolithic living by hunting continued to be easy and rewarding, in contrast to the difficulties of farming in the northern forest, so that adoption of a full Neolithic existence was held back. In some parts of the Mediterranean shore there are signs of an intrusion of farmers *without* pottery, and thus evidently very early. Their descendants or followers began making pottery of local forms, which looks as though the idea of pottery making had traveled from the East, but without actual pottery styles, so that they made pots on the model of their older containers—bags or baskets. Such are the people who appeared in Spain, France and England.

A more important colonization of Europe was that of the Danubians, people whose culture took shape in the Balkans, apparently under increasing influence from the East. They advanced up the Danube, reaching southern Germany before 4000 B.C. and fanning out from there. They made good pottery, decorated by meandering shallow grooves at first, and later by other markings. In fact, because of this new kind of evidence, archaeologists can almost study their migrations tribe by tribe.

They came with grain agriculture, and with the animals of the original Neolithic center of southwestern Asia. Pigs were important and useful because they could do well in the forests of the time, and so could cattle. Sheep, on the other hand, prefer open country, and only came into their own later on. In Germany and Poland the Danubians built good-sized villages of well-made rectangular houses, with timber or mud-plastered walls and thatched roofs, and apparently with wooden floors supported on posts. These were large houses, up to one hundred feet in length, and for some reason certain villages made them broader at one end than at the other. Better houses than these were not made in Europe for a very long time.

However, all was not peaches and cream for the Danubian farmers. They had no plows; instead, their gardening was of a primitive kind which goes under various names: the geographers call it milpa agriculture, and the anthropologists call it slash-and-burn. It is used today in

FIG. 21. *Reconstruction of a typical Danubian long house.*

places, and was very common in pioneer America. Trees are cut down, or ringed and allowed to die; then wood and brush are burned over, with no clearing of stumps; and the natural soil, slightly enriched by ashes, is turned up with hoes or sticks (the Danubians had stone "shoe last" hoe heads), and the seeding is done all around between stumps. There is no manuring or other treatment. This gives a good soil but wastes it quickly, so that a new patch must be cleared after a crop or two, and the old one is ruined until a second growth of trees has come along, years later. So the Danubians, like other slash-and-burners, ended by using up all the virgin forest around them, after which they could only move along to a new place. Thus they had villages but not cities; like the hunters, they still had to move, if only once a generation.

Furthermore, the grains are hungry plants, using up the soil quickly. Hence the Danubians moved rapidly, settling in much of the middle of Europe. They came up, choosing the not too heavily mixed oak forest, which grew on the areas of fine loess, good for the browsing of cattle and pigs, and easiest to work with a simple hoe. They followed this soil until they got as far as the Rhine and Meuse valleys. But as the Neolithic people spread in Europe they were forced into the rest of the deciduous woods (the northern evergreen forest was altogether too poor for their kind of farming), and things were harder.

Soils were more difficult to work, and keeping stock was a serious problem in fodder. For Europe was not open meadows. In spite of the farmers' inroads the forest grew up again on the wasted soil, and it was only the steel axe in the Middle Ages that finally pushed back the woods for good and all. By now most of Europe was populated by farmers, either immigrants from the East or missionized Mesolithic people. Only in the North did a Mesolithic way of life persist, where farmers could not yet make a living.

The megalith makers

The immigrants had come, as we have seen, in various ways, and not only up the Danube. One of the latest Neolithic manifestations, or streams of culture, was also the most peculiar, that of the megalith makers. It started in the western Mediterranean and is believed to come from the idea of chamber tombs, by this time important in the developing centers of Greece and the eastern Mediterranean. It spread up the Atlantic coast of Europe and had its greatest impact on France, the British Isles and Scandinavia.

The Megalithic people constructed monuments of huge rough stone which nowadays go by the name of dolmen, menhir, pierre levée, giant's tomb, passage grave, horned cairn, long barrow and so forth. Some of them are nothing but a sort of crude archway, two vertical stones capped by a third, each weighing many tons. Others have chambers behind the arch, sometimes with a skeleton or two buried in them. Still others have a long passage or even a sort of courtyard in front of door and chamber, suggesting that they were used for rites, perhaps over a period of time, and perhaps associated with the dead. They were generally finally covered over with rocks and earth, to make an oval barrow or tumulus.

The most unusual megaliths are the long rows of single great standing stones at Carnac, in Brittany, and some of the stone circles of England. Nobody knows what went on around any of these things, and you can paint your own picture of the doings. But the fact remains that a cult of great appeal had seized on the Megalithic people, because the structures must have called for a good deal of human labor (such as hunters could never have afforded, you notice), as well as for the building of earth ramps to place stones in position or to set capstones, and for various engineering tricks like the use of rollers.

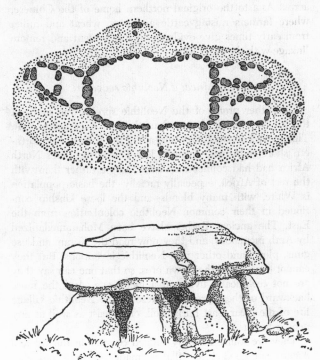

Fig. 22. *A dolmen with capstones in place, and (above) the plan of a large mound in Ireland with a court and several chambers.*

All this was happening about 2000 B.C. and shortly after, in an age that seems vastly remote from ours in

culture as well as time. Although diminishing areas long
kept up an almost Neolithic way of life, Europe as a
whole grew apart in later times from its alma mater, the
Near East, as both of them attained high culture. Furthermore, Europe was not the only direction out of Southwest
Asia in which the Neolithic culture spread. It stabbed
southeastward into Afghanistan and western India, though
we still know very little about this. It reached all the way
across Asia to the original northern home of the Chinese,
where farmers raising cattle and pigs, wheat and millet
from early times give evidence of this ancient and remote
linkage with the Near East.

North Africa: a Neolithic souvenir

One other prong of the Neolithic spread was south of
the Mediterranean, rather than through it or north of it.
This moved across Egypt and along the Riviera-like northern shore of Africa. Even in late Paleolithic times North
Africa had had connections with Europe rather than with
the rest of Africa, especially racially—the basic population
is White, with many blonds—and the loose kinship continued in their common Neolithic colonization from the
East. The ancient Berbers have been Mohammedanized
by Arab incursions, and they now read the Koran, and use
guns, plows and other post-Neolithic inventions. But they
cannot even smelt their own ores, so that one can say they
are not technically living in a metal age. And the more
backward of them probably preserve the Neolithic village
life of the Near East fairly well, or at least as well as any
people living.

They are found in fairly rugged country in the Rif and
Algeria, in good-sized villages, made of stone and clay
houses with wooden beams. Some houses have two stories,
but these are somewhat collapsible. They do not move
their towns, however; their gardening is broad enough, and
their land well enough irrigated, to support them in one
place. They are mixed farmers—very mixed. Their cattle,
cared for as well as they can manage, and used for milk,

meat and hides, are nevertheless runty, and goats and sheep are important. They are Moslems, in a nominal sort of way, and so it will not be tactful to consider whether they ever eat pigs; they will not discuss the matter, but things looking very much like pigs are apparently kept by some of them. They have the familiar grains, including rye, which will grow on poor hillsides, and oats, which they can gather wild. Along with this familiar pattern they grow various garden vegetables, and, more important, they are orchardists of no small means, raising olives, figs, nuts, oranges, lemons, apples, pears, plums, peaches and apricots. On top of this they use much wild food, which they speak about as their oldest foods of all: wild olives, acorns, cherries, mulberries, asparagus, celery, mushrooms and so forth.

So they serve to remind us that, in the Neolithic proper, the people of the Near East (if not of Europe) doubtless had broader food resources than we can always detect from archaeology. They also show us at once how much more complex social life may become in large villages than in the bands of hunting peoples. Later on we shall see how varied its forms may be. Probably the Riffians' customs are more familiar to us than are those of other cultures. For example, like the hunters, they reinforce their food-getting and its distribution with certain practices: they have sharecroppers, and harvesting bees, and regular charitable institutions. Gleaning is allowed (see Ruth 2), and in fact any hungry person passing a man working in his garden can hop over the fence, pitch in and help, and the gardener will owe him a meal.

Their towns are made up, not so much of families of our style, or by anything like the fearsome organizational schemes of the Australians, but of extended families consisting of the actual households of a group of brothers. They call this large family a "vein," in the Rif, and the vein decides such matters as buying and selling. A group of such big families will make up a "bone," which may be either the same thing as the whole village or a major part of it; a sort of superfamily with a council to decide its affairs.

Over this there are councils of whole districts and finally of tribes. (In the Kabyle region of Algeria they have instead local parliaments.)

With all of this they have a highly developed code of their own laws, and also a strong code of honor. In other words, in our own best traditions they love to argue and they love to fight. They are great cracker-barrel lawyers, and councils meet to settle affairs with every anticipation and wish for an orderly denouement, but the admired legal process is only too apt to lead to an increase in the temperature and finally to a pitched gun battle between opposing bones, with dead and wounded all over the town.

10. The Spread of Modern Races

We can gaze far back along the trail in Europe. Large-skulled men—White men—of the Upper Paleolithic displaced the Neanderthals and hunted in the changing climate until the end of the Mesolithic. Then we see, though dimly, the establishment of farming in the Near East and Egypt and its spread, by new waves of people, also White, westward through the Mediterranean and northwest into the European forests.

If only we had something as clear for Africa and Asia, we would be pleased indeed. But we have not, and we should recognize the fact in order to view what little we do know in the right light. We find ourselves at this point in the story—the founding of the modern world through the knowledge of farming—checked at many places by ignorance. Specifically, we do not know how the modern varieties, or races, of man developed and distributed themselves about. Nor do we know just how the various cultures, principally farming, arose and spread, nor how far they were transported by their proprietors (the Danubian farmers, for example) and how far they were simply passed along from neighbor to neighbor.

Races, of course, are a special problem, and one that stretches far back of the Neolithic. Races did, however, probably undergo a considerable amount of redistribution and mixture during the Neolithic, leading up to the picture of humanity in known historic times. Now racial types change by biological principles, not cultural ones, and so they change much more slowly. Their origins go back at least beyond the beginning of the Upper Paleolithic when White people took over Europe, and when other racial types, all of modern form (Homo sapiens), apparently existed elsewhere. Just how their common stem arose is very much under dispute, but we have already gazed on this enigma. Some scholars, compromising with the extreme view of Dr. Franz Weidenreich, think that different kinds of Lower Paleolithic fossil men mixed with the original Homo sapiens (our kind of man), so that the different hybrids which resulted became our different races. I doubt myself that this is widely true, since present races are so much alike in skull form, but it is certainly a possibility. For example, the natives of Australia might get their especially long, low heads and heavy brows from Solo Man, who lived in this same part of the world not long before them.

Origins of race

The reason for races in man, as in any other animal, must be looked for in the processes of evolution. We must suppose the existence of a human stock already possessing, even if in primitive form, the basic features distinguishing Homo sapiens. We must also assume such expansion of this stock that different major populations of it became sufficiently isolated geographically from one another so that they could come to differ slightly; so that any hereditary differences appearing among them would not be at once lost by thoroughgoing intermixture.

The origins of differences themselves are to be looked for in mutation, selection and drift. Mutation means the appearance of new traits through accidental new genes; it is the material of long-range evolution but has usually been overstressed, as far as we can tell, for the smaller differences distinguishing races. For example, the appearance of pygmies has sometimes been ascribed to one or two major mutations toward small size, certainly a wrong view. Though small, stepwise mutations may have been involved, much racial evolution probably took place through the sorting out of genes already present in the population, a sorting out that is accomplished by selection and drift.

Genetic drift means accidental change in the gene proportions of a population. Some parents simply have more children. Or the possessor of a given gene dies by accident. In a small group, or population, something like the gene for blood group B might, by a series of such accidents, diminish and disappear and so two such small populations, originally from the same source, might drift apart in the averages of their characteristics. Statistically, it is like this: suppose you draw at random a number of playing cards —twenty—from the usual deck. You expect to get half red and half black. But you also know that this is only the normal expectancy, and that in fact it is much more likely that you will get unbalanced numbers, say eight red and twelve black. Now this is your new "population," or "generation," and you must now draw from a deck with these proportions. Your most likely drawings will therefore have these proportions. You might by chance get a swing back to fifty-fifty, but the fact is that red now has a disadvantage more likely to lead to its disappearing from the deck entirely, especially in small drawings of "populations." The same thing applies to genes for hereditary traits. This is genetic drift, a force without direction.

Natural selection, of course, is a force *with* direction; the tendency in favor of greater adaptation, which is the main key in evolution. If forces of any kind favor individuals of one genetic complexion over others in the sense that they live so as to reproduce more successfully, such individuals will necessarily increase their bequest of genes to the next generation relative to the rest of the population. Thus differences in environment might, in a relatively short time (geologically speaking), cause adaptive racial differences to emerge between once similar groups. Much would depend on the intensity of selection, and genetic drift would be operating as well. Of course, mixture among distinct racial groups *after* they have become distinct will produce still other racial types, and there is absolutely no real distinction between "pure" and "mixed" races. But selection and drift may be expected to have done all the work necessary to produce the most different races of Homo sapiens without calling for mixture with outsiders like the Neanderthals, and so I prefer to leave these other folk in the Lower Paleolithic graveyard for good.

All the above is theoretically correct, but it has been possible to show evolution actually producing changes only on lower forms of life—for one thing, we cannot observe ourselves evolving because we only live as long as our subjects. But also, it is very difficult to find demonstrable or even logically appealing examples of racial features that are adaptive. The most clearly shown (and they are not usually considered "racial" features although they have the same nature) are the effects of the rules of Bergmann and Allen.

According to the first, as an animal of given shape gets larger, its inner bulk increases faster than its outer surface as a matter of simple geometry, and so in warm-blooded species the ratio of heat produced to heat dissipated through the skin is higher in larger individuals. It has been shown that human populations go up in average weight as annual mean temperature goes down (that is, as one goes away from the equator), in general and considering only peoples who have been long in one place. By Allen's rule, extremities (limbs, ears, muzzle) make the same kind of response for heat conservation, being longer and skinnier in warm parts of a species range. Man obeys this rule as well, and different body shapes thus seem to have become matters of social inheritance. In the same sunbroiled desert live the Arabs of Arabia and the Tuareg of the Sahara, both of whom are of the White stock (and who protect themselves with clothing, even over the face in the latter case), and also the Dinka and the Shilluk, of the White Nile, who are of the Negroid stock (and who wear no clothes at all). Now these populations are all extreme in lankiness, with the Nilotics being the tallest men on earth. They are in marked contrast to some extreme Northerners like the chunky Eskimos, who are thick-bodied and particularly short in the limbs.

It is almost certain, as we shall presently see, that the flat, squint-eyed Eskimo face is also a special adaptation, serving to protect the eyes and nose from severe cold. It would seem similarly obvious that other racial features, like a protective dark skin in the tropics, or a light one in the cloudy North where healthful sunlight is at a premium, are also responses to the environment. But in fact there are various difficulties in the way of simple explanations of most such traits, and little is known anyhow of their actual biological meaning. For the time being, the argument that they are forthright adaptations is less a scientific proof than an appeal to logic, however strong. Eventually we will know for a fact how racial differences came about; now we do not.

Dark-skinned races of the tropics

Suppose we look instead at the races as we actually find them, and see how much of a pattern we can make out. First of all, in the tropical parts of the Old World—Africa below the Sahara, India, the western Pacific, and Australia —we perceive what seems to be the home of the dark-skinned peoples. Here are those whose skins are deeply pigmented and whose eyes also have a dense brown coloring of the iris. Of course we are at once taken back to the idea that these things are connected with the intense equatorial sun, to protect the tissues of the body and the interior of the eye from the harmful effects of too much light. But notice that this is not the outstandingly sunniest part of the world, all told. Some of it is desert (in Australia), but it does not include the great Arabian and Sahara deserts. Much of it is savanna and parkland. But a good deal of it, what looks like the central part, is rain forest, humid but shady. And this forest was, if anything, more extensive rather than less so during any period when the human races were becoming distinct. So this does not help out the argument for dark skin as simply a sort of super suntan, becoming a racial feature in response to an overabundance of light. Drs. C. S. Coon, S. M. Garn and J. B. Birdsell have interesting things to say about this dilemma,[1] suggesting that there may be other advantages for tropic-dwellers in dark skins (such as resistance to certain kinds of disease), too subtle for us to understand in the present state of our knowledge.

The Negroes of Africa seem to have their proper area in the forest of the Congo basin and along the Guinea coast, all near the equator, even though Negroid peoples occupied almost all Africa south of the Sahara. Besides their dark coloration they have woolly hair and puffy lips. Both of these traits are distinctive, or specialized, making the Negroes seem what an advertising man would call different; they are certainly not primitive traits, and they suggest that this human line has pursued its own racial development for some little time. The woolly hair is likely to be an adaptation insulating the head from excessive heat, by forming an air-filled mass and allowing evaporation from the scalp. The thickened lips are a puzzle; possibly they are a secondary feature related to thick and deeply pigmented skin.

The history of the Negro stock is a blank. It seems solidly entrenched, probably long since, south of the Sahara. But men of the same general type, though shortish and apparently mixed with other dark- and light-skinned races, are found in the islands of Melanesia, from New Guinea eastward to Fiji. The essential puzzle is that between Africa and Melanesia—more than the width of Asia —they are not seen.

This is not true of the Negritos, a branch of the Negroes who share their essential racial nature except for size. They are pygmies, usually simple hunters, and their wide spread through this whole enormous tropical space is one of the most astonishing things that the study of race provides. Everybody knows about the Pygmies of the Congo, who wander in the forest and bring game to exchange for iron and vegetables with the Negroes of the villages. But fewer people are aware that these Negritos form the population

[1] *Races: A Study of the Problems of Race Formation in Man* (Springfield, Ill.: Charles C. Thomas, 1950).

of the Andaman Islands, at the opposite side of the Indian Ocean, off Burma, and that they occur also in the mountains of the Malay Peninsula and in many of the Philippines, and in New Guinea as well. Definite traces of them are found in other parts of Melanesia, Australia and the East Indies. Finally, and perhaps most important, there is evidence among the wildest people of India that her original population was made up of the dark-skinned races, and that the Negritos were an important element among these.

What could have given rise to this strange state of affairs, which makes the Negritos seem almost more important in racial history than the Negroes? There have been various explanations, ranging generally from dubious to absurd. They are not, for example, leftovers from a time when all men were small, because all true men of the Pleistocene, at least, were of our size, and thus the oldest form of Homo sapiens must have shared this size. So the Negritos have somehow become diminished. Further, they must have had a common origin with the Negroes, since they have the same special, strongly evolved traits. Though it has been suggested, they could hardly be Negroes or some other kind of men who, in half a dozen different places, shrank in size under the influence of the environment. Even one such shrinking must be looked on as a special event in human history, and in fact it would be less of a stretch of the imagination to suppose that the Negritos evolved small size, dark skin, woolly hair, thick lips and so on all together, distributed themselves around the tropics, and then in one place or perhaps two, grew up again to be full-sized and what we call Negroes. This has been suggested also. I think the least stretch of imagination is needed if we assume that somewhere, and I should guess in Africa, a basic Negro stock developed, in sunny open country like the Sahara border, and gave rise in the forests to the south to a stunted offshoot, since small size has various advantages to forest hunters. Then, in a favorable climatic period, with a wider extension of forests (and grasslands?) these peoples both extended themselves eastward, with the Negritos being the more successful in reaching and surviving in more places. But every bit of this is imagination.

In any event this does not finish up the dark-skinned races. There is one more, represented in the natives of Australia. But these people do not seem at all closely related to the Negroes or Negritos. With them they share the dark skin and eyes. They also share large teeth and somewhat protruding mouth regions. These things may be retentions of ancient, more primitive features on both sides, rather than evidence of brotherhood. For the Australians have certain other probably primitive traits, such as hairiness of the face and body, hair that is wavy or curly or nearly straight, beetling brows, and receding foreheads. All of these are definitely not traits of the Negroids but they *are* traits of the Whites. So there is at least as good—possibly better—reason for thinking that the Australians go with the Whites as for thinking they go with the Negroids.

In fact most anthropologists, following Earnest A. Hooton, have simply classed them as a primitive branch of the White stock. I prefer to regard them as a generally antique form of Homo sapiens, representing more closely than any living men what such a form might have been. Instead of saying the Australians are primitive Whites, I would rather say that the Whites are evolved Australians, which would even allow the Negroes to be evolved Australians also, but evolved in another direction.

On top of this, the Australians seem to have been a long time in their part of the world. You have seen the ancient pattern of their culture. Such fossilized, probably ancient skulls as are known are all of the same racial type, and the one well-dated specimen, the Keilor skull, has an age of some 15,000 years. Thus the Australian racial form has a considerable antiquity in Australia itself. And the occupation of the continent definitely took place in the Pleistocene, arguing that the primitiveness of Australian culture was no accident. Elsewhere were found the well-known fossilized skulls from Wadjak in Java, Australian in type and probably Pleistocene in date, demonstrating in any event that the East Indies were formerly populated by this kind of man.

Today, of course, the type is found only in Australia, but its racial stamp is clear in the islands north and east of that continent—New Caledonia, New Guinea, New Britain—among the obviously mixed peoples of Melanesia. The type is barely suggested in other places, including India again, where it seems to show up dimly among the remnants of the most ancient parts of the population. In fact, judging by simple inspection of appearance, the study of nose shape and hair form, and certain indications from blood traits—and we really have little else to use—it looks as though this original stratum in India might have been made up of two elements, the Australians and the Negritos.

So we have Australians in the East, having come long ago from Asia; we have Negritos throughout the tropics; and we have Negroes in Africa and in Melanesia, and a puzzling question as to where the Negroes formed in the first place. To make it worse, we have the Bushmen of South Africa, another people who, like the Australians, have an old hunting culture and an impressive claim to antiquity in their own home. In spite of their smallish size and their ultra-woolly hair, they differ considerably from the Negroes and Pygmies; and yet certain similarities in blood type do suggest some kind of relation or mixture, as I have said already. What does this mean as to Bushman origins? We do not know.

Whites and Mongoloids and Indians

All these tropical and southern people are separated from the northerly parts of the Old World by barriers of a sort, such as the deserts of Africa and Arabia and the great Himalayan mountain range. But only the last is a really effective bar, since changes in climate once made the present desert lands more inviting. In any case there are gaps in the barrier, in China and in the Near East. Nevertheless it is to the north of it that we find the other great racial stocks, the Whites and the Mongoloids.

The Whites, of course, are at home in Europe, North Africa and the Middle East. In our own centuries they have been pushing themselves into other people's property everywhere, but this is an old habit. They evidently did it thousands of years ago in India, coming in from Iran and Afghanistan and overrunning the darker aboriginals to form the variously colored but predominantly "White" India of today. And they did the same thing in Europe thousands of years before that, evicting the poor Neanderthals entirely.

The Whites are all light-skinned, obviously, but they have developed an exaggerated phase of this in blondness, so that especially pale skin, blue eyes, and fair hair are common, often in combination, around a great center in northern and eastern Europe, and are sporadically found in other regions as well. Both the basic lightness and the

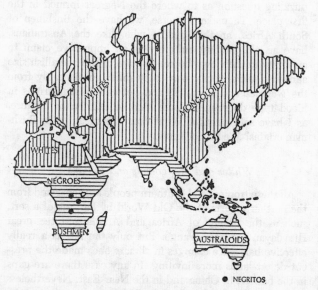

FIG. 23. *Main areas of the principal racial types of man (greatly simplified).*

extra blondness may have come about, as I have said, because of some advantage, or at least no disadvantage, of a
thinner skin under the cloudy skies that hung over Europe
and Asia during the long time while the last glacier was
in retreat, and after. Even if this is so, we have no definite
idea as to how quickly such evolutionary changes—even
such slight ones as this—might come about: whether blondness might have flowered rapidly, among the Mesolithic
and Neolithic populations, or whether it was actually developing even among the first of the blade-making invaders
of the Upper Paleolithic. In spite of all the splendid animals the Paleolithic artists painted, only one good portrayal
of a man has come to light, a Magdalenian painted bas-
relief, found in 1949 at Angles-sur-Anglin in France. This
Magdalenian, clearly a White man, has dark eyes and hair
(and a huge nose). This tells us nothing, because most
Frenchmen still have the same coloring.

Chinese also have dark eyes and hair together with
various traits of the Mongoloid racial form. Such traits are
straight hair, sparse beard and, above all, a flattish face
with a small, nonprominent nose and a slant-eyed appearance because of a fold of skin over the inner corner of the
eye opening. Not all Chinese have these features, just as
not all Scandinavians are blond-haired and blue-eyed. Furthermore, the real center of this exaggerated Mongoloid
kind of face seems to be eastern Siberia and the Eskimo
Arctic. Drs. Coon, Garn and Birdsell have ably argued
that this whole visage is a prize example of a racial feature coming into being as a result of evolutionary adaptation: if you sat down to remodel a human face to protect
it against the cold, they say, you would finish with the
face of an Eskimo.

The cold of Siberia today is fearful enough. Now, during the last glacial phase, this area was ringed around and
cut through with sheets of ice, but was not completely
covered, remaining a space in which Paleolithic hunters
could live with proper clothing, and from which they could
not escape. Here was a selection machine, and a struggle
for existence, that would have made Darwin happy. For

many thousand years the inhabitants were in danger of
frozen faces and eyes, infected sinuses, and pneumonia.
Supposedly they were not killed off entirely by the cold,
and instead gradually evolved a face that is a protective
mask. The brows became flatter, reducing the sinuses over
the eyes, always a vulnerable point. The eye sockets added
fat around the eyes, and an overhanging fold of skin gave
extra protection, against snow blindness as well as frost.
The cheekbones became broader and more forward-thrust-
ing, or "high," further helping the eyes, and also protecting
the sides of the nose, which itself became lower, and perhaps longer and narrower (as in Eskimos). This change,
and still more fat on the cheeks, acted to preserve the air
chamber of the nose and the sinuses inside the cheeks.
Finally the broad flat face gave as little skin surface as possible for freezing or for penetration of the cold. In addition to all this, whiskers became coarse and sparse: no
beard at all is better than one full of icicles from your
breath.

We assume, then, that this special face, almost the hallmark of the Mongoloids, came into being under great pressure. It conferred an advantage in intense, dry cold. But
it does not appear to confer disadvantages in other kinds
of climate, and certainly there would be no new kind of
pressure to undo what the cold had done. Therefore this
face was entirely suitable for export once the glaciers had
gone; and these specialized Mongoloids spread southward
even into the tropics, taking the face along, and bestowing
it in some measure on such indigenous peoples as they met
up with and married. Its home remains Siberia and Korea,
but the Chinese exhibit less marked versions of it, and it is
to be seen all down into southern Asia. It is in fact particularly characteristic of certain tropical peoples in the Philippines or Borneo. Except for the generally broad cheekbones, the various traits of the face (low noses, flatness
and roundness, eye folds, reduced brow ridges) are much
less common among the American Indians, but they are
present in full force in the Eskimos, who are set apart
physically in this way from the other Americans.

Now if, in the last twenty-five or fifty thousand years, the Whites have been becoming in part blonder, and the Mongoloids more Mongoloid, then we might ask whether they were formerly more alike, or at least what they started from. For the Mongoloids the raw material was, I think, something like the American Indians. The latter have dark, more or less straight hair, dark brown eyes and typically large faces. However, they usually have large brows, and not seldom prominent noses, and signs of the fully developed Mongoloid face are rare. In the Americas they vary a good deal in type, and they are so to speak racially nondescript, though they certainly are more like the Asiatic Mongoloids than anything else. One may imagine such a former population in Asia—small hordes of late Paleolithic hunters with a culture recalling the Australians, Bushmen or Aurignacians—of which some fractions crossed the Bering Strait into America and some fractions became caught in the Siberian ice trap and went through a rapid evolution of the face.

There is further license for such imaginings in certain facts. One is that there are still many peoples, especially in southern Asia and Tibet, who either strongly resemble American Indians or at least are not very Mongoloid, and who can be looked on as still other fractions of this ancient population which underwent neither migration nor selection. Another fact is the three skulls from the Upper Cave at Choukoutien, China—the same cave group as Locality 1, the cave of the Pekin men, but in this case of Upper Paleolithic date. One skull looks rather Mongoloid, one is alleged to look Negroid and one, a large male, has big brows and a deep jaw, and would cause us no surprise if seen among skulls of either Upper Paleolithic Europeans or certain tribes of American Indians. Now I cannot imagine, as can some of my colleagues, a sort of convention of the races having been held in this cave, nor any Stone Age international marriages. I can see in these skulls only the sort of unspecific and varying form, with apparent resemblances of individuals to other racial types like Negroids, which has been clearly described in a collection of crania of American Indians from a single recent village. I think the Upper Cave people were Indians still resident in China.

Explaining the Mongoloids as coming from something like American Indians makes them in turn somewhat more like the Whites, but it does not make the Whites the same as Indians. There is still a difference, and we can go no further back. We know the Whites from the beginning of the Upper Paleolithic when they arrive in Europe, in a form not actually more primitive than today. They seem to have come from western Asia or the Near East. But if that is so, they were not confined to this part of Asia, nor do they seem simply to have been one end of a range of peoples which merged gradually with "Indians" at the other, unless these first Indians were almost "Whites."

For there are signs of "White" peoples in the Far East. One of these signs is the Ainu, the ancient inhabitants of at least the northern half of Japan, who are brunet, but hairy and generally "White" in nature. Other signs are found among people who seem to be mixed in their racial origins and to include a White strain in their ancestry: possibly the Japanese and various groups in the East Indies, but above all the Polynesians of the whole eastern Pacific from Hawaii to New Zealand, who must originally have come from southern Asia. Thus the Whites would seem to have penetrated the Far East, north of India and the mountains, perhaps to the south of the area where the parental Indians and Mongoloids held sway, and perhaps before an expansion of the latter peoples almost completely submerged the eastern Whites.

Beyond this we can hardly probe the racial past at all. Only long and thorough work in archaeology, coupled perhaps with lucky finds, will do more. A single skull found under the right conditions could tell us volumes. We see that a White race existed by the middle of the last glaciation somewhere in western Asia, and that very likely the early, Indian-like Mongoloids were present too, as well as the natives of Australia, who were probably in southern Asia and perhaps already in Australia as well. We may suppose that the special—what are usually called typical—Mongoloids, those with the flat faces, were forming in the time since then, sending their representatives into the New World only in the Eskimos, after the main groups of Indians, showing a far milder degree of these traits, had gone before. As to the Negroes and Negritos, we are simply at a loss.

And, of course, a principal reason why it is so hard to determine how and where races arose is the fact that the moving around of peoples has been a continuous process. It is not as if our main racial types had traveled once and for all into the places we later find them, and then had stayed put. Changing culture and changing climate have sent peoples repeatedly on the move, and we should only be fooling ourselves if we did not realize the great complexity of all these ebbs and flows, which in some cases must have led to the total replacement of one population by another. That is what seems to have happened to the late Neanderthals, as first one wave and then others of the Upper Paleolithic Europeans came drifting in. Surely climate must have somehow made it possible and desirable for hunting groups of a similar kind to move across what is now the Bering Strait into North America, a movement that began not long after the Cro-Magnon invasion of Europe. And then later in Europe we have seen how the first influences of Neolithic culture filtered in from the Near East, followed by actual migrations of Danubian farmers with the farming culture full-fledged, who, compared to the Paleolithic and Mesolithic occupants, made a different and fuller use of the land.

Repeatedly, cultural advances must have opened fresh territories to man, or changed the same old countryside by making it usable in a new and different way, quite apart from such climatic changes as the retreat or advance of ice, and the spreading or shrinking of forest. You might realize that, for all the splendor of our own science, there are great parts of the world which are still barren to us. We have hardly surpassed the Eskimos in figuring out what the Arctic is good for; nations compete for pie-shaped pieces of Antarctica without knowing why they want it. Irrigation is still only promising us the key to the deserts; and we are still content to leave a large share of the tropical forests of South America to the Indians. The same is true of much near-arctic land: we push into it only for spot exploitation, as when we find coal on Spitzbergen or uranium around the Great Bear Lake, and we do not really call it home. We are just as unmoved by such territory as hunters may have been by some of the finest farming land; or both hunters and farmers by such things as the great natural seaports, or coal and iron centers like the Saar and the American Midwest.

So we may be very sure that there has been migration and countermigration from the Paleolithic to the present, increasing if anything in more recent times. At any rate the "Neolithic" people of the modern world, meaning most of the supposedly primitive tribes known to history, are the net result of all the involved developments I have hinted at.

11. Asia and the Western Farmers

The Neolithic pioneers of Southwest Asia, those Near Easterners whose first villages are just now being dug up, probably had a newly made-over culture to go with their newly subjugated grains and stock animals. We know about their mud-walled houses, of course, but we cannot excavate their marriage customs. We can, however, put two and two together. Statuettes from various places (of somewhat later date) suggest that they dressed simply, in loose garments, probably a short wrap-around skirt or kilt for either sex, and a shawl, perhaps worn over one shoulder and under the other. And the painting of designs on the skin may have been popular.

Socially they seem to have placed an accent on the male and paternal side, and to have been willing to put their affairs into the hands of strong, not to say despotic, rulers. We do not know this, of course, but such ideas have been prevalent among many cultures of the West. Notice, for example, that even at this late date we ourselves seem to regard giving simple equality to women as a most noble, generous and highly civilized achievement, not the natural thing. In religion, if we can judge from the Norse, the Greeks and India, the ancient culture revered a group of powerful gods, derived from nature, and tending to be formed into a sort of family themselves. At any rate we may suppose that the kernel of such beliefs goes back to the early taking-shape of this culture.

Once it had become established, after its gradual development, it was ready to travel, and travel it did. I do

not mean at all that a particular set of civilized people began moving out to every part of the world, bringing a new
culture with them, a belief that long was popular in one
guise or other with would-be historians. Nor do I mean
that the culture was boxed for export and sent everywhere
in the same form, much as we do with farm implements
and try wistfully to do with democratic government.
Rather, it moved as might be expected, partly by migrations of peoples, partly by the migration of crops, and
partly by the migration of ideas alone. The new achievements, like all such important advances, were a force that
could not be resisted, and from which there was no turning back.

We have seen that the Neolithic, as goods or as ideas,
went to Egypt and North Africa and, later, into Europe.
At home in the Near East it held on, changing with time,
remaining primitive in some places but advancing in others
until it finally became the matrix of our own civilization.
But that is getting ahead of the story. Let us see what happened to it in other parts of Asia.

India and the castes

It went down into India. Its tracks cannot be followed,
for Indian prehistory is almost a void. When this prehistory begins to be deciphered it will be a great addition to
our knowledge of the past. For in India there was surely
a meeting of North and South, and of East and West,
which produced a greatly varying culture and a caste-
bound social system of such complexity that it now seems
to be its own worst enemy.

What must have happened is that Whites from the
Persian and Mesopotamian regions (modern Iran and Iraq)
moved into western India with their crops and animals,
meeting dark-skinned peoples of a Negrito and Australian-
like variety who may still have been hunters like the Vedda
of Ceylon. This might not have been the first time that
White westerners came in, by any means. But whether
it was a beginning or a continuation, there was evidently

a fusion of racial types which ended by being predominantly White, and by giving rise to a sort of scale of color from a lighter west to a darker east and south.

The above is "what must have happened," given the picture of later times. As for archaeological fact, we know that there was a general advanced Neolithic culture in the westernmost part (Pakistan and eastern Iran). Just to the east, along the Indus Valley, there grew up an important civilization, by 2500 B.C.; it was related to that of the Near East, but it shows that new elements had joined the complex, especially animals and food. It had elephants, humped cattle, buffalo and chickens, all of which must have come from the other direction, the east. India also came to use cotton in place of sheep's wool, and rice as well as the other grains.

India of today, with its philosophical and artistic developments, is too far along the road of complication for us to consider. But let us look at her castes, which are a unique social system. They do not seem to be extremely old, at least in their modern form. It has been guessed that they arose first through the mixture of races, or that they originated with ancient totemic groups of aboriginal times. They may actually go all the way back to the ancient Indus cities, but traditionally the caste idea stems from the Aryan invaders of about 1500 B.C., rather barbarous village people who came in from Iran (same word as "Aryan") long after the Indus civilization. We know about these people because of the Vedic hymns, the great record that has made their language, early Sanskrit, so important among the earliest forms of the "Aryan" or Indo-European languages. (In fact, discovery of this language connection was the reason the word "Aryan" eventually became so thoroughly misapplied to an imaginary race, which supposedly civilized Europe at an unspecified time in a manner not known, but which is the classical example of a chimera with great political usefulness.)

The Aryans had four castes—priests, rulers, cultivators and servants—establishing the doctrine that people must be divided by occupation. And it is occupation which in recent centuries has given rise to the great number of modern castes, with elevator men and chauffeurs forming new ones; if there is not a caste of television repairmen now there will be soon. But whatever may have started things off, this is how Professor Alfred L. Kroeber explains what it has become:

> *The racial explanation is obviously inadequate. Castes do represent race to a certain extent, but they also represent nationalities, tribes, common residence, religious distinctness, occupations, cultural status. Whatever sets off a group in any way may be sufficient to make it a caste in India. If groups diverge within an established caste, they become recognized as subcastes, perhaps finally to develop into wholly separate castes. Priests, nobles, clerks, fishermen, street-sweepers are castes; so are the Parsis; so are hill tribes that maintain their primitive customs—the Dravidian buffalo-milking Todas, for instance, are reckoned high socially. Clearly we have here a generic system, a pattern of organizing society, into which every sort of group as it actually forms is fitted. Caste is a way of thought that the Hindu has tried to universalize.*

That is the secret: "a pattern of organizing society." No other "reason" could have made it so important. It is strange to us and to our ideas to see how an Indian is locked into the caste he is born in, and how the castes keep aloof from one another. For their main purpose seems to be to preserve their distinctness. You must marry within your caste only, or face being outcasted, which is serious. And you must live up to the ritual requirements of ceremony and purity of your caste, which are more exacting the higher the caste. The topmost must not eat beef or pork, or drink wine, and may have to avoid or be careful about a variety of other foods or kinds of cooking. And they are strict about women and marriage, keeping the women secluded and not allowing widows to remarry, or sanctioning any divorce.

Further down, caste members may live lives less strict, may eat more kinds of food, do things no high-caste Hindu may, and be freer about permitting widows to marry again, and so on; penalties for doing the wrong thing will be less absolute and severe. But this laxity makes such a caste relatively "unclean," so that its members may pollute the food of the higher castes if they are used as servants, because of food they indulge in themselves. So the high-caste person must keep an eye on what's cooking and on who's cooking also. The lower caste may be so free and easy in its ways, or so automatically contaminated by its occupation, as to be untouchable to the higher levels, meaning that contact between them must be careful or the higher person will be defiled and have to go through a ritual cleaning up.

So there is a ranking of castes, starting with tradition, in which the superior ones pay for their status by observance of custom and apparent self-denial. For individuals, the castes have windows but no doors, and one escapes only by jumping out of the window, with the effects increasing the higher the story. But the castes themselves may shift a little bit: the council of a local caste may decide to ban widow remarriage and in other ways put itself on a higher level of purity, and so look for higher caste status. It can hardly move far up in this respect, being anchored by tradition and by the status of the same caste in other places.

Now all this exclusiveness might look like a struggle by the castes to have nothing to do with one another. But it would be a strange society which actually managed to break itself up into little pieces. On the contrary, the Indian caste system apparently exists in order to create pieces that can be fitted together usefully. It does insist on defining the pieces clearly. But—and this is the other side of the coin —it also says where the pieces belong and what they do. For each caste has its occupations, and its rights to those occupations, established as a labor union could only dream of. Whether the caste does the plowing, the housework, the laundry, or makes pots, does smithing or cuts hair, it is apt to have the hereditary right to perform these services, and its hereditary customers, especially among the land-owning upper caste.[1] This last, indeed, serves as something like a pivot for the scheme, making the greatest use of the services of other castes, and in return (apart from any money transactions) giving out food, the use of land, and so on. So everyone does his own particular job, never dreaming of doing anything else, and the whole thing fits together neatly.

Now this is one way of organizing a society, but a rather extreme one in the emphasis it gives to the social units (castes) of which it makes use. It is foreign to us in the completeness with which it takes away the individual's scope to arrange his life or to change his position. It also rejects the chance for the whole society to progress by al-lowing, as ours does, one class of people and then another to seek fulfillment and expend their energies in new and more efficient ways, even while they are interacting. At the worst, the caste system seems static. At the best, it does say, "You're the catcher; you're the pitcher; you're third base," and so gets the game going. It reflects Indian phi-losophy, which does not value change, but rather predes-tination. Each one has his place, accepted by him and ev-eryone else as proper and satisfactory, getting a social and personal security which may be forfeited in other societies where your occupation is looked on as your personal re-sponsibility.

This gives us a fine chance to pass judgments. Let us not take it. The point is simply that here is a way of putting a society together, not our way, but a successful way. It is certainly post-Neolithic, but I have described it here be-cause it does bear on a problem that Neolithic peoples began to face when their new ways of producing food finally made their communities considerably bigger than the bands of hunters, or the bands of howling monkeys.

---

[1] For an excellent account of the system, see "The Division of Labor in an Indian Village," by Morris Opler and Rudra Datt Singh, Chapter 17 in A Reader in General Anthropology, edited by Carleton S. Coon (New York: Henry Holt & Co., 1948).

The problem is that of keeping the bigger group from becoming unwieldy, and making it socially and economically effective. That is the meaning of social organization at this new stage.

Herders of the desert and steppe

We must leave India and go back to Southwest Asia and into the Neolithic, whence we started. The farming system that appeared here spread outward with both grains and animals; and in parts of the dry, grassy belt that runs right across Central Asia and Arabia (and on into Africa), it was the animals, rather than the crops, that the people eventually found most profitable to depend on as their mainstay. A herding life was thus a special offshoot of this Neolithic basis. One such development took place in Arabia: it was actually rather late, but it was spectacular.

Arabia was formerly better watered, and much of it was occupied by farmers of the regular variety, as it still is. Part of these, living near the grassy region, have their villages where they raise crops. They leave the villages during the winter wet season to drive their flocks of sheep and goats through the grass region on the desert's edge, while they themselves live in tents. But some of them, the Bedouin, live mainly in the desert itself. These are the Arabs you ordinarily think of.

Camels make this possible. They were domesticated long after the original animals, and came into Arabian use in biblical times, before the twelfth century B.C. Now the camel is the ship of the desert, you will have heard, and it became the key to transportation and trade. And by making over their own lives so as practically to become parasites of the camel, the Bedouin Arabs formed a culture able to exist in the poor grass region, which is useless to other farmers, and even to pass through the sandy desert itself. Their products are camels and camel's milk: the latter they drink, and the former they trade to the people outside the desert, among whom they spend a month or so out of the year, getting in return other kinds of food,

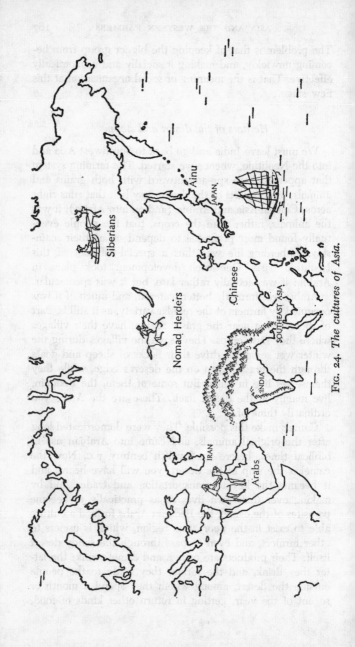

FIG. 24. The cultures of Asia.

such as sheep, grain, dates and coffee. But there are (or used to be) further items in the economic balance as well, to wit, collecting tribute from other tribes and villages, and raiding to steal camels and horses from other Bedouin camps.

There are smiths, slaves and occasional peddlers in the camps, but life revolves around the camel. Herding them is the pleasure and pride of the men, whose other great pleasure is fighting and raiding. They are not at all averse to being raided themselves, and like to keep some white camels, because these are easier to see at a distance than ordinary camel-colored camels and so are more likely to catch the eye of an enemy and tempt him to a raid. There is only one thing more valued than a camel and that is a horse. Horses are not at all suited for ordinary travel in the desert, which means that they need much care, and this in turn makes them all the more prized. And horses are vital for fighting and raiding.

So Bedouin life was geared to the Bedouin ideal of getting into a fight. For to expose himself to danger, to show courage, and to exult in victory to the point of drinking an enemy's blood were what a man should want. Society was strongly paternal, and the sheikh of a group or tribe, who should be an able war leader, had a strong, almost military authority.

Out in the grassy plains and steppes of Asia, an enormous area running from Europe and the southwestern Asiatic home of farming all the way to China, there appeared another pastoral culture, and one much more general. Its originators were doubtless early farmers moving out of the Near East, or people who soon learned farming at that source, who for one reason or another turned their backs on grain growing and gave their attention wholly to their livestock. Not that farming became extinct in the area, but rather that a new kind of nomadic culture gave the highest dividends, as shown by its great endurance and in fact by its historical importance.

Perhaps a degree of drying up of the climate was one cause. Perhaps the adding of the horse was another. For the horse was not among the animals of the original Neo-lithic group, and must have been tamed in the middle of Asia by the farmers who came there. It was first used for carts, but before 1000 B.C. it came to be ridden; and this probably so solved the problems of herding other animals, and of moving about after pasturage, that the pastoral life then became a highly successful one.

It is, however, a difficult one as well, as it is lived by such people as the Mongols, the Kirghiz or the Kazaks. Horses and sheep are their particular sources of food, with the horse being the delicacy and the sheep the everyday meat. Both are milked as well as eaten, and mare's milk is made into koumiss by keeping it awhile in a skin bag that has already had koumiss in it: it is fermented this way into a kind of milk beer. The people live in permanent sheltered homes for the harsh winters, leaving them and hunting for pasturage in the spring; the new grass soon dries and so the hunt for good grass keeps them on the move.

Their summer house, for which they are famous, is the yurt. This is a round, tentlike object: a frame made of a collapsible lattice which is pulled out and set up ring-shape, some poles which are pulled together at the top, and a ring for the smoke hole to which the poles are tied, the whole thing then being covered by sheets of felt. As if this were not easy enough to knock down or set up, they formerly had smaller versions of the same thing which were simply kept on carts—the first trailers. As for felt (used also in boots and hats), this is made from wool which is spread out and tamped down on one big straw mat and covered with another. Then the whole thing is rolled up like a jelly roll and tied; two teams of feltmakers sit down in opposite lines, and roll the roll back and forth for an hour or so between them with their feet; and so the wool becomes all felted together into a large sheet.

The culture, counting its early forms, is essentially the story of inner Asia for perhaps the last six thousand years. It has been partaken in by various kinds of people. There can be little doubt that those who first had it, from South-

west Asia, were Whites; and the Scythians of about 600
B.C. and before were actually remarked on by the Greeks
for their blondness. The raiding barbarians on the border
of the early Chinese Empire, before 2000 B.C., were apparently not Mongoloids, for their descendants, the Huns,
were Turkish in the type of their speech and their physique. However, the culture enlisted Mongoloids as time
went on, so that in later history these have been its main
practitioners.

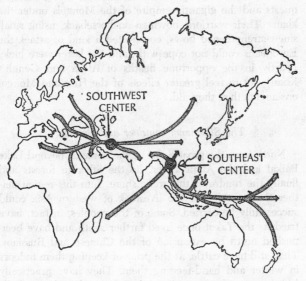

FIG. 25. *The two homes of farming and Neolithic culture in the
Old World, and their hypothetical directions of spread.*

Like other higher nomadic cultures, it was warlike. This
has probably nothing to do with open spaces where men
are men—that is to say, essential hardiness—but rather
comes about because nomads, having small establishments,
little to lose and the mobility that suggests attack, are the
natural attackers, while sedentary people have larger establishments, accumulated goods and facilities mainly for

defense. So the nomads not only filled the gap between the West and the Far East but also provided them both with a joint and familiar menace for thousands of years. The Hiung-Nu and other barbarians were the scourge of the Chinese for twenty centuries, until at last the Han emperors struck back with such force into the nomad territory as to throw these peoples into confusion and turn their attention toward the Western world. The Huns were their vanguard in Europe, beginning the westward movement of Turkish and Mongol peoples, and foreshadowing the conquests and the gigantic empire of the Mongols under the khans. Their warriors, bowmen on horseback, using small sinew-strengthened bows, constituted a kind of attack the Europeans could not cope with; and the latter were lucky (partly in the opportune deaths of Attila and Genghis Khan) not to feel greater effects of the Hun and Mongol onslaughts than they did.

The Siberians: reindeer and shaman

North from the great home of the nomads, beyond Lake Baikal and the Amur River, lie the Siberian forests and finally the tundra of the arctic shore. Into this region neither the farming nor the livestock of western Asia could successfully be carried. Some of the peoples, in fact, have tried it: the Yakut once lived farther south and have been pushed north by expansion of the Chinese and Russians. They still have cattle, at the price of keeping them indoors in winter and hand-feeding them. They have practically lost the use of horses entirely, though they kept horse skulls to use in ceremonies, a relic of the time when horses were important in their culture.

But this did not mean that the idea of domestication— of breeding animals for milk, meat or riding—could not penetrate, providing there was some animal to domesticate. And there is: the reindeer, who is at home and happy in this snowy zone, as he was in Magdalenian Europe. It seems clear, in other words, that this represents the last wisp of influence from the invention of animal breeding in

Southwest Asia. In Central Asia horses (and yaks) were added to the usual stock, but here the idea itself was applied in a new setting. Not only that, but we can almost see the process at work. The Tungus, a major southerly tribe, possess domesticated reindeer herds, of a variety different from the wild ones, which give them milk and meat. And the reindeer are used as well for riding and for pulling sledges. People to the north, on the other hand (Koryak, Chukchi), have herds which are not really domesticated but which are theirs nonetheless, and which they keep in touch with, so as to lasso an animal for dinner when it is needed. Still other people are without even this, and are hunters and fishers only.

The Siberian area is therefore one in which the people have taken up reindeer herding to a greater, lesser or no degree. It is one containing a conglomeration of peoples, though with certain general similarities in culture. (It surely comprises, for one thing, the home of the specialized Mongoloid racial type.) Subtract the domesticated reindeer, and the basic culture is a high-level hunting one, having small settlements and living in tents, small wooden blockhouses or partly underground earth lodges. Clothing —and this is the area which is still horribly cold in winter —is of furs and reindeer skin, well sewn and well decorated with appliqué designs. Furthermore, garments are fully fitted, with trousers and sleeves. This is where our own tailored clothes came from, imported to Europe by the Central Asiatic invaders, some of whom at least must have been originally recruited from this older Siberian culture themselves.

The Paleo-Siberians, the non-reindeer-herding people, are interesting for their material objects and for certain likenesses which these, and their myths, hold with North America, suggesting some fairly recent contact of an unknown kind. But they are socially simple, and the most interesting person here, and in the whole Siberian region, is the shaman.

This is the man, or woman, who talks to spirits. He may call them forth, just as a medium does, in a séance. This is a performance held in a house or a yurt with the lights, to be sure, put out. The people gather, the shaman beats softly and rapidly on a tambourine, and begins to sing. After a while a new voice is heard in the house, and then others: the spirits have come and may be heard moving around; some of them may be animals who can speak human language; some of them may speak unknown tongues; the drumming and singing go on, with a confusion of mingled voices and noises, some giving messages, while the audience sits in great excitement, occasionally giving encouragement by shouting at the right moments; finally the strange voices diminish and stop, lights are brought, and the shaman may be found sitting or lying in a trance.

Part of the performance has been the shaman's ability as a ventriloquist, producing a variety of voices and sounds as he moves about; part of it comes from the excited state which he has induced in himself, which he himself will think of as his shamanistic power, and by no means as simply a job of acting. Shamans, make no mistake, are great conjurers, and give demonstrations of ordinary parlor magic that are remarkable. But they do not at all look on themselves as clever operators, pulling the wool over the public eye, since they believe in their own shamanizing and in their ability to get in touch with spirits.

For here in Siberia they are professionals, with an actual calling which they cannot refuse. A spirit comes to a man (or woman) and bids him become a shaman, whether he will or no. It would seem as though this admired position would be sought, but few seek it. And it is apparent that those who do, or who are forced into it, are often those who are not well adjusted in our own sense, being over-repressed or hysterical by nature. One tribe believes that a future shaman can be recognized as a child by his meditative nature and his tendency to fits. And shamanizing is sometimes taken up as deliberate therapy, because of a decision that the only cure for a patient's particular illness or depression is to become a shaman, and to go on being a shaman. That is how it seems to work for such people, because it gives them both a respected place in society and a vent for their unusual excitability.

Shamans thus are special people, with special personal powers, not like ordinary men or women. And theirs is a life of peril as well: it is dangerous to have dealings with spirits and to go among them. More, a shaman acquires an animal familiar which gives him power and protection, but which may turn and rend him. Worse, it might die and so cause the shaman's own death, because they have but one soul between them. In some Siberian tribes a shaman wears a distinctive costume, with designs alluding to his particular familiar and other spirit helpers, and perhaps with trailing strands of leather by which inconsequential sprites may attach themselves to his retinue.

At any rate the shaman sticks out like a sore thumb from the rest of the community. The same kind of personage is found widely in the rest of the world among similar simple societies: hunters, less developed "Neolithic" tribes, and those on the border between the two. Here in Siberia he is the one religious expression of importance. It is he who keeps this world, the everyday one, in tune with the world of spirits (there is no worship of major gods).

He has special jobs to do all the time. If somebody falls sick, it may be that his soul has gone awandering; the shaman, who alone can see it, sets after it and brings it back. When, on the contrary, someone dies, and the family yurt must be purified by sending the soul, which has lost its body, off to the place where souls go, then it is the shaman who is called.

Once again he gives a heroic performance, this time in full view. In a dramatic dance, he catches the soul with his drum and drumstick, tells it what it must do, leads it to the gate of the old spirits' home (in this performance, he is both there, before the spectators, and far away, on his errand), and persuades them to take the neophyte in. If things go wrong in the village, he holds a séance and thrashes things out man to man with the spirits. So, in this way and that way, he can deal with most of the up-setting circumstances that may befall a small community, through his ability to get into direct contact with special powers. The more so because he can give the whole group an emotional straightening out by one of his rousing dramatic performances. A very useful man.

The Neolithic cornerstone of China

Starting with a continent, we have come down to a man in a cluttered skin tunic beating a tambourine. Let us go back to the continent. We saw the outward flow of the grain farmers and their successful pioneering in all directions, including India. We saw a special offshoot of this existence, pastoralism, founded probably on horse riding in inner Asia, and certainly on camel riding in Arabia. We saw this idea, herding, intruding among the primitive forest hunters of Siberia, so that the reindeer became the major factor in the lives of some but not of others. There is one more thing to see as the result of the Neolithic discoveries in Southwest Asia: the founding of China. For agriculture here was of the same type, originally.

China today runs south to Indochina and north through Manchuria, and one thinks of rice, tea and silk. But the original China was a small region, north and inland, in the great bend of the Yellow River. Here it is that the empire of history goes back into the past of legend and archaeology, and finally to a farming center of the Neolithic. What apparently happened was that the original Southwest Asiatic type of farming thrust all the way through the southern edge of the steppes, of Russian and Chinese Turkestan (Sinkiang), prior to the strong development of pastoral herding, and probably at a time when the region was less deserty than it is now. This farming was probably spread, or transmitted, by people we might guess to be Whites, since the Mongoloid spread in the opposite direction in Asia seems to have been later.

At any rate, at the end of the line the culture reached the Tungus-like, Mongoloid ancestors of the Chinese, who took it and carried forward their own version of it. Wheat (this is not rice country) must have come from the West, but probably the most important early grain, common millet, is a native and may have been domesticated on the spot as a result of the arrival of wheat and barley. Cattle must also be from the West, but in striking contrast to the Near East and to the nomads of Central Asia, the Chinese have never consented to use milk. On the contrary, they have always been fond of pigs which, though present from the beginning of the Neolithic in the West, have been notoriously "unclean" in the cultures that derive from the Near East, except in Europe.

The early Chinese made mud-walled houses (preceded by pit houses), but of a style different from those of Southwest Asia. Their religion of gods, their emperors and their family life share a general character with the West, but they are nonetheless distinctly Chinese. Now China has not been as isolated as you might think, for there has been trade and contact across Asia at all times; but she has been far enough away so that the exchange was at several removes. Her culture has always had its native character, drawing from the regions to the south as well as from the far West and from the nomads. What we see, in the beginning, is one more child of the Near Eastern Neolithic, but remote, and even racially distinct from the rest, doing its own upbringing.

12.   The Pacific and the Eastern Farmers

Down in Southeast Asia lie Indochina, Burma and Siam, and beyond them the islands of the Indies, including the Philippines and Formosa. This is all an area of tropical forest and heavy rainfall. And it is not as close to the rest of Asia as the map makes it look. Its boundaries with China and India are rugged, and so are the interiors of the islands, and therefore it is not easy to approach (remember the Burma Road to China). The same ruggedness within much of it, its many mountain ridges and river valleys, tends to isolate its people, cutting them up into small communities.

It is the home of another culture development, distinct from the web of Neolithic cultures of the rest of Asia. By this other culture, however, I do not mean the civilization of the last two thousand years, the kingdoms that rose in response to massive waves of influence from China, India and Arabia. By the beginning of our Christian Era, Indian colonies, or states on the Indian pattern, were growing up all the way from Burma to Borneo, and a thousand years later major empires appeared on Sumatra and Java, building many of the great temples and casting their shadows northward beyond the Philippines as far as Formosa. This set the Hindu tone of Indonesian life and art. Then Islam, on the crest of a wave of Arab trade and expansion, replaced Hinduism as a religion almost throughout the civilized area in the south (as did Buddhism in the north), and had the effect of breaking down the larger empires.

This final culture, the one we are familiar with, was a high one, with large states, writing and impressive architecture. Nevertheless, the chopped-up island and mountain geography has enabled forest and valley to shelter remnants of older cultures for what must have been thousands of years. We can, in fact, almost peel off the layers of higher culture, and so look backward in time.

Jungle hunters of Malaysia

If we carry this peeling-off far enough, we come down to nomadic and seminomadic hunters of the forest, especially the Negritos, whom we find in sole occupation of the Andaman Islands, and also in the interior of the Malay Peninsula and various islands of the Philippines. They use the bow and arrow, and live in rock shelters or impermanent villages of moderately well-made but flimsy huts. The Andamanese are the most fortunate in having shellfish and turtle; their villages are the best built and longest occupied (a few months), and they even make a poor grade of pottery. Though these are the only surviving colonies of Negritos, signs of them turn up in ancient historic references in parts of the region where they are no longer found, and also in mixture with other people who may be presumed to have absorbed them. They reveal their traces in small size, dark skin and woolly hair in Borneo, Sumatra and Celebes, and especially in the farthest islands of the Timor chain, such as Flores.

But the Negritos are not the only such hunting remnants. There is another distinct strain, seen in such peoples as the Sakai (Senoi) of the Malay Peninsula and the Kubu of Sumatra (and the Toala of Celebes?). These are also nomad hunters, using a blowgun. They are hard to place racially. They are taller than the Negritos, but still short; they may have Negrito blood in them, but they seem instead to be most like the vanishing Vedda of Ceylon. This is to say that they are something like the Whites, but smaller and darker, and also something like the natives of Australia, but not so primitive in head and face form. They are possibly another suggestion of a deeply submerged White strain, ancient in eastern Asia.

The hidden Neolithic of Southeast Asia

The living people I have described are only two examples of hunter-gatherers, and archaeology has unearthed various pre-Neolithic or early Neolithic cultures throughout the area, to say nothing of remains of the earlier Paleolithic. Too little is known of all this at the moment to make much sense out of it. If, however, we stop the peeling-off process before going down so far, we find a simple Neolithic culture, among the uncivilized peoples of the backwoods, below the historical level but above the hunters.

Such people live in many parts, from the mountains of Formosa and the interior of Borneo to the islands strung in a line south of Sumatra and back up to the mountains of Burma and Indochina. But for all this scatter, there are strong resemblances among them that argue a unified culture based on gardening, native to the area. The people themselves are Mongoloid in nature, though shading off into unmongolized, American-Indian-like types with vague evidences of a White strain as well. No Negroid or Negrito-like ingredient can be seen, but otherwise this unholy jumble of inscrutable ancestors tells us nothing about the age of the culture or the time of arrival of the now dominant Mongoloid element, which we may assume to be the latest, and to have come from the North.

The "culture" of these largely pagan peoples covers a great many different tribes, and is not exactly the culture of any one of them, so please insert the word "typically" before any statement in the description which follows. Their villages are isolated and sufficient to themselves in their affairs; they may recognize their general tribal affiliation, but the tribe does not function as a tribe. They ask only to be left alone, and offer danger to the stranger. They are glad to welcome him, on one condition: that he leave his body behind. For this is the home of headhunting, a persistent and important custom from one end of the area to the other, and something of a deterrent to neighborliness. Against this, villages in many parts are palisaded for defense, or otherwise protected by having a ditch, being built on a hill, and so on.

Houses themselves are well constructed, of heavy timbers, and are usually on piles, raised off the ground, and reached by something like a notched log for a ladder, leading to the door, a landing, or perhaps an entrance through the floor of the house itself. Defense may be the basic reason for the raising up of the houses, though in this damp climate, where the pigs may trample the ground around the house into a mire, it is doubtless a comfort to be above the ground even in the most peaceful times. In some places each family may have a good-sized house. In Borneo, on the contrary, families have their own apartments, of a few rooms or alcoves, in a single long house for the entire village running along a riverbank for several hundred yards, with a porch or gallery its whole length. This kind of house is a major piece of engineering and construction, in some cases being set with its floor twenty feet up, and holding five or six hundred people.

But all this solidity of the house does not mean that its owners never move. For the method of clearing and planting is that of slash-and-burn, cutting and burning the trees and brush, and planting and cultivating with a digging stick. In Borneo the nearby land along the river is all used up in the course of about twenty years, whereat the people may literally chop the house down, cutting the piles off at the ground, dismantling the timbers and floating the whole apparatus, or as much of it as they can use, downstream to a new spot. But in other parts the people manage to avoid moving by taking in so large a territory roundabout that the trees will have grown up again on the oldest used land and it will be fit for cultivation once again.

As to the crops, everybody knows the place of rice in East Asia. But that kind of wet rice, grown in paddies and in terraces on hillsides, and plowed with the buffalo, is the "civilized" staple, and not part of the culture we are looking at. Some of the pagans have it (as in the Philippines), but it is obviously a later introduction to them, just as are American corn and various other vegetables. An older crop

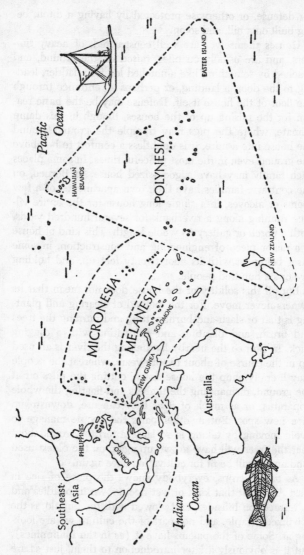

FIG. 26. Southeast Asia and the Pacific Ocean.

is dry rice, grown more like other grains and usable on hillsides without terraces; this is important for example in Upper Burma and in Borneo. And millet, ancient in China, gives signs of being also ancient here, more so than either kind of rice.

But the vegetables that seem to be most at home—not necessarily the most important except rarely, but grown very widely—are yams and taros. Yams come in many varieties and are, practically, unsweet sweet potatoes; and taro is something like a big turnip. These are plants that are suited to a humid forest. They are of course quite different in their doughy nature from the grains of Southwest Asia. This is a disadvantage because after they are harvested they will not keep as seeds will.

As for domestic animals, these people are poorly off compared with the west. The only ones they have long had (always excepting dogs) are the chicken, who is a native himself, and the pig, who seems to be native just about everywhere, since he was a member of the cast in the Neolithic of Southwest Asia as well. With this small barnyard retinue, you might think that the people eat eggs until they begin to cackle, but here is a surprising perversity. They eat chickens and eggs very little (the hens are not prolific layers anyhow), just as the Chinese do not drink milk; instead, chickens are kept largely for sacrificing and for fortune-telling, augury-fashion, from their bones. So there is a considerable amount of hunting and fishing as a source of meat for the pagans, with spears and blowguns, and with a variety of nets and a multitude of mechanical traps of the most ingenious and effective kind.

In arts and crafts there is other evidence of borrowing of things probably not present when the "Neolithic" culture was first founded. The people are good workers in iron and brass, making swords and ornaments, but the use of metal seems to belong to an upper level of the culture, meaning that they originally relied on stone tools. Weaving and dyeing, mostly of their own cotton, is also widespread and excellent, and dress nowadays is often a long skirt or a full toga for women, and a breechclout and an open-fronted waistcoat for men. However, the more out-of-the-way peoples give evidence that dress was formerly slighter, fashioned mainly of bark cloth, which was made from the inner bark of certain trees, especially the paper mulberry, beaten into pliability and endurance. Now of course there is no way of knowing that bark cloth in turn does not go back to a Mesolithic stage of culture, but that is neither here nor there; it certainly was an element in the culture we are talking about.

In any event one thing about which the Southeast Asiatics and the Indonesians have long been enthusiastic is decorating the body, clad or not, in more permanent fashion. Karen women of Burma stretch their necks with high collars of brass rings. Dayak women of Borneo wear similar-looking things around the torso as a sort of combination corset, etc. And infants in several parts have tourniquets put around the head while it is still soft, to give it a more unusual shape or to flatten the forehead still further and so exaggerate that round Mongoloid face.

But these are local specialties. More generally beloved is tattooing of the skin, and above all accessory adornments to one's smile. One such is filing of the front teeth to points or other designs, with sometimes the knocking out of a selected few, or the nailing onto the gums of a decorative metal plate. Another is the darkening of the teeth themselves in some permanent way, often by chewing betel nut, which not only has a minor narcotic effect like smoking but also turns the teeth to the shade of mahogany. One final, well-nigh universal effort for loveliness is the stretching of ear lobes by means of big buttons or plugs set into pierced holes.

Class, clan and social teamwork

Socially these people live in isolation, having at best some nonaggressive contact with others, especially their own tribe, keeping to themselves and marrying within the village. They have few internal problems. There are chiefs of a sort, without much authority; the chief is more like a magistrate than like the stronger rulers of many cultures in the west of the Old World; and affairs are largely in the hands of a council. If you look at the social structure of communities, you find social classes and rules of descent but, as you see them here, those two things are less familiar to us than the names might imply.

They have, in many parts, upper classes, commoners and slaves. But wealth, not power, is the difference between upper and lower classes. The "best people," an informal aristocracy, give feasts, and have more social cachet, but able commoners carry their weight readily enough in council or public affairs. If there is a difference in appearance, it is in the greater elegance of dress, bearing, tattooing and so on of the upper class, while a commoner is freer to be uncouth.

The upper crust would not think of addressing others as "churl" or "varlet"; they are the social leaders but not through arrogance, and their daily pursuits in general are not different from those of the lower class. As for slaves, these may be war captives or the descendants of captives, but they are not like Uncle Tom; they are unpaid servants but they are not bought and sold (except in a few spots, under Arab influence) and they are pretty much members of the family. After all, they do not differ in origin or background from their masters, in this relatively simple culture.

There may even be intermarriage between classes, though this is taking chances with one's own status, and is usually frowned upon. On the whole there is a certain democracy in society, both as to politics and in the sense in which we normally misuse "democratic," to mean "not uppity," "willing to rub shoulders with all sorts."

Another way of dividing society, found in parts of Indonesia, is by clans, a matter of descent. We ourselves go by families, and we follow the male side. To do so may have been characteristic of the general Southwest Asiatic culture, and you have seen the elaboration of our idea of a family in the "veins" and "bones" of the Rif. But clans are a different tack. They do not emphasize your particular personal blood relationships. Instead, the community is broken down into a number of well-defined units, and you are born into one of them because it is the clan of your father, if the clans of the tribe are patrilineal (or your mother, if they are matrilineal). You know well enough who your blood kin are, just as we do, but it is emphatically those kin who are members of your clan who are your important relatives in life.

The whole clan is considered to be descended from one ancestor, however remote, and to be tightly related anyhow, so that any member of it is a closer relative than half of your actual blood relations. The clan contains, of course, your brothers and sisters, and also your first cousins through your father's brother (talking about the patrilineal variety). But this clan does not contain your first cousins through your father's *sister*, for she has married a man of another clan, and her children take their clan from that man. These children are your *cross*-cousins, as are those of the brother of your mother, since these (your mother and her brother) also must belong to a clan other than that of you and your father.

For clans are exogamous, which means that you do not marry within your own. Its women are practically sisters to you, and such marriage would be incest. Thus clans are different from the castes of India, which are endogamous; there you avoid actual incest but you marry inside the caste.

Clans are also different from the complicated kinship systems of the native Australians. But here a certain likeness appears, for clans can and do fit into this kind of system. The Australians distinguish between cross-cousins and parallel cousins (which are children of a pair of brothers, or of a pair of sisters); so do clans. The Australians recognize big classes of those who cannot marry and those who may or should marry; so do clans. Kinship in Australia controls a lot of behavior among the individuals; so do clans. And in fact clans are imbedded in the Australian machinery itself. In a manner of speaking, if you should try to do what the Australians seem to be aiming at, but do it by simplifying and lumping, and omitting the formidable terminology for your kin, so that you give everyone a convenient segment of society to serve as his relatives, you would have clans. This is a manner of speaking, to be sure, not a theory.

The clan, then, is a man's background and his strength. Clans also have their mutual relationships and duties. Here in certain areas of Indonesia, for example, one clan may normally get its wives from a particular one of the other clans, and may exchange certain kinds of traditional presents with it. At the same time it sends its own girls as wives to a different clan still, and has different obligations in this direction. These gift exchanges are very important, and are not a simple item of the social amenities, as they would be among us.

Sometimes the clans are grouped into two major, opposite units of the community; or else the major, balanced division may exist without clans (or be practically the same as a single pair of clans). These divisions are called moieties (halves), and marriage takes place only between them. They emphasize the importance of exchange between social units, not only of mates but of various things of symbolic value. Knives, for maleness, for example, are given in the same direction as husbands; cloth, for femaleness, in the same direction as wives.

For they express a general idea of how life, spiritual as well as social, is divided, and how it is related to the universe in general. One moiety may be identified with certain principles: earth, the outside of things, youth, the coast; while the other has the opposites: heaven, the inside of things, age, and the mountains. The two thus ceremonially trade and make presents, and in so doing they make the world go round, so to speak, because they recognize accepted social and spiritual values, and see that they are properly distributed.

This idea of dualism even has a more definite counterpart in a few places, in a pair of gods, a male of the sky and the mountains, and a female of the earth and the sea. But such gods are not notable in the religious ideas of the region, which run instead in two other directions: to hordes of minor spirits and godlings (associated with all kinds of natural things, or with special assignments like frightening your enemy) and to a very widespread ancestor worship.

Lacking well-defined high gods, they lack well-defined public cults. The religious approach is highly itemized, and their prayer book, if they had one, would have more the spiritual quality of a Sears Roebuck catalogue. By this I mean that observances are practical and suited to the occasion. The Filipinos have legions of little gods who seem like technicians, waiting to be invoked to do the one thing each knows how to do. And everywhere a great proportion of spirits are simply pests, to be avoided, driven away or destroyed. This kind of work, as well as healing and fortune-telling, is carried on by shamans, whose ministry is basically like that of the Siberian variety, including trances and séances, and who are responsible for a certain amount of ghost control. Along with all the above there is a mass of omen-taking and spell-making, which anyone can do and which everyone does.

If there is one rather special rite, it is headhunting. Although old heads are kept, and people are glad to have them as trophies, that is not why they are hunted. In fact they are not usually taken by individual men but rather by an organized raid on an enemy village, in which only the needed heads will be cut off, from fallen defenders when possible, with other victims being captured alive as slaves.

There is glory for the taker of heads, but the impulse is not blood lust; rather it is almost sacramental. It may stem to a large degree from the idea of capturing and controlling the soul of the dead man, almost as if you were making him your own ancestor in that way, instead of an ancestor for the village he belonged to. In some places this is definitely the reason, and they may tell the head as much, while they speak to it in friendly and apologetic fashion and feed it some native beer—but let us stop there. In any case neither the head nor its owner is in a good position to talk back.

But along with this, the immediate reason for taking a head is apt to be a direct ritual purpose: in Formosa for ancestral rites, in Borneo to end mourning for a chief, in

Nias to invest a chief in office, and in Indochina, as in many parts of the whole region, as a necessary prelude to the marriage of a young man. Head-taking is like the official seal on a document, without which the document is no good.

A problem of beginnings

Here, then, is a broad kind of culture in the southeast of the Old World which is still a good deal of a mystery. It has a considerable unity, and tribes may be found on the northern and southernmost fringes with cultures much alike. It is obviously independent in type from the cultures of western Asia. Does this mean that it was based on an independent discovery of the uses of domesticated plants and animals? It certainly looks so. The plants that are apparently the oldest in use (like taros and yams as well as the plantain-banana group) are the ones most unlike the original plants in the West, and show some signs of having been long domesticated.

Further, Professor Carl O. Sauer, the geographer, believes that here was the first, the original, discovery of plant domestication by man. According to his belief, Mesolithic fishing people living along the rivers and shores of Southeast Asia were sufficiently sedentary (like some American Indians you will see later) to allow them to experiment with domestication, under the impetus of increasing the plants that they used for fish poison, for net fibers, or for bark cloth, and not only for food. This kind of planting involved the simple setting out of roots and shoots; that is, a rather obvious method of duplicating existing plants, rather than grasping the whole cycle of plants which can be propagated only from seed. The sowing of grain, Sauer thinks, was actually achieved later, when knowledge of planting had traveled to western Asia, to open valleys and hillsides where seed planting was easier, and planting from cuttings more difficult.

In this reconstruction we have a useful hypothesis for the domestication of the roots and fruits of Southeast Asia.

However, few would give this region credit for the invention of agriculture generally, in view of the obvious and gradual adoption of grains as food, in their native habitat in Southwest Asia, beginning at what is now known to be a very early date just after the end of the Pleistocene. This process is clear from archaeology. Things were evidently so much later in Southeast Asia that it would be hard to prove that domestication did not come the other way, from west to east, in spite of the differences in food. Be that as it may, another kind of Neolithic life and culture did appear there, however it got started. But here again, who was responsible? Mongoloids? Proto-Mongoloids (often called Indonesians)? Still older strains, even the dark-skinned peoples? And are there yet other layers to this culture than those we have allowed for? These are all unknowns, and archaeology cannot yet tell us this history, as it is doing in the West. But we can learn a little more by pushing out into the South Pacific, into other areas.

The Melanesians: the host who gives the most

Beyond Indonesia, and north and east of Australia, a continent never reached by any but hunters (the Australians and a Negrito strain), lies Melanesia, the Black Islands. It would need a lot more introduction if it had not been the great theater of our war in the Pacific: our early forward bases in Fiji, the New Hebrides and New Caledonia; our slow moves from Guadalcanal at one end of the Solomons through New Georgia to Bougainville at the other; our pounding of the great Japanese bases in the Bismarck Archipelago and our seizing of the Admiralty Islands and part of New Britain itself; and finally our progress along the north coast of New Guinea until we jumped at last to Halmahera, across the line into Indonesia.

Except for this, Melanesia would be generally unfamiliar. It is also generally unhealthy, with a good stock of insects and tropical diseases, headed by malaria. But it is possibly the most fascinating part of the world for the study of man. Consisting as it does of islands, some close to

Indonesia and some far out in the ocean, it tends to keep cultures from mixing freely, the exact opposite of the plains of Asia. And the islands have a great variety of climate and form. Some are large—and New Guinea is enormous—so that the inlanders, especially those in the cool highlands of New Guinea, might as well be on a continent far from the water. But the coastal Melanesians are typically pretty good navigators, so that water, a barrier to long trips, is nevertheless a boulevard for short ones.

All this means that, when men began to arrive, and group followed group, some kept themselves more as they were when they came, by settling in some out-of-the-way place, while others mixed, borrowed, exchanged and changed with those before them or after them, in every kind of combination. What can be seen today is the final result. The opportunities for untangling the skein of history have been appreciated by everybody, but few people have proposed to untangle it the same way.

It is evident that the first modern men to come were hunters, of the Australian and Negrito variety, probably in that order, since these strains must have passed through New Guinea to get to Australia. New Guinea may have been about as far as they got in Melanesia, simply because there is not enough game and food to hunt elsewhere. The Melanesians of our own times are all Neolithic gardeners —really Neolithic—but signs of Australian parentage are present in the faces of many of the people of New Guinea, New Britain and New Caledonia. As for the Negritos, actual villages of these live in the mountains of New Guinea, where they are cultivators rather than hunters; and diluted strains of them are visible more widely, in New Britain and possibly in the New Hebrides farther east.

The languages tell a story of a similar sort. In the interiors of large islands, especially in the west—nearer Asia— there is a great variety of different tongues, not clearly related to each other, but having something in common as to type (which also recalls the languages of Australia). But on the coasts, and in the eastern islands, are found languages all of one group, the Melanesian, which is itself related to the great family of Indonesia. This group is obviously the newer arrival. Who brought it? Perhaps no very specific lot of people. But the later population does seem to be more what we recognize as Negro proper, like that of Africa, showing signs of having itself been affected by Mongoloid mixture in its latest, minor waves.

So it is not easy to say anything simple about Melanesia, and in seeming to do so I shall be committing a fraud, emphasizing the likenesses rather than the great and significant diversities. But it is fair to say that the general culture stems from that of Southeast Asia, and represents what must be an early form of it. For the leading crops are the roots and fruits, without rice: yams and taro, and also the banana-plantain family and the breadfruit tree, all of these things having been imported, along with pigs. (Pigs are reserved for feasts; they are uneconomical because they must be fed on taro, and so they are usually allowed to run wild and are hunted.) Various other things are grown (or gathered): coconuts, sweet potatoes, pumpkins and sago from the sago palm, in different places. And the people are fine cooks. For reasons not clear (richness of the land? crop rotation? low population density?) villages are not forced to move by soil exhaustion.

Houses on piles are not universal, though common. Clothes are, quite typically, a grass skirt for women and a bark-cloth loin piece for men, wherever the men wear anything which can be called clothing at all. Tattooing is rare, being found only on the light skins of known recent immigrants, since tattooing a dark skin is a patent waste of time. However, patterns of scars on the skin are common, and may be the corresponding idea. At any rate the same penchant for decoration by mutilation that occurs in Southeast Asia is evident, for everybody pierces his ear lobe and puts something in it, and many people pierce their noses as well, for a bone splint or a big shell ring.

Ties with Southeast Asia are plentiful in social life. Clans are of pronounced importance, having great solidarity, and there is commonly present the division of a tribe or community into two exogamous moieties. The clans are usually matrilineal, and often totemic, meaning that they have a mystical association with a species of animal or fish or bird. Villages are apt to consist of a few related clans, and chiefs are of even less consequence than in Indonesia (except in Fiji, which is partly Polynesian). Also much in evidence are certain other elements of Indonesian life: formal gift-giving, and pride in the wealth that makes possible the giving of gifts and feasts. What comes out of the mixture of these elements may be something different from Indonesian culture, but the general ideas and values are there. Certainly a love of formality stamps all kinds of Melanesian social affairs.

The *kula* ring, of the islands off eastern New Guinea, is a famous illustration of this. Here prominent men are traders, who have partners, to the north and to the south, with whom they exchange visits. When a man goes to see his friend who lives in the direction which is clockwise around the ring, that friend will ceremonially give him a bracelet made of a white shell. It is not just a shell bracelet but one which he has himself been given by a friend in the very same fashion; it has a name of its own, and has passed around the kula ring through the hands of other honored kula traders.

That is what makes it desirable to have, or rather to *give*. For the whole purpose of having is giving and spending, and a man who made any show of keeping and amassing such things in Melanesia would be just as silly as a New Yorker who came into bankruptcy proceedings and showed as his assets the parties he had thrown on Long Island: bear that in mind. Then in due course, not too long after, the giver will make a return visit to the man to whom he gave the bracelet, and he may expect to be given a necklace of red shells, which is at least as "valuable" as the bracelet he gave, in the sense that it already has a name and a history of being passed around by traders of high standing. The bracelets, going to their new homes, thus actually move counterclockwise, in a direction opposite to the necklaces, and so there is a hint of the reciprocity, the balanced but not identical exchange, which marks relations of clans and moieties in Indonesia.

On the surface, the kula looks like trade, but it turns out to be quite different: a ceremony encrusted in careful etiquette which is social rather than religious in its nature. It is something high in the social interests of the group which partakes in an expedition, and of course vital to the social status of the man who is the leader of the whole thing, the kula trader. But look once more and it turns back again to trade. The kula exchange is the reason for a trip, the reason everyone thinks about, and yet a lot of important ordinary commerce in needed objects goes along with the ritual part, between the islands. And cordial, useful relations of a general kind are kept up, between the groups but above all between the partners, a sort of antidote to the distrust and isolation among communities of this part of the world.[1] It is really a surprising and unusual institution in one more way, in that it is the joint property of several different cultures (in the different island groups), and not of one only; it is like a miniature Common Market.

This is only one method of social advancement by the use of wealth and party-giving, a motive about which the Melanesians are even franker than we are. In the Solomons a man can practically lift himself up by his own bootstraps, if he has the energy. On Guadalcanal the way is clear, and the work cut out for him, if he wants to become a *mwane-kama* (which simply means person of importance, big shot). He begins to increase his food resources, enlarging his garden by getting relatives to give him a little spare-time help, and begging a few extra young pigs, which increase his work load because food for the pigsty must be grown. Having his plans laid out, he announces he is going to build a larger house. This is taken as a sign of what he has in mind, and now other men are willing to pitch in and

[1] The kula is beautifully described and explained in one of the most celebrated accounts of a primitive people (the Trobriand Islanders) ever written: Bronislaw Malinowski's *Argonauts of the Western Pacific* (New York: E. P. Dutton & Co., 1922, reissued in 1950).

give substantial aid, under his organization, with skilled builders acting as foremen, others doing heavy work, and everyone in general partaking in such subcontracting as making thatch for the roof.

They know that when the house is done there will be a feast. A feast there is, the thing that quickens every Melanesian pulse, and all his food is eaten. Morning comes, as to a little boy on the fifth of July whose firecrackers are all gone but who knows content. The food is no more, but he has his house and his credit is good. Now he can more easily persuade people to help, and give him advantageous deals in food and shell money. He will probably add a wife or two, young widows perhaps, who have to work hard but who are already trained, and are glad to get a husband, especially a mwanekama, which gives them position in society. The rising mwanekama himself goes on, giving next a dance festival, on a bigger scale than ever, with feasts and presents to the whole community. It is a career none but an energetic man can undertake, and he has to slacken off eventually, but he has made his mark and will always be remembered for his public services.

In fact a mwanekama is Guadalcanal's only person of consequence. The same kind of a person on Bougainville is called a *mumi*, but this man takes his duties as presiding social leader more earnestly. He actually erects a clubhouse and gives feasts which attract to his court followers, who owe him a sort of social allegiance and act as a claque. And he will hold parties in honor of a rival mumi, showering presents on him with the idea that the rival must reply in kind or lose his influence. This may go on, each man topping the other, until one is bankrupt and disgraced. Hospitality is a snake in the grass; but the ordinary citizen gets his heart's desire, a feast.

The idea of a clubhouse is a common one throughout Indonesia and Melanesia; and in the Banks Islands, eastward from the Solomons, it is the thing which gives a man his standing. For here the great clubhouse may have a large number of ranks in it—so many that some of them may stand empty at times—and a man simply buys his way from the bottom up, as far as he can, paying the members of the grades above him with shell money which is like wampum. So of course a rich father is a great help to a man.

If a mwanekama represents a frontiersman, practically clearing his own land, this *sukwe* of the Banks represents entrenched wealth. In the same island group there is another custom, a *kolekole* feast, the name of which means to sponsor something: you simply make that thing extra good socially (if it is a house) or extra important (if you have gone up a grade in the sukwe) by honoring it with a fine feast, which makes a permanent difference between that thing and other things of its class.

As if formality in trade and in social strife were not enough, it rules in military strife as well. General hostility and weakness of tribal ties make a certain amount of raiding and fighting natural, but also there are Tweedledum and Tweedledee battles between villages which fight each other as a matter of course, perhaps every five years, at the same battlefield. Even if the cause of trouble is something more immediate than renewing old rivalry, like charges of black magic, or stealing women (who have probably run off by invitation), the approach is usually something to remind you of knights and tournaments, with perhaps a declaration of war by heralds, and agreement on the day and arrangements for the two sides to tidy up the battlefield jointly. One death may stop things, or at least end play for that day. In any case women, children and certain others are not molested. Taking of heads or eating the dead are not usual accessories to these traditional fights, and belong rather to more malicious raids on real strangers. At the end everything is made up as carefully as it was started, and the people seem to have got out of their systems all their malice and fear of sorcery for the time being.

For sorcery and the making of spells are prominent in the supernatural ideas of Melanesians. Gardening magic, for instance, is especially necessary, to make your yams grow, or perhaps to keep somebody else's spells from mak-

ing the yams in your plot leave and go to his plot. The rest
of Melanesian religion can be summed up in "ghosts" and
"mana."

As in neighboring Indonesia again, it is ghosts and small-
scale malevolent spirits that dominate the spectral scene,
not gods; and ghosts are connected in many places with
the secret societies, and are impersonated by dancers. Mana
is another idea: it is a special quality, or strength, in something, that makes that something into a sort of charm. It
can reside in a bone or a stone, which you can use to make
your garden grow well, or your boat seaworthy. A man
can have it in himself, explaining why his skill or power is
greater than another man's. Mana is all the same, something like electricity, making things work, or work better,
according to their natures.

The Polynesians: birth, rank and the divine right of kings

If we now leave Melanesia and cross the date line, in
the middle of the Pacific, we come to yet another ocean
culture rooted in the Neolithic of Southeast Asia. We are
in Polynesia, the widely separated island groups in the
triangle Hawaii–Easter Island–New Zealand, and we see a
people who are a surprise and a puzzle. Whereas the
Melanesians are dark-skinned, the Polynesians are light
brown, seemingly part White, part Mongoloid. But above
all, where Melanesia has variety, Polynesia has homo-
geneity. The languages, of a type closely allied to Indonesian and also to the main Melanesian group, are mere
dialects in their differences from one another, and the culture shows nearly as great a uniformity. This is partly
because the great sailing skill of the Polynesians made
the open ocean a road between distant islands, and so
allowed repeated contacts, but it is mostly because they
arrived in their separate homes in the not too distant past.

They brought those vital plants of Southeast Asia in
their canoes. This is a fine illustration of how a Neolithic
people could find a tropical paradise in islands that would
be only a scenic desert to hunter-gatherers, since the natu-

ral island foods could hardly support man. To a great extent the Polynesians came to depend for vegetable food on coconuts and breadfruit, the latter of which has doughy flesh and is something like a large knobby avocado. Since both of these foods grow on trees, this leaves the men free to devote themselves to fishing, in an enormous number of different ways, to fill out that side of diet. They have plenty of other foods, including birds, and most islands keep pigs and hens as well.

But life is not hard, and the people have time for arts and games. Houses are handsomely made, of timber, mats and thatch, but not raised off the ground, except in some islands where they are built on stone and earth platforms. Dress, in the old days, was of tapa, finely made bark cloth which was a major craft; and tattooing and love of decoration by using flowers, feathers and the like were rife. The Maori of New Zealand actually carved grooves into the skin of the face in bold curved lines, and put color in the cuts. But this (moko) was the extreme of Polynesian self-defacement, and they did not mutilate their teeth like the Malaysians or stick bones in their noses like the Melanesians.

Social ceremonial reached a peak in Polynesia, in such things as visits between important men. But the plan of society took a different direction from that in Melanesia. Clans were present, but the accent was on family lines in our sense. Genealogy and primogeniture—being as nearly as possible the firstborn of the firstborn of the firstborn, etc.—determined rank, and rank was important. For the class idea of Southeast Asia was improved on with a vengeance.

In Samoa a village or district was ruled over by a sort of House of Lords, composed of men with hereditary titles who formed a council. In the east, however, the nobles, with the king at the top, lorded it over the commoners, with slaves at the bottom. Such a hierarchy made possible the expansion of authority, and this happened in Hawaii, in Tonga and in Fiji, where kings managed to conquer and rule large territories or a whole archipelago. And religion backed the whole thing up, for the ancestor worship of Southeast Asia also appeared in a new form: the gods carried the human lineage over into the divine, for the gods were the great ancestors, and the king was their highest descendant on earth, and so on down.

Added to this was mana, in the Polynesian sense, more refined than in Melanesia: a man had a given degree of mana, partly by practice and skill but largely by descent, so that the king had most, less only than the gods. So much had he that contact with a man of lower class might drain it off—pollute him—and kill the lesser man, whose constitution could not stand the extra mana. Thus the king and others of high rank were "tabu," in a word, and in a Polynesian word to boot. That is why the king was sometimes obliged to marry his sister, the only woman equally tabu. So the Polynesians seem to have taken material that was lying around loose in the cultures of their relatives in Indonesia and Melanesia—social class, ancestor worship, mana—and constructed a single coherent scheme with high gods, elaborate worship and philosophical ideas, and a strongly defined social structure.

This is shamefully short shrift for the glamorous Polynesians, but I cannot do justice all around. I want only to show how the Neolithic pattern of Southeast Asia was probably used by different kinds of people, in the tropical areas where its foods would let it travel. Polynesia adds its own special problems to the general ones. The Polynesians, judging from their careful genealogies, from language studies, and from radiocarbon, could only have arrived a few centuries before the opening of the Christian Era, forming their special societies and modeling their gods on their pioneering ancestors when they had reached their new homes.

Nobody knows where they came from, except that it was originally eastern Asia; and guesses have placed the homeland all the way from India to China, not forgetting that a few things like the heaven-descended king may even ally them with an element in Japan. Perhaps they came through Micronesia (the Marianas, Carolines, Marshalls and Gilberts), serving an apprenticeship in ocean voyaging here. They have myths about the old home, too vague to show us definitely where it was. They seem to have lost the use of rice on the journey, and they stopped making pottery sometime after they arrived.

How does all this fit into the puzzle of culture in Southeast Asia generally? We still do not know whether the Negroids (parents of the Melanesians) might have been the founders of this center of food growing, or whether the Melanesians simply learned gardening from Indonesia by transmission.

But the culture must have been moving out into the Pacific fairly early. Fragments of pottery of a good grade have been found on Saipan in the Marianas, in a level dated by radiocarbon to about 1500 B.C., and the Marianas also had rice in historic times. The modern Micronesians are something like the Polynesians in culture and type, and also a little like the Indonesians, though they have their own variations as well. It may be that because of war or population pressure one ancient group of Micronesians broke into the eastern ocean and became the founding fathers of all Polynesia. As to the beginnings of this whole southeastern Neolithic, however, we are left juggling Negroids, Whites and Mongoloids, and a culture pattern without a history.

13. African Herders and Gardeners

Africa used to be called the Dark Continent, for reasons you can probably think of. It has now been pretty thoroughly explored, however, and it is clear that Africa's riches in prehistoric remains are enormous, sufficient to make Europe seem like a sideshow when enough digging has finally been done.

Africa has given us not only the oldest known tools of man but also a sequence of stone industries as full as Europe's, and apparently more varied. The two continents were, furthermore, related, having their own developments of the same Acheulian and Levalloisian forms and methods of stonework. But in only two parts of Africa have we a good idea of who was concerned in all this, or how it may have connected with the present. In North Africa there were Cro-Magnon-like people in the Upper Paleolithic, preceding, as in Europe, later White immigrants who brought Neolithic culture. In the south, the once widespread Bushmen were still living their archaeological past as they were pushed and cramped into their desert refuge. We have looked over the Whites and the Bushmen already. Between these populations are the Negroes, a puzzle as always.

The Sahara Desert—really continuous with the Arabian Desert on the other side of the Red Sea—is a good deal of a barrier to human beings, primitive or civilized, and usually has been, in spite of the fact that at some times in the Ice Age it was more hospitable. For this reason North Africa is cut off and joined instead more to Europe, as the other shore of the Mediterranean. For the same reason the Neolithic newcomers bearing the culture of southwestern Asia were forced along this Mediterranean shore as a channel. For a time life ran parallel above and below the Mediterranean, until Rome defeated and destroyed Carthage (in modern Tunis). Since then North Africa has fallen back, with Mohammedanism increasing its isolation from Christian Europe. The incoming Arabs have had a great influence on the ancient Berbers, and this is the most important development of historic times.

As for contact with the Negroes south of the Sahara, the desert relaxed its vigilance only in the face of the camel. Camels, which had come from Asia to Arabia earlier, arrived in North Africa about 400 A.D.; whereat some of the Berbers, like the Bedouin before them, moved out into the desert to become the camel-raising Tuareg, whose own name for themselves is "The Plunderers." In this way trade

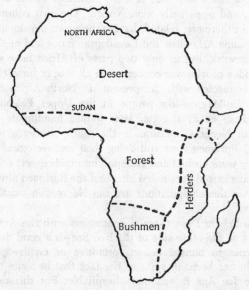

FIG. 27. *The cultures and areas of Africa.*

and slaves, and later on Arab influence and religion, began
to cross the Sahara. Even so, the jungle below, and a west
coast unfavorable to shipping, have been dampers on free
contact with the Negroes.

But if the Sahara has cut the continent in half, this does
not mean that no other impulses reached the southern part.
For in Negro Africa there are two main kinds of culture,
both "Neolithic" and seeming to owe their origins to the
two Asiatic centers of food raising, that of the Near East
and that of Southeast Asia respectively. These cultures exist, as you might guess, in two different environments, the
forest and the grasslands.

Cattle keepers of the east and south

At some time unknown, cattle and grain arrived in East
Africa, either up the Nile or down Arabia and across the
strait into Ethiopia. Whoever brought them, or handed
them along, this is an area in which a basically White
stock was anciently entrenched, and which also shows signs
of some contact with Egypt beginning several thousand
years ago. The first arrivals were sheep and goats, cows
coming later, but in recent times there has been a huge
sweep of cattle keepers from the middle Nile to the Cape.
The people will seem different outwardly, should you visit
different parts, or see them in some of the good movies
that have been made in East Africa: those human bean-
poles, the Nilotic Shilluk, Dinka and Nuer; the lion-hunt-
ing Masai and Nandi; the dancing Watusi and the other
dandies of the lake country; and the great tribes of the
south, the Zulu, the Basuto and the Bechuana. But there
is a certain pattern nonetheless, as there is in Indonesia or
Melanesia. The natives live in villages, kraals of round,
mud-walled, thatched houses, perhaps protected against
lions by fences.

A man is expected to be a warrior, a spearman, and he
wants to be a herder. For cattle are the center of attention.
The people are not pronounced pastoralists, like the Asiatics. Some of them move out to pasture for part of the

year, but they are not true nomads. Milk is important, but beef is eaten sparingly and meat is had by hunting. Actually, agriculture is more important as the staff of diet. The central crop is a millet (sorghum), a very old grain as we have seen, though others have been added, such as maize from America, and a number of common vegetables. Nevertheless, if you are going to live in East Africa you had better speak well of cows.

Cattle are no mere livestock; rather they are both pets and money. In some tribes, greater love hath no man than his favorite cow or bull. Sometimes this feeling mounts to something a psychiatrist should describe, so obsessed are the people: the Masai use special language about things that pertain to the cattle, as distinguished from ordinary things. More commonly there is found the kind of special ritual law which you may find in the Old Testament as well, about not eating meat at the same time you eat other foods. But in most of the area the cattle simply take their special place as wealth, on which one's social standing greatly depends. This may be a family affair as well, especially in the way cattle have come to reinforce marriage, in the custom known as the lobola.

The lobola is the bride price, paid by a man for a wife. But before you blaze with indignation at so barbarous a usage as wife-buying, let us look a little closer at its meaning. True, cattle are paid by a boy to his fiancée's family. True, the more cattle in payment the more pleased is that family. But the boy's kin are not anxious to look cheap, or to have an inexpensive daughter-in-law, and the arrangement is, actually or in feeling, a matter of concern to the whole family on both sides, meaning that several relatives of the boy may help out in making up the lobola, and several relatives of the girl may share in the proceeds. For it is, where the institution is strongest, a long process and a major transfer of wealth, not simply a bargain struck in cattle over a young girl.

Payments of cattle begin with betrothal and continue as the marriage approaches. The amount may be so great as to delay a wedding some years; payment may even go on after marriage, until the birth of children. And on the side of the bride's family this does not mean steak for everybody, because the cattle are family wealth—social wealth, not unrelated to the social value people get through the kula, or through buying degrees in the secret societies with shell money, in Melanesia. And this wealth must be husbanded, and looked on as the source from which brides may be found for the young men of that family in turn. Poor people may be forced, in different tribes, to use goats for the lobola, or even iron, but these things are only imitations and lack the meaning of cattle.

If you grasp the social poundage which the cattle carry, you begin to see that this transaction is actually not a recompense but rather a bond between families, and a continuing one that is more than a bond between bride and groom themselves. Families are somewhat more closely knit than among ourselves, and when the lobola creates the bond between them it strengthens each internally as well. And as for the marriage, the fact of the matter is that it consists principally of the cattle, and that is the East African view of it. This puts it a little strongly, but the nuptials of boy and girl are more the occasion for the lobola than the other way around; it is the marriage which makes the cattle move.

This is borne out by events. A Shilluk wife cannot fully divorce her husband unless the cattle are returned by her family; he would keep the children, who are the fruit of the marriage, without the cattle. But a Shilluk also takes care to please his wife's family, because they can demand more cattle if some of the basic lot die. The lobola *is* the marriage, and the children are the children of those who paid the lobola. If the husband dies, and the widow remarries, future children are her dead husband's; she may be expected to have children, married or not, probably by a brother of her husband's, in order to "raise seed" to her husband in the grave. This is not really outlandish, because the marriage survives, between the same families, with the same grandmothers, aunts and uncles, as if the husband were still alive. Actually the most usual thing is that she marries her husband's brother and keeps something like her original position. Looking at it from the point of view of the lobola, it is the same marriage. If, on the other hand, it is the young wife who dies, especially with no or few children, her family is expected, or obliged, to send along her sister—same lobola, same marriage. Finally—and this is no rarity, being found even in West Africa—an older woman, a widow, of important social position, may increase and insure her line by "marrying" a young girl herself: she pays the lobola, and pays selected men to become the fathers of the "wife's" children. In view of the lobola, all is proper and rational. You may note, in passing, that a child's true father and his social father may not be the same man at all.

Perhaps you will raise an eyebrow hereabouts, but I shall not ask you to adopt any of these ideas for yourself. I have not asked you to be a gibbon, nor have I asked you to approve of caste in India. I suggest to you only that strong relationships between important families, and stability of marriages and of family relationships, especially for children, are ideals inherent in the social system of the East and South Africans; and that the lobola makes use of the social and economic value of cattle to foster and strengthen the whole thing, and bring it into focus. This is even managed without making marriage so formal a family matter as it was in nineteenth-century Europe, for the Africans usually leave the choice of mates to the young, and have plenty of pretty customs of courtship, betrothal and wedding to emphasize this personal side.

Not only that, but there are in some parts schools for marriage, as one form of the schooling for adulthood, or initiation rites, which are so common in the world. Such rites may be more or less severe and more or less direct, from tribe to tribe, but among these African cattle people the girls are subjected to them as well as the boys, whereas girls generally get off more lightly in other parts of the world. The Venda of South Africa separate the boys and girls when a group has come of age, put them through a rigorous course of lectures on etiquette and sex, while they are starved, kept awake, made to stand in the cold river, do bizarre dances, have their fingers squeezed or hold hot ashes, have things thrown at them (boys) or wiggle along on their stomachs (girls), all on the evident principle that misery makes for memory. Then they are brought together for another course, lasting several months and conducted by symbolic representations, on the meaning of marriage and correct deportment, with more hardships and humiliations. The Zulu are more restrained and do not beat the boys; and as part of the training they put youth in charge of the kraal for a while, to learn at firsthand the right way of doing things.

But in general the boys have a bad time. Commonly they are circumcised (and the girls may have some parallel kind of attention), and they may have deep scars cut into the forehead or some of their front teeth knocked out, along with the other disagreeable formalities, which commonly consist of being sent out into the wild to care for themselves. The boisterous and belligerent Masai have at least relieved initiation with a few features calculated to appeal to the teen-ager. When a band has been made up of boys just beginning to have whiskers, they are allowed to go from village to village demanding presents, which are then given to the tribal elders in request for permission to hold the ox-seizing ceremony. A black ox is chosen, and from far and wide boys come in. The game is to hang onto the ox by hump or horn, and to pull off anyone else hanging on, unless he is your clan mate, in which case you help him. Casualties are not few. There is no particular score; they simply stop, and if the ox has survived to this stage he is killed and eaten anyhow, and the boys all put on finger rings made of his hide. After varying intervals each lad is circumcised without ceremony, something which hurts his mother almost as much as it does him, because if he cries she gets beaten. Then they go through a novitiate, wandering about for a period, to gather once more to have their heads shaved by their mothers and be given weapons by their fathers.

Now they are men, and forthwith give us an example of

another East and South African institution: age grades, or warrior classes. This group, like a draft call, becomes the youngest part of the standing army. The new Masai warriors dress and decorate themselves in striking fashion. While in this grade they cannot marry; they live in their own bachelor village, where their mothers come to cook for them and the uninitiated girls come and live with them. After their own initiation, which is late, the girls must act more strictly; it may seem rather tardy to come to that, but such is the rule. Like the Masai, tribes from one end of the region to the other have this system, the new group of initiated boys becoming the newest warriors responsible for the defense of the country, and each senior class moving up, changing status or retiring, and perhaps with officials or elders of the tribe being chosen out of a specific higher grade. It is the same system that Chaka, the infamous Zulu Napoleon of the early nineteenth century, put to his own ends, by turning the age classes, a militia, directly into regiments for the army that he used in his conquests.

The local isolation found in Southeast Asia is notable here for its absence, and tribal agglomerations under a chief or a king are the rule. Clans and kinship systems are both characteristic; clans may enter into affairs, and it may be that the head of a certain clan is automatically the king. But the important units are families, under head men, which fall into a hierarchy, making up villages, then districts, then tribes under paramount chiefs. Individual families or leaders may transfer allegiance from one chief to another. This free ability to form and change large political groupings is so important as to figure in colonial politics: modern Basutoland results from the swelling of the original Basuto tribe by new adherents seeking a rallying point and a refuge from the Zulu under Chaka.

As to the king, he may be important in religion, and perhaps divine himself. Among the Shilluk he is the rainmaker, the descendant and living embodiment (something like Egypt) of the divinity Nyakang; and the king must not in any way be allowed to grow senile or lose his vigor, so that the divine spirit in him shall not suffer. This is easily done: strangle him or wall him up in a hut before he is old, and then find his successor among other eligibles of the royal line. In South Africa the king may similarly be concerned with crops, but more as a kind of seer, determining the time to plant and being responsible for the goodness of the seed.

Across the grasslands of the Sudan, which run east and west, in the other direction from the long East and South African region, there is strung a variety of cultures also based on herding and agriculture. Here the Berber and Arab influences, and Mohammedanism, are all strong, and the mixture of peoples results in classes and castes, in which there is a tendency for herders to be overlords. But there is a whole spectrum of tribes, these more White, those strongly Negro, these mainly nomadic herders and those mainly settled farmers. Some of the people form large nations, and some have lately been ruled by medieval sultans.

The Congo forest

South of this, in the forests of the Guinea coast and around into the basin of the Congo River, is a second major region of the Negroes, which also harbors, in parts of the Congo, wandering bands of hunting Pygmies. The Negroes do no herding, because the forest keeps the cattle out, abetted by the tsetse fly, which carries disease. But they keep goats, pigs, chickens and some sheep, and if they want more meat they have hunting to fall back on. Some tribes have special expert hunters; a few of them let the Pygmies do the hunting and pay them for the meat with things the Pygmies cannot make or get themselves, like iron and garden vegetables, which are Negro specialties.

The real source of Negro food, indeed, is the forest garden, cleared by slash-and-burn and worked with a hoe. They have a long list of crops, delicacies and condiments and, like the Melanesians, they are good cooks. Much of their present stock is new, like manioc and corn from America (as well as tobacco), or rice from Asia. But old and important foods are yams, taros and plantains, apparently from Southeast Asia. To some extent they have plantations, for the kola nut (an important spice and narcotic), and for palm wine and oil, and they may go on using such trees long after they have moved their village and fields to another place.

In its simplest form, their dress is some kind of bark cloth loincloth for men and a "grass" skirt of palm leaves for women, which is unlike the skin clothing of the East Africans and makes you think of Melanesia. Also as in Melanesia, they cut scar patterns in the skin, especially on the face, and they go in for a certain amount of tooth-filing. They also are fond of cutting their hair in patterns, like little formal gardens for the scalp.

But the Negroes do good weaving in addition to this, and in fact they are admirable artisans and artists in many ways. They are indifferent potters but excellent wood-carvers, so that their fetishes, stools and free carving have not only appeared in art shows in the civilized West but have influenced Western painting itself, as witness the "Fauves." They do good work in leather, basketry (many wear basketry hats) and ivory. And this is the country of drum language, and of highly developed native music.

One of their most impressive arts is the working of iron (and other metals), for the Negroes of Africa are the best of uncivilized iron founders, from ore to finished blade. The East Africans also make iron, but among them there is a strange tendency to set smiths apart as people of low esteem, sometimes to the point of not allowing them to marry among the rest of the community, in contrast to the position of respect smiths hold in the Congo. In North Africa also smiths are a despised and servile group, apparently Negroid as well, an effect that may be connected with the importation of Negro slaves to do the smithing. The Congo peoples make hoes and weapons from their iron, including a fearsome throwing knife, a starfish-shaped affair, flat and keen, which is thrown whirling against an enemy. Now as to the use of iron, it may seem strange to have this Negro culture described as Neolithic when it appears to be in an Iron Age, but you will remember that Neolithic refers to the kind of economy, the food-producing, and the iron is just a material replacing stone and not making any other difference in life. In fact iron points and knives obtained in trade are used by the Pygmies, who at best are otherwise in a Mesolithic stage of existence.

The Congo forest tribes are not unlike the eastern herders in their social ideas. Communities or villages are apt to be small, but "kings" and large groupings do exist. Relationships are similar, and a bride price is paid for wives. There is a fairly complicated legal and judicial system; but in both areas there is also much reliance on magical ways of settling disputes or criminal cases. In the Congo the poison ordeal is used: a defendant is given poison, which itself will judge his guilt and allow him to be affected, or not affected, accordingly; or two people will settle a civil case by seeing who can resist an intoxicating poison longest; or poison will be fed to a chicken, while it—the *poison*, a conscious agent, not the chicken—is respectfully asked a question, and asked to kill the chicken in whose stomach it is residing if the answer is yes, and to spare it if the answer is no.

The basic religious cult is ancestor worship, of a simple, pleasant kind. The young men are also initiated in harrowing rites, but where in the eastern region the hazing is all clearly for instruction, in the Congo it is often connected with secret societies which are vigilantist and rather terroristic, and which are not above killing and eating an occasional novice. These societies are a difference between grassland and forest areas, and a likeness between the Congo and Melanesia (and the same can be said of cannibalism), for they go in for the impersonation of ghosts and for the use of fright, to keep the whole community law-abiding but also to keep it in partial subjection to the society, for it is something outside the usual institutions, and a little like the old Ku Klux Klan.

One other feature of life in the Congo is more attractive: its markets. Simple trade, of course, exists everywhere in the world, and the Negroes conduct it with the Pygmies, but among themselves they hold markets, perhaps every four days (the usual Congo week), to which goods and food are brought for open sale. Payment may be in kind, i.e., by food or oil, but they have an actual currency, consisting of cowrie shells, from the Indian Ocean, or of iron hoes. This, as you can see, is putting trade on the threshold of a new kind of organization, and one that is familiar to us. With markets, random exchange is replaced by a fixed institution, which exists frankly for the bringing together of buyers and sellers just as does R. H. Macy's. It does not rely, as a trading institution, on the social egotism that makes the kula ring go round.

I do not want to press the distinction very far. In such a simple farming society the markets do not make the culture radically different from other such cultures, and may not be too distinct from a Pueblo Indian woman sitting beside U. S. Highway 85 with half a dozen pots in front of her. And other kinds of Neolithic peoples make definite trading expeditions, or other plans for trade, and some, like the Riffians or the Bedouin, have long been in contact with more advanced ways of life. But nonetheless "market" is not a word that can be used for the usual primitive farming culture.

Some African question marks

So much for this Congo area. What was its past? We are largely in the dark, as we always seem to be in dealing with the Negroes. We can attach the East African cattle-herding culture to the Near Eastern Neolithic base with no great quibbling, much as we would appreciate knowledge of dates and places. But can we attach the Congo culture to that of Southeast Asia? Some of the likenesses, especially with Melanesia, are rather striking, but it must be remembered that certain of them would be coincidence anyhow, because of the forest itself, or the kind of life. While yams, taros, plantains and chickens must have come from the East, they were a success in Africa on their own merits, because this is the sort of tropical forest region into which these crops *can* spread.

In fact these very crops almost certainly are the ones that opened the Congo Basin to a gardening, Neolithic culture for the first time. But to whom? A Mesolithic culture with tiny microlithic blades and a poor form of pottery is known to have survived for a long time in the Congo, after there were already Neolithic peoples in the Sudan to the north. This Mesolithic seems to have given way in the Congo only before iron-using peoples coming in. Was it a Pygmy culture? And did the Negroes appear here very late? Or were there Negroes in the Congo already?

Iron spread from the upper Nile into Negro Africa after the birth of Christ, originally coming down from Egypt. How and when some other things, especially yams and chickens, spread through this area is not known. Africa has interesting likenesses with Melanesia and Southeast Asia. Both West and East raise chickens, and both tell fortunes by sacrificing them. Both dress in bark cloth and "grass" (leaf) skirts, and like to scar their skins or file their teeth; both go in for ghostly secret societies and ancestor worship. But any actual transfers, such as crops, are probably quite late, and there is much room for coincidence and independent invention in other matters.

West Africa: a very simple civilization

Whatever the source of this Neolithic culture of the Congo, the same thing did give rise in turn to a more advanced form in West Africa. Here the population flourished and became dense. Certain major nations grew up, extending into the southern Sudan, of which the best known and most important were Dahomey and Ashanti. Old contact with Arabs crossing the Sahara may have had an effect on this, but it is a Negro culture, and consists of a further development of the same institutions that are proper to the forest area in general.

It was not a matter of material inventions, although some of the arts, like weaving and metal-casting, stood at a higher level than in the Congo. Daily life was a good deal the same. Rather, political organization came into its own. The king of Dahomey was an absolute ruler of great power, surrounded by a full corps of officials (ministers, marshals and magistrates) and governing also through local viceroys and chiefs.

Taxes were collected carefully and systematically from everyone, including the king, a nice gesture. This in turn was based on censuses of the people (kept by storehouses of pebbles) and on censuses of their possessions, gathered secretly by agents of the king, who kept tabs on everything in the kingdom, even to movements of travelers. The king maintained a standing army, adding the famous regiments of Amazons two hundred years ago, and important sections of the kingdom were the result of conquest. (The Amazons were technically all wives of the king, and were commonly beheaded for "adultery," but few of them ever met him, being simply husky girls who would look well in the army.)

The native culture is flourishing today. While life is still of the village variety, there were already, in pre-European times, large towns which later became the modern cities of the region. Markets are highly developed, being held in various parts every day according to a schedule. (The most important ones fall on the first of the four days of the week, and religious ceremonies are not held that day; the gods themselves are shopping, and it would be impolite to call on them when they are not at home.) Markets use standards of value and of measure, and were originally regulated by officials to prevent cheating; they have practices of wholesaling and retailing, of price agreements and profit regulations, and co-operative marketing. This degree of organization has been highly encouraging to trade, which in turn was encouraging to artisanship and specialization, allowing men to devote themselves full time to the manufacture of particular goods without having to garden for themselves, while the gardeners were able to farm for the market as well as for the table.

The Dahomeans today also have co-operative work

associations for the young men—they are not a lazy people and good work is an ideal—which exist to do certain kinds of community labor like opening new fields. They even have mutual insurance societies. All these things probably reflect the fact that the whole functioning society had become enlarged.

Another such thing, probably a better indication of this large size, is the churches. Now the normal religion in Dahomey is ancestor worship, and the king's ancestors are the national cult, as well as the cause, in the past, of a good· deal of human sacrifice. But there has grown up a set of churches that are very much like our idea of such a thing and are addressed to a set of nature gods, families of the earth, and the sky, and the thunder, who resemble, let us say, the pantheon of the Greeks. These churches exist simply for those people who want to believe and worship, as in some of the higher religions, rather than as the normal recourse to make the crops grow or the enemies weak. They are not tribal cults, and nobody has to belong. Yet a large proportion of the population nowadays does belong, going through a novitiate representing death and resurrection which is much more extended than the baptism or confirmation of Christians. These churches are in fact the parents of the mixed "voodoo" religion of Haiti (*vodun* is the Dahomean name for a god), which does not consist of black magic and hexing as everybody seems to think.

So we behold in West Africa various improvements and embellishments of the forest Negro culture, topped by a few highly developed governments. These governments may have been barbaric and arbitrary in the extreme. For example, the king of Dahomey could collect taxes in the usual way. But he once also had a corps of private burglars, and he used to smooth their path by the graceful device of giving a great lawn party, from which, naturally, nobody could be absent. Everyone was there; no one was at home. And he could collect fines for the breaking of royal decrees, sometimes made for the purpose. He could ban, let us say, the wearing of the same pattern of cloth

by anyone but himself, immediately dress up in one of the
more popular current patterns, and send out the cops before the citizenry could get home and change.

When I say "highly developed" government, I mean
high for the society in question, since it changed that society from a tribal to a national one, making possible the
inclusion of other peoples and giving a sort of stability
which might allow the culture and the economy to expand,
always within their own limits. West African governments
and institutions, the high point of native Negro culture, are
not to be sneezed at by uninformed snooters and sneezers,
for they are far along on the scale of human progress.

THE NEW SOCIETIES

14. *The Organization of Society*

The Neolithic way of life was a success, to say the least, for most of us would literally not be here at all without it. Throughout the Old World, it pushed aside the ancient hunters and increased the human population manyfold, as food became more plentiful and dependable, and could be drawn from smaller areas of land. As this happened, a problem moved out of the background into the foreground for the first time: how to get these much larger groups of people to live harmoniously and to co-operate efficiently for their own welfare. In other words, how to form societies out of them.

The problem is present only in embryo among hunters or the other Primates. These nature-raiders ordinarily make up such small bands that they can be their own committees, so to speak, and meet their problems through the natural teamwork that comes from constant close association. But suppose the community is so large that this will not serve? Then it has to have some kind of internal structure. If you are satisfied with a very small house, you can stick boughs in the ground in a circle to shelter you, but if you want something larger than the individual boughs can compass, you must take a number of pieces—bricks, stones or timbers—and fit them together in an organized way; then you have structure.

Put it in other terms. Suppose you must have an army of 100,000 soldiers. You might round up 100,000 men, put them in uniform and give them the tools of the trade, but if you stopped there you would have a rabble, not an army, and one that would shortly begin to fight within itself over the food it did not know how to distribute. Only when this body of men is structured is it any good. Everyone in it must have a status, which he and everyone else knows and can depend on. If you have two bars on your shoulders you will be given the attention and deference of a large proportion of the 100,000, a certain body of whom will in fact act by your dictates, so closely are they related to you in structure; however, you in turn will hurriedly raise your hand to the vicinity of your forehead when a man with oak leaves, birds or stars upon his own shoulders draws near. Thus each individual has his status, or place. He also has particular roles to play, like blowing a bugle while others sleep, which are connected with his status, and are also connected with behavior expected of him which he personally must fulfill if the whole structure is to stand up and do what it exists for.

In addition to giving a status to every one of the 100,000, any soundly conceived army would also group its members into large and small units, some for fighting, some for supplying, some for engineering and so forth, and it would have traditional ways for relations and communications between the various groups. For it could hardly expect to send an envelope with personal directions daily to each member. Instead the structure must take care of ordinary matters routinely, so that not only individual men but also large segments of the whole can co-operate effectively.

So the army gives everyone his status and his immediate role, and makes them as plain as it is able. This is structuring of a high degree. And it may seem strained to apply this to normal living, because an army is an artificial affair, and not a self-sustaining society. Nevertheless, the example is a good one, especially as most societies have more structure to them than you might think. This is still more true of the kinds of people we have been reviewing, since they leave more of the regulation of their lives to their social organization than do we.

It begins even among the Primates. They have perfectly good societies, you will recall. The members of a howling monkey colony are all habituated to one another and, although they have no names to know it by, each has his or her status (as a female, or an elder male, or a young sprout) and his or her roles (as a mother, or a leader through the trees, or a defender against another colony by howling, or an adolescent jackanapes). In any case they understand their relations as we might describe them in these terms—each knows his place, and the usual reactions he gets from each of the others—and they do not start to learn about one another afresh every day. This is the very simplest kind of organization, growing up through the constant interaction of the individual monkeys.

It is strongly based on the fact that the individuals are not all alike; they differ biologically. They are born either male or female, like us, a difference most pronounced in adults. Like us also, they are born very young, and gradually get older, changing as they do so. And even among monkeys of the same age and sex there are usually differences in dominance—strength and personality. These kinds of difference are quite enough to give the members of a monkey group a set of individual roles to play and practice at.

And the same differences do the same thing in man, which should not be astonishing. The women are going to be the mothers, the babies are going to be immature, and the men are going to be the most efficient hunters. The closest resemblance to the simple divisions of primate societies occurs, as you might expect, among hunting-gathering peoples. But the great distinction, even here, is the element of culture. What might correspond, in human society, to the free expression of these natural factors in primate social behavior is taken by culture and put into set patterns and finally into institutions. And that is, of course, why human societies differ one from another, while those of howlers do not.

For example, what women can do is the same anywhere; but what they *should* do is not. Their roles are always different from the men's, so that the two normally work co-operatively. Among hunters, for example, the men hunt and the women gather vegetables. And the women look out for the younger children, as you might anticipate. Also, the greater actual strength of men does not mean they do a greater amount of work. They may be expected to do those things that call for great effort, like hunting or fighting or breaking up new ground, but to leave the continuous drudgery to women.

Women do the housework but are not always the cooks. And when the higher arts come in, among "Neolithic" peoples, there are no special rules for all cultures, though of course in any one culture no normal man would be seen dead doing women's work. Ordinarily it is the latter who are supposed to make pots and do weaving, but not always. The men make their own tools, and take social precedence, and usually conduct religious rites, not uncommonly to the exclusion of the women, as among the Australian natives. And the whole status of women can be high or low according to the culture, instead of being fixed by nature as wretched, as it is among baboons.

Age has its dispensations too, and especially among the more primitive. Maturity arrives, bringing the full powers of man and woman, but instead of letting this merely happen, it is signalized in a majority of cultures by dramatic initiation rites, as we have seen. Nor does the time of these rites necessarily fall together with biological or sexual maturity, because the rites celebrate social maturity more than anything else. In later life heads grow wise as blood grows cool and shape grows shapeless, and the whole group can benefit from these wise heads. So the direction of affairs in an Australian band is given to them by cultural consent. And in the Andaman Islands age is the principal factor in social structure.

The Andamanese, who live fairly comfortable lives for hunters, often adopt other people's children, and thus are used to treating all children much the same (many a suburban mother must feel that she is bringing up the whole neighborhood in the same way); and so strict family groups are a little vague. Especial respect is paid to elder people, and they are addressed by titles of honor and more or less treated as community parents. It is these people, of both sexes, who form such government as there is (and it is not much, for they trust that nothing will go wrong, and simply go and hide if a row breaks out). Andamanese seldom use words for "father" and "mother," because they have the honorific terms instead. And in place of typical kinship terms like "brother" and "sister" the significant words are "older," "younger," "married," and so on. They simply have no nouns for most of their relatives, because they put such stress on age, and lack the kind of organization or behavior that goes with the idea of relatives as we see them.

Now this does not mean the Andamanese are some lower grade of man, but only that they have fastened to an unusual degree on age as the key to social structure and the way to distinguish individuals; and it does not mean they do not know how they are related. Where we might say "she was my second cousin on my mother's side," and an Australian could put the whole thing, sex included, in one word,[1] an Andamanese would have to ask for silence while he concentrated and told you a long story of who had married whom and who their children had been, back and forth. He knows, but his language and his culture simply consider that all this is excess baggage, because they do things differently.

People with larger and more elaborate societies than the Andamanese and other hunters—i.e., "Neolithic" societies —are apt to make use of more kinds of status than those relating to sex and age, and more of the sort of thing we would call social position, pure and simple. Between a pair of baboons, dominance would hold sway: a couple of barks or a short engagement would settle the matter of who was No. 1 and who was No. 2. And even among Andamanese and Australians the ablest man will, age being equal, have the most influence. But if there is a hereditary chieftainship, or social classes, or castes, then natural dominance may be

[1] In the Karawa tribe, for example, this would be *Djibari* or *Gogarlina*, depending on whether she was the child of one's maternal grandmother's brother's *son* or of his *daughter*.

offset by a cultural framework that holds people in particular positions. We compliment ourselves on our own democratic society, but you might as well know that it makes a great deal of difference, to you, where and to whom you are born. A child of a Masai smith will have to be a smith himself and marry the child of another smith, whether he wants to or not, and we ourselves could furnish parallel cases. This sort of thing all implies rank, but there may be other kinds of position that relate more to the group you belong to (example: "Yankee"; properly, a New Englander; to a Southerner, anyone from north of the Mason-Dixon line, be it Minnesota or Brooklyn; to an Englishman, someone from the U.S.A., which includes South Carolina).

At any rate a great function of etiquette is to take care of status: to preserve your own and recognize that of others, so that no injury shall result from some improper clash of position. Etiquette is not basically a matter of whether you hold your fork like a screwdriver, which will not elevate your status at all. It is rather taking action that belongs to the pattern, and so not only registers status but reinforces it by the very exercise. Let us start quite simply with the French *tu* for "thou," instead of *vous* for "you" (which is all we ever say in English). If you say *tu*, you are speaking to a relative or a friend, a social equal. For anyone else it is unthinkable, and people of low breeding may in fact use it as an insult. The same holds for German and other languages. And in Japan, or Samoa, or South Africa, much more involved differences in speech have to be used. A Samoan commoner could say to a friend, "Have you bathed?" but this would be too personal for him to say to a chief; instead, it would be "Are you dry?" There may be as many as five different ways of saying one thing. (We are great Nice Nellies ourselves: all women are "ladies" and we have changed "graveyard" to "cemetery" to "Memorial Park"; and "belly" is horrid so we took "stomach," which is not the same place at all, and now we cannot stomach "stomach" so we say "tummy.")

In the societies I have named above there is a good deal of the grading of individuals which calls for such etiquette.

Among the Zulu and their neighbors, age, sex and position all count, with wives of an important man having their own relative rank as well, and with especially polite behavior being demanded of a wife toward her in-laws. A Venda, for example, may show four grades of respect by the pronoun he uses, going from second person singular to second plural to third singular to third plural, always using the last for a chief. He or she must also employ polite gestures for greetings and conversations, perhaps kneeling or squatting, or sitting with legs tucked to one side, all depending on who is speaking, who is spoken to, and who spoke first. And the really urbane person, politely listening to someone else, must continually interrupt with exclamations—"Lion!" "Great one!"—which are strict equivalents of "My goodness!" and "You don't say!" And a Zulu wife is obliged to use *hlonipha* behavior and hlonipha talk to her husband's parents, which means dressing in a certain way and not eating or chewing in their presence, not using their names or even words containing syllables of their names, and also putting her words in an unusual order, as though she were talking pig Latin.

All this sort of position is what Ralph Linton has called "ascribed" status, as distinct from "achieved," since it is what falls to people through the accident of birth and their normal progress through life. But achievement, a beautiful word in our ears, has its counterpart as well in other cultures. Among the simplest, a man may stand out somewhat by virtue of particular force or hunting skill, though a shaman or magician has practically the only kind of really special status. Up the scale there are more possibilities, so that people may become artisans or priests or people of property. In Polynesia a skilled canoe maker or architect generates his own mana by his accomplishment and so he actually becomes a priest of his trade. And in a really complex society there may be all the shades of standing that we recognize ourselves: in West Africa, aside from wealth and good birth, a person may be known as a gentleman and a man of principle by his demeanor.

Money is almost everything

But, in the middle cultures especially, social standing may be changed through what is aptly called a "prestige economy," meaning that one can amass a surplus of the world's goods (hunters cannot) but can manage to spend it only for prestige. We can take good, hard money and invest it in a Cadillac or a Matisse. The Cadillac runs beautifully and looking at the Matisse gives us great personal pleasure, quite apart from the impact that our possession of these things may have on other people. We can spend our cash on good food, travel and every kind of personal comfort, perhaps on a new heating system which is hidden in the wall and will come out for prestige purposes only if we discourse about it to every unfortunate who comes to dinner.

But such opportunities, art possibly excepted, are denied to Neolithic village dwellers, who can turn their wealth, energy and ability only to personal enhancement. You have already seen plenty of examples. For East Africans it is done through the simple possession of cattle. In Arabia it is horses, and not, you notice, the camels, their basis of subsistence. In Melanesia, where they understand all this very well, a mwanekama through party-giving can translate his bodily energy directly into prestige, while a club-man can go in for lending shell money at interest, and otherwise caring for his fortune, so as to buy his way upward in his lodge. And the kula is another fine example, because the worth of the kula necklaces and bracelets is purely their prestige value and nothing else. So it was with the stone money of Yap, in the Caroline Islands: big mill-stone-like rings, which were difficult to make and transport and which therefore had a sort of natural value and limitation, until a rascally Yankee brought in a load of actual secondhand millstones, and very nearly wrecked the system.

On Ponape, another of the Carolines, there exists a well-rounded case of this kind. Its principal expression is a contest of the growing of yams for a feast held by a chief at the end of the season. Each man brings in his best yam to contribute, and a consistent winner will be given a title of honor by the chief, as well as the admiration of his fellows. A good deal of effort goes into this. The yams for entry are planted in the dark and raised in secret, and the family is willing to go hungry rather than eat into their chances of winning, though there is feasting enough at the end. But here is the oddity: once the yams are on display, Ponapean manners insist on the most overdone modesty. Everyone is on the watch for any sign of smugness or satisfaction, which will unleash the gossips and turn all pride to shame. The exhibitor of the largest yams is obliged to look about in wide-eyed innocence and protest that somebody else's yams are much bigger than his.

This is such a general rule of behavior that a Ponapean should not admit he can do anything well. You may imagine the arrival of American administrators after the war, brought up in a culture that demands you say you are twice as good as you really are, and double that again if you are in civil or military service. Try to recruit labor on Ponape; say, "Expert shovelers stand forth," and any well-brought-up Ponapean, demon though he might be with a shovel in his hands, would be expected to blush and hang back. Here, then, is a custom where status may come from work and skill, and where the desire for it may control other values, often useful, so as to determine a whole code of behavior. It actually fosters industry and husbandry (as in the Solomons, or Africa), and competition without aggressiveness, something we praise but scarcely practice.

Kinship: the importance of being related

I have been talking about the distinctions between individuals in a group, those things that, according to the culture, give them their roles to play and the cues they can confidently follow. What now about the way individuals are formally related to one another, by kinship and by family groupings?

Kinship is not simply blood ties and marriage relationship. A female baboon knows who her husband of the moment is, and who her own child is. Kinship is rather a cultural pattern, based on these things, but not the same from culture to culture and usually more complex than you might think if you were judging only by our own. You have seen the postgraduate systems of the Australians, and the fact that, unlike ourselves, they usually make a sharp distinction between a parallel cousin and a cross-cousin—you will find you must stop and think before you can say which kind your own cousins are. But whatever the complications and whatever the variety, there are certain things all such systems do: they provide you with relatives, they tend to increase the number of relatives who are considered important, and they govern the behavior that you should hold toward them and they toward you.

In other words, kinship enlarges your resources in people. This may be the last thing you think you need, but you are exceptional. Make yourself into a native Australian for a moment. I have already tried to make plain how these people stretch their resources and offset their poor culture by their enormous skill in tracking, hunting and finding food generally. They go further to defeat their difficulties by maintaining relations and mutual obligations with other bands, through kinship and intermarriage. Thus a man need not be a stranger, even when he has come to a band where no one knows him, because by carrying through his kinship relationship from the last band, he knows how he stands with everyone. He can feel at home and be sure of committing no offense: he knows which men are his "brothers" and which women he may be familiar with and which not.

Kinship thus makes for stability among persons. Its meaning, and that of the family, is reinforced by certain important rules, especially the incest tabu, and what is probably best called avoidance.

Incest is not only banned but considered horrible in all human societies, and the exceptions permitting brother-sister marriage (kings in Hawaii, Peru, Egypt) do not count. Now we think we feel this antipathy instinctively. But we do not, for gibbons and other Primates do not and incest, alas, does occur in man; in fact, if it did not there would be no stated rules against it. It has some biological disadvantages because of the possible appearance of recessive heritable defects, but the popular idea of all this is not very correct, and certainly the gibbons have not withered away. Actually we learn from our culture to reject the notion of incest sternly, and learn it pretty thoroughly; and the tabu seems to have been a fundamental social invention of humanity.

The last word has not been said about incest, but the fact is that it would be a great source of trouble anywhere. Not all societies have equally complicated kinships, but all are equally clear about the existence of kinship and the notion of families. And incest, particularly the abhorred mating of brother and sister, would set any system of relations at naught. In almost every society, mother and mother-in-law are quite different people, socially. Having them fuse into the same person would be intolerable incongruity and a clear loss to that family. Anyone's network of relatives would collapse like a pricked balloon, and the maintenance of the family's future would be threatened because boy and girl were not marrying new people, and this would be the community's loss as well.

See what the Arapesh told Margaret Mead on this particular point. These, the Arapesh, who live in northern New Guinea, are somewhat unusual, or exceptionally "human," in their feelings about incest. They look on it not as an enormity but as an absurdity, being unaware of its existence and hardly comprehending Mead's investigation of it. "No, we do not marry our sisters. We marry other men's sisters." Says Dr. Mead:

> When I could get no better answer and no illustrations of incest, I sent the young men to ask the old men what they would say to a man who wanted to marry his sister, and the replies were almost identical: "What? Do you not want brothers-in-law? If you

marry another man's sister and another man marries your sister, you have two brothers-in-law. If you marry your own sister, you have none. With whom will you visit? With whom will you talk? With whom will you hunt? Are you mad, not to want brothers-in-law?" . . . Thus incest is regarded among the Arapesh not with horror and repulsion towards a temptation that they feel their flesh is heir to, but as a stupid negation of the joys of increasing, through love and marriage, the number of people whom one can love and trust.

What incest would do to any higher system of organization, like large families or clans, may be evident upon a little thought. At any rate the force with which it is rejected is impressive proof of the importance everywhere of relationship and family structure.

The same end seems to be expressed in another kind of custom, not universal but fairly widespread. This is special behavior toward certain relatives, usually consisting of some degree of avoidance, but sometimes of just the opposite: expected familiarity and joking, or even coarseness. By all odds the commonest manifestation is the rule of avoiding one's mother-in-law, to the degree that some Melanesians may have to climb a tree at sight of her; otherwise it may be a question of not passing her, not looking at her, not speaking with her, or simply being most reserved and polite, like the Zulu. Other people may observe other kinds of peculiar behavior. All this may apply between father-in-law and daughter-in-law as well, and brothers and sisters are also apt to be the object of one another's avoidance, in various degrees again, as they become adults.

Now the reasons for this are not obvious, and I am not inclined to embrace the first Freudian explanation that comes along, even after noting the popularity of mother-in-law jokes among ourselves, which are notorious for their malice and lack of humor, and for their simple insistence that she is a disliked person, or ought to be. These avoidances seem to support the incest tabu along many lines, and they or their opposites—familiarity—also seem to mark down certain kinds of relatives as those whose social dealings are best not allowed to be ordinary, because of any conflict or difficulty they might give rise to. Either avoidance or familiarity provides these relatives with a special etiquette by which to recognize their special statuses and deal with one another.

Marriage is for everybody

If there were in the world only one man and one woman there would be no society to disturb, and so none of the above problems to worry about. The two could be mated—married in the sense gibbons are married—and so meet the needs of sex. They could have children, and provide the children with parents and upbringing, although unless they had a definite culture to guide them they would have some awesome problems to face. And they would have a simple economic unit, man and wife, to do their several tasks for their joint benefit. These are the things for which a basic family—man, wife and children—exists. But such a family as I have described is really an abstraction, because it never exists apart from society. For human society always demands formal marriage—not the gibbon variety—and then uses it as the building block by which to make a structure of bigger units. This is another aspect of the social structure or organization I mentioned earlier.

For one thing, isolated families of the above kind are quite impractical, even among the crudest hunters, for both social and economic reasons. If either husband or wife becomes ill and cannot do his or her normal work, the mate and the children are in dire straits unless they can turn to others for support. There are a few cultures where families may live by themselves for periods, but this is probably practical only when the food supply is such that anybody can make a living from it. This might be true of gibbons. But even among howling monkeys too small a group might be unable to defend its territory and so its food. And among the native Australians, hunting calls for long training and practice by the men to develop the skill they need, and a lone widow would simply not have that skill. So in hunting peoples, just as you find that the number of people in a band does not run very high, so you find that it does not run down to a single family. This is added, of course, to the fact that a larger group is more efficient anyhow, and that man is a social animal.

Marriage itself is affected by such considerations. We ourselves are strict monogamists, meaning that we have only one wife or, perhaps more correctly, must take our wives one at a time. Other cultures allow more than one wife, a few allow more than one husband, and a couple allow a sort of group marriage, although this is actually stretching a point, and does not mean what it seems to say. Enormous amounts have been written about marriage and its evolution. Let us ignore it all, and only say about the evolution that it is a snare.

We doubtless have good reasons, quite apart from preference and religion, for insistence on monogamy in our own society, and the other people doubtless have good reasons for fostering other kinds of marriage. They are not necessarily lower forms in an evolution of marriage any more than other languages are lower because they cannot say "trinitrotoluene." Such institutions, as I said earlier, do not evolve in isolation from the rest of culture. Rather, they suit the cultures they belong to. Even if such a culture is more primitive than ours, nonetheless no evolution of marriage is involved. This sounds like a paradox, though it is not.

But the main point is this: monogamy, meet and right for us, might be catastrophic if it were enforced on a band of Australians, depriving them of a way of taking care of any extra adult women there might be. These women cannot live with their parents indefinitely because hunters weaken and die early anyhow; and they can hardly live with other households in any capacity except that of a legitimate wife.

Similar and other reasons exist for the permission of polygamy (more properly polygyny) in higher societies.

Its presence does not mean that every man has several wives. But women outnumber men everywhere, especially where the men engage in hazardous pursuits or go to war, and polygamy reduces the number of spinsters while at the same time it may ease the work in a household with two wives.

Kin, family and clan

Let us leave the forms of marriage and go back to the building up of societies by putting families together. Ideally they may just form a band, for mutual benefit. But then matters of kinship enter in, even among hunters, and this gives rise to more complicated units, and in fact to the sort of thing that seems to have become important and useful when groups become larger with Neolithic life. You find among the societies of this kind, as we have seen them in Asia, Oceania and Africa, a great variety of schemes of social organization, arising from just what rules they have chosen to follow in putting families together and deciding where they will live.

There is in this a rigidity that is basic to tribal life and that we in our open national life cannot easily see. We do, it is true, invariably give the wife and the children the husband's surname. But apart from that, the family may live with his family, or her family, or they can move to Cincinnati. The young provider may go into his own father's business and inherit it, or he may on the other hand marry the boss's daughter and become boss himself when the old man can be persuaded to retire. All of this would seem shockingly untidy outside the West. Our simpler people abide by their particular rule of lineage and rule of residence. These rules do not invariably both favor the same side (male or female), which is one cause of variety in social organization.

The result is generally an approach either to a joint family or to a clan. The joint family is a superfamily, made up of the households of a man and his sons, or of a group of brothers (or, matrilineally, of sisters with their husbands and children), or some such array, perhaps extended over more generations or relatives. The Riffians gave us an example of such a kindred, in the "vein" that acts as a unit in many kinds of activity.

A clan is a more extreme and arbitrary alignment, for a joint family depends on tracing family lines for a given distance beyond which it may break up into several such families, while a clan is permanent. The clan will, if it is patrilineal, contain your father and his brothers, and your grandfather, and so on, but it will also contain members with whom you can no longer trace relationship by blood. It will contain your brother and sister, but your sister will have to marry out, and have children belonging to another clan, though she still belongs to your clan and takes part in its affairs.

If it is a matrilineal system, then your clan is your mother's, and your father is the outsider. Family matters are for your mother and her sisters and brothers to decide. The important man in your life is your mother's brother, who has responsibilities to you and from whom you will inherit; your father is just a nice fellow to go fishing with, whose own property will go to his sister's son in his own clan, which is not yours. Thus our kind of father is divided into two men, which has some advantages. This particular case may seem clumsy, but only because we are used to our way of looking at things. Whatever its precise form, such a system is consistent.

You will see why exogamy applies—why you have to marry outside, even if some women of your clan are only distantly related to you by blood: the whole system would begin to crumble, and the social organization with it, if members of the same clan married. Another common custom that acts as a prop for this kind of organization (joint family or clan) is the double-barreled one I described along with the lobola: the levirate, by which a widow is taken as wife by her husband's brother, and the sororate, by which a man's second wife is sister of the first (who may be living). This, as I said, keeps all the lines in proper order.

A clan, or a joint family, is of great importance to a member. Its other members are his real relatives, whatever feelings he may have for his blood kin in other clans. They are the people with whom he shares property, with whose affairs he is concerned, and with whom he holds religious ceremonies. They are the people he trusts and confides in, and the ones who will be his strength and his defense as he needs them.

This is how such a unit as a clan acts in organizing society, as an army puts men in manageable groups. It makes a number of households into a larger, well-knit group that can take care of many social and religious affairs. And it thus gives roles to whole clans, and allows relations between clans that in turn build them up into a functioning society of the whole. They intermarry, by the rules of exogamy. They commonly have mutual obligations, or certain reciprocal required behavior, perhaps as to presents and feasts as in Indonesia, perhaps as to the parts they must take in general ceremonies, as in our own Pueblos. And they usually have responsibility for the acts of their members: the clan will rise to protect him, but if he has committed a crime it becomes the clan's responsibility as a whole, so that he must answer to the clan. And so the clan is a regulator of behavior and keeper of the peace.

If such a degree of social organization is to be seen among our Neolithic people, why have we not a higher one still? Why have we slipped back into a simple family system, with our most obvious concern being monogamy? The answer probably has to do with something that we have which the Neolithic peoples have not: politics. If, among hunters, basic family organization and kinship, plus general consent and the decisions of the older men, seem to be adequate for the harmonious action of a band, then among the villagers the more complex social organization and the expansion of kinds of status do a great deal of the work necessary for the operation of a larger society.

Clans or other extensions of the family are not the only subdivisions that can go into the structure. Social classes like those of Southeast Asia may interact with a similar effect, and so may the castes of India. But such cultures are not as a rule strong in political institutions. Councils are the most important arm. Law codes are found in few places, notably among such as the North Africans and the Indonesians; elsewhere justice may go by the hazards of the ordeal and other kinds of fortune-telling. Rulers are only too apt to be despotic.

We, on the other hand, under the umbrella of our complicated constitutional government and our law for everyone, written for everyone to see, need not rely on the Neolithic kind of ward-and-precinct social organization to help us govern our lives and relationships. And our open economic system allows people to maintain themselves as bachelors and spinsters. So we have regressed socially from what must have been something more complicated, and perhaps we are still regressing.

Perhaps too far. Are we glad when, in our once-patriarchal system, we see Mrs. Smith divorce Mr. Smith and go back to her mother, Mrs. Jones, taking along her daughter by her first husband, little Alice Robinson? Our children of divorce have no lobola to tell them where they stand, and no clan that will be always theirs; and their status as persons is made that much more difficult.

15. *The Meaning of Religion*

Is life complete with food and society? It is for the monkeys, but then the monkeys have no culture, and we have lots of it. Culture consists, as I have said more than a few times, of patterns, or abstract ideas that are translated into concrete objects or actions. Now that man has become able to handle such patterns he can no longer take them or leave them alone. Instead, he must accept them as his way of understanding his whole universe. And this in turn has brought him the most abstract, non-animal side of all his culture: his religion.

This is a sort of top level of culture, symbolic in nature, and so above the technical and social levels. Man meets some of his problems with concrete tools, which are so easily perceived and comprehended that apes may imitate their use. (Be it remembered, of course, that the tools themselves are the products of abstract ideas.) He meets other problems—raising children, let us say—by various practical rules (though rules are more abstract than tools) which he follows to give his society more definite shape. Now man's handling of abstract ideas shows him still other things that no animal can recognize and that correspond to nothing concrete.

For example, an animal may be aware of what it is like to be hungry or sick, while a man may be aware of what it is like to *foresee* being hungry or sick and to be apprehensive about it. But this is something he cannot lay his hands on or give orders about. He cannot pull it down from its abstract state. He must rise to its level with cultural weapons of a symbolic kind. In the awareness of such things as sickness and hunger, mankind has been introduced to problems that cannot be attacked with spears nor yet with regulations and that must be met with a third kind of resource, philosophy and religion.

There may be a dozen ways of looking at religion, or of describing it, but for purposes of culture we might take this one. Man views the universe and, as animals cannot, he forms abstract ideas about it, such as "day" for the hours of light. He also takes note of his own place in it: his needs and wishes. He will be only too aware that the universe is not a tidy system, harmoniously responsive to his wants, and that there are ugly gaps that must be filled somehow if he is to be safe. A hook and line will serve to close the gap between himself and finny food, and so satisfy hunger. But illness must be met with equal assurance, or it will have a strong demoralizing influence on everyone.

How to close the gap and somehow handle the illness? The illness is recognized not only as a bodily feeling but also as a something, in an abstract way. So is the need to get rid of it. If the illness can be symbolized in a manner easily grasped by ordinary human imagination—as a spirit that has possessed you, or an evil charm—and if the emotional need to drive it away can also be symbolized—as a drink the spirit will not like, or as a countercharm to break the first charm and send it back on its maker—then the situation has been put into a form in which it can be handled. The action taken may not work. That does not matter, because the main result is the completing of the system of ideas or symbols connected with the situation—the closing of the gap—so that anxiety may be stayed.

I am not trying to reduce all religion to a treatment for heartburn, or even to give it an inclusive description. I am only trying to show its symbolic nature. I have used the fear of illness merely as an example. Religion is more than answers to problems. It is rather a way of putting the world into a shape that is comprehensible and satisfying. And I am suggesting that man's mental advance made religion, as a final area of appreciation of his world, not only possible but essential.

Myth, the storehouse of ideals

The limits of religion are not easy to fix on, and in fact I should prefer to speak of religious behavior rather than religion. For one thing, the attitude of a culture toward a belief or an action might be the thing that made it religious. Compare Little Red Riding Hood and the Bible. The first of these is a folktale, dealing with the supernatural to the extent that it contains a talking wolf; we are amused to repeat it to children, but it is not religious simply because it happens to be supernatural. The second is our Scripture, the heart of our religion, and I need hardly dwell on the strength of the reverence it commands.

These would represent the two extremes of feeling that cultures might hold about what may generally be called their folklore and mythology, which loom large in the lives of those who do not write their literature but who keep it alive by telling it. Some of their stories may be nothing but pleasant romancing. Many may seem like this but may also have an extra philosophical value or hold moral lessons. Such may be tales of origin, for example, or other explanations of important things, which may by suggestion teach people to honor their culture. Or they may be myths of violence and obscenity which, even while the listeners enjoy them, recognize and uphold, either directly or indirectly, the ethical idea that this is wrong behavior.

These myths may be recognizably religious in character. The Bakongo of Central Africa, for example, tell all sorts of things about Nzambi Mpungu, supreme being who made the world and the laws and who is good, punishing all evil: the breaking of oaths, perjury, adultery, and disrespect for parents. Yet the Kongo do not know what Nzambi looks like, and they do not worship him—their gods are the ancestors.

Finally there is the kind of myth that is deeply sacred, as in Polynesia or Australia, existing along with the other kinds but forming the basis of ceremony, being kept alive by repetition and drama, regarded as we regard the Bible, and perhaps so sanctified as to be kept secret from the uninitiated.

So myth and folklore are means by which people express to themselves a lot of their joint ideals. Among ourselves, two novels may deal with strife, lust or terror. The author of one has moral values which he is clothing in action, and in his book the story shows forth these values in strengthened form. The author of the other, innocent of such values, produces only a lascivious sensationalism. Doubtless, as a myth is retold, it is such moral values—those important to the culture—which make it survive, and the very retelling has in the past molded the myth in that direction. Thus a people's myths are the main repository of their philosophy. Probably many kinds of myth should qualify as religious, and not simply as philosophical, if we go by the definition of religion as using supernatural symbols or parables to fill out gaps in man's understanding of the universe.

This view would certainly put within religion a lot of activity that we ourselves would not, offhand, recognize as religious. But we are used to thinking of religion as something well defined, like the Christian belief in God and the Christian church, or like a rival religion such as Mohammedanism, which resembles Christianity in its highly developed and international character.

These are great world religions, helped in development by prophets, saints and scholars, and having scripture, dogma and strong ideas about heresy. They contrast with the disorderly and unexclusive nature of pagan religions, as those of the tribes, outside the great religions, are called. When we are considering human history and the past of culture, these pagan cults are important, for the very reason that they are not international, and belong to local societies in a single region, answering the Mesolithic and Neolithic needs of these societies by a process of natural development. And so they show us what the needs are, and what the answers have been, in the form of certain beliefs and practices which occur again and again.

Magic, or how to do it

One of these is magic, perhaps the least religious of such things by any standards. You have heard of it before, and you are doubtless aware that this kind of magic does not mean sleight of hand, or something incredible in our sense. It means rather the working of spells.

Black magic is evil, done to injure someone else or at least to help you at another's expense. Always with us, even today, is some sort of hexing or image magic, by which you make a dummy of your enemy, name it, curse it, and then injure or kill it by stabbing it, burning it or poisoning it with a charm. In this satisfying way, your wish to injure or kill is symbolized and carried over to your actual victim through his image. And if anything happens to him—even though it is not exactly what you hoped— you can feel it is your doing.

Now if this business is so universal and so persistent, it is not hard to apply the same interpretation to the animal pictures in the Paleolithic caves, especially when some of the pictures actually show spears striking into the animals as well. So the animals (almost always game animals) were cunningly brought within the control of the hunters, whose intent might be to prekill them, so to speak, or to bring them to the neighborhood, to make them fertile, and so on.

Magical villainy is everywhere. Australians secretly "point the bone," sending the magic like a death ray toward a distant victim; Riffians of North Africa will take a spell drawn up by an unprincipled student of the Koran and written in bat's blood, and soak it in the victim's drink or tie it in a tree where he must pass. Et cetera. But surely there is far more belief than actual practice, far more time spent in worrying what your enemy is doing to you than in scheming and executing some kind of a low blow yourself.

White magic has greater practical importance: the many spells that are used to help out in everyday work and to go beyond the things a man can do with his hands and his tools. Hunting people use hunting magic, to make their arrows fly straight, make themselves silent and sharp-eyed, make the game stupid and slow. Gardening magic is a major possession of a Melanesian, who cannot expect his yams to grow properly without good spells. And there is war magic, fishing magic, pot-making magic and love magic: the magical formulas of any tribe would literally take a book to catalogue, and if you put down even your own little magical tricks I think you would be surprised. Or did you never wish on a shooting star?

Probably everywhere the two outstanding kinds of magic are healing and fortune-telling, or divination. And well they might be, for illness and uncertainty are every-where the most pressing causes of personal and social anx-iety. That is why we ourselves are blessed with palmists, card readers, fortune-tellers, astrologers and the like, and why we still see acceptance of every kind of old wives' cure or quack treatment, even in the face of the great knowledge and integrity of modern medicine. Can we really look condescendingly upon a Zande of the Congo, who will not so much as go to the next village without asking his rubbing board (a small contrivance like our Ouija board) whether he may? (Anything of slightly greater import, of course, would call for poisoning a chicken.) Or should we laugh at our own ancestors in Europe, who used the ordeal by combat as the Africans use the ordeal by poison? They solemnly believed that the justice of his cause alone would make a good little man triumph over a bad big man, who would otherwise chop him into catmeat. The mind boggles at the endlessness of divination and its procedures, and we had best go no further into it.

The same might as well be said about curing. We may note only that a particularly common practice is to let something out of the patient, or remove it by sucking. The doctor applies his mouth or a tube to the site of the illness, sucks, and then shows that he has removed the trouble by bringing a stone, bone, cinder, ball of fur or some such thing out of his mouth. If you know the feeling of relief and relaxation that comes over you when the dentist takes a last look at the cavern he has been drilling in your tooth, says, "There, that's all," and puts up his burr, then you can appreciate the positive good and comfort a primitive patient may get when the cause of his pain seems to be taken away, after which his system can go to work to effect a natural cure.

Of course, if the illness is fatal, it is fatal and that is that, but the chances are in favor of the cure anyhow. One other common feature of uncivilized curing is the taking of medicine, as we do. The medicine may be good because it seems related to the trouble (liverwort has liver-shaped leaves, so it must be good for the liver), or because it is rare and expensive, or for reasons nobody can remember. And it may be perfectly good in our own eyes, like many primitive treatments. For it would be strange if such things were not discovered by trial and error, just as natives discovered tobacco, beer and wine. But this would be an accident rather than medical science; it would strike its users simply as particularly good magic.

To them, magic is both scientific and religious. To us it is neither. Science, when you strip it to its essence, consists in recognizing the difference between (a) a reasonable guess and (b) a fact that can be proved. This is the very distinction that magic, along with most other primitive and civilized thinking, neglects. Magic attempts the same practical ends as science, but it does not care to dig out the explanations for what it is doing. It assumes that throughout the universe there are supernatural connections like telephone wires, running between actions and their results, and that these connections can be discovered and used; also that none of this is any more extraordinary than water turning to ice when the weather is cold. A lot of magical "logic" stems from what Sir James Frazer, in *The Golden Bough*, called the Law of Sympathy (like produces like), and I have just cited examples: another would be a row of young girls in New Guinea being obliged to sit stiffly quiet on a log in a hut, and so keep a sailing canoe of the village, away on a voyage, on a steady keel by a sort of distant body english. But such obvious "logic" is not necessary. Magic just works. I do not know, for example, any explanation for knocking on wood, or why a rabbit's foot is lucky, or why a wishbone should grant wishes.

As to religion, if you feel that Christianity offers a philosophy based on compliance with God's will and His omnipotence, then perhaps you can see that such a religion cannot contain any area where it degenerates into superstition and hocus-pocus by which nature can be controlled by spells. So our churches condemn magic vehemently, recognizing how enduring it is among the uneducated. But for people without such a philosophy it does not seem evil, and in fact it sustains them in the weakness of their poor culture, assuring them that they have ways of meeting problems that absolutely must be met.

So true is this that a good deal of primitive magic is public, meaning it is not done for private ends, as we might use it, but for the common welfare. This gives rise to the office of medicine man, to whom the people will turn in need, to find the cause of a general sickness, or a drought, or to catch an evildoer by divining. So there is a group dependence on magic, almost like a cult in itself, though not quite. The Dinka of the Nile have semidivine kings whose principal duty is making rain; even so, they have lesser medicine men to help out at times. Such a one takes a perforated gourd full of water and makes a miniature shower. Then he goes into his house "to keep out of the rain."

Shamans and witches: powerful people

Magic is impersonal. Supposedly anyone can use it. The magician, or medicine man, is simply an expert in the business. So he is different from a shaman, who has acquired powers of his own and is a special person.

I described the type specimen of that species, in his Siberian habitat. This is by no means the shaman's only haunt. Precisely the same man is found far away, among the Zulu. Here he has a different climate and a dark skin, but in detail after detail he is like his Siberian brother or sister: the shaman may be of either sex, he is a highstrung person, subject to visions and melancholia, going through a trying novitiate and getting a familiar spirit, as a method of cure for his neurosis, and ending as a professional who dances and divines through his insight. It is plain that shamanizing everywhere gives a neurotic personality a satisfactory means of adjustment, while at the same time it gives a simple society a useful person, in the form of a diviner and minor religious functionary.

So, ideally, there is a contrast: the shaman with his spirits, his second sight and his tensions; and the magician with his lore and training, otherwise as wholesome as a Boy Scout. But this is ideal. The Zulu recognize the difference, since they have both kinds. But other peoples may not. Shamans are apt to know a good deal of ordinary magic anyhow, and the culture may dictate that the magician should have some of the peculiar attributes and personal powers of the shaman. Thus it comes about that recognizable shamans, though less extreme than those of Siberia, South Africa and a few other spots, are found very widely in the primitive cultures of the world.

If shamans have special powers, they are not the only ones so blessed. Mana is another kind of power, which is apt to reside in a thing in Melanesia but in a man in Polynesia. But after shamans, the most striking manifestation of supernatural power is witches. Or rather the belief in witches, since witches, I hope you will agree, do not exist. The emergence of this notion, that living people supernaturally attack their innocent neighbors, have animal familiars, and fly through the night, perhaps in changed form, to a sabbath where together they eat the souls or bodies of victims—this emergence all over the world, and especially among Europeans, Africans, Melanesians and some American Indians, is truly astonishing.

Evidently it is a common human fantasy, a particularly natural projection onto the screen of the imagination of people's fear of the malice of others (educated perhaps by feelings of malice of their own). For that is the essence of witchcraft: the conviction that witches have the power to harm you or your soul through the simple desire to do so. This is quite different from black magic. And all the stories about witches boiling a potful of eye of newt, toe of frog, wool of bat, tongue of dog, unbaptized infant, and goodness knows what other delicatessen, are secondary inventions to the plain charge of witchcraft that got people hanged in England or Salem, or tried in Africa, as a close look shows.

Perhaps a witch has a special internal organ that causes him or her to be a witch. Or in some other way he may inherit his witchcraft, without wanting to. A *ndoki* in the Congo may show his nature only through a kind of restlessness, and the fact that his eyes cannot be closed after he is dead; or he may not be distinguishable from an ordinary man even to the most practiced eye. And still he is able to bring death with a glance or a touch. If anyone is so evil by nature as to want to become a ndoki, there is a way open: he searches out an old man who has "opened the heads of bats," and makes him presents to win his friendship. After several months of ingratiating himself he tells the old one:

"I want to become adult."

"But you are adult."

"Not *really* adult." (Heavy wink.)

"Who are your relatives?"

"Such and such a clan."

"Well," says the old man, "hand over so-and-so, and we will eat him together." The novice consents, and by a powerful magic the old man changes them both into ants or spiders, and they come by night to the victim, go into his nose and suck his heart's blood. They return and change back into human shape—alas! they look like anyone. So the people say, and while nobody has ever seen any of this happen, almost all deaths are caused by this witchcraft, they say, and so of course witches are rampant.

Witchcraft may seem like a strange exhibit to admit to a discussion of religion, especially if it does not even happen. But it does give people a symbolic explanation of some of their persistent ills. If the trouble can be blamed on a faraway witch, then at least it keeps blame from falling on friends and relatives. But it often creates as much trouble within a community as it might solve, or more, as was the case in Salem. Only the Zande of the Belgian Congo, who are deeply obsessed with witches, have worked out a system of legal etiquette which keeps suspicions of witchcraft from having explosive effects.

Gods, and a better world

Witchcraft, shamanism and magic are things we call superstition. They all perform their little services to society, in their rudimentary way. They occur everywhere, but shamans and magicians are better able to minister to the needs of small and simple groups like those of hunters, and it is there that you see them standing forth as important figures. Where then do we see what we customarily call religion: the worship of gods? We see it very widely, but more in the higher or larger societies of man, or those that are, at least, large communities of settled farmers.

For these more complicated societies have more complicated problems; and mediums and magic workers are not enough. A re-creating of society itself, in another world and in a more ideal form, to which the people can give their strong attention and allegiance, is one way of helping the society here on earth to govern itself by dramatizing its own philosophy. This would be too simple a way of explaining the gods, but it does put them in the light I have chosen to use: as elevated symbols of a supernatural kind by which people round out their conception of the universe, so as to deal with it.

By the same token there is a natural tendency—not a rule—for the more advanced societies to have the more fully developed cults. There are all kinds of gods and spirits, and some of them are nothing but devils, spectral vermin who hang about inflicting damage out of bad temper. They are thus something like witches as a cause (meaning an explanation) of ill fortune and sickness; they are not worshiped, but only propitiated and avoided. If the devils are roused to anger by human uncleanliness and carelessness, as are the jinns of North Africa, then they are actually on the side of the Lord, because they are an argument for proper behavior, but that is all; they simply exist to enforce a list of "don'ts." The more usual tribal religion has true gods.

You will not find a monotheism of our exalted kind, even if you find some belief in a supreme being, for such supreme deities or creators are recognized even by Bushmen, without any great worship given them. Instead, ideas in advanced cultures run in the direction of a group or family of gods, like those of the Greeks, the Norse or the Hindus. Such are the gods of the churches of Dahomey.

And in Polynesia, where native theology flourished, there was a whole lineage. The universe built itself from chaos, out of the principles of existence—light, breath, thought—and then appeared the first gods, the Sky Father and the Earth Mother. The children of these were the great gods of Polynesian religion: Tane, god of light, of maleness and of the forests; Tu, god of force, of the right side, of war; Rongo, god of peace, plenty, rain and fertile nature; and Tangaroa, usually ruler of the ocean. The Sky and the Earth had other divine children, but humanity was fathered by Tane, who fashioned his own wife, the Earth-formed maid (and that is why woman is earthly, dark, inferior to man). This is the pantheon of ancestor gods, known throughout Polynesia, to which junior ranks were added here and there as the gods' own descendants, the great human ancestors, became gods themselves in one or another of the island groups. The worship of these gods was carried out in temples, with long traditional chants and invocations addressed to them which, reciting past doings of the gods, renewed their mana to perform their special functions for the universe and man.

These gods, and their colleagues elsewhere, are very apt to have their particular aspects of nature and life to look after. They are departmental, something like the government of the United States, as though you prayed to the Secretary of Agriculture for the good of your crops or to the Secretary of Health, Education and Welfare if you wanted children. Such gods come to personify various human concerns, and so are symbols of them. But this is certainly not the only quality of gods and spirits. They represent permanence, power and freedom from the restrictions of mortal flesh, and so they symbolize these human aspirations too. That is what they share with human souls, which merge insensibly with spirits and gods anyhow.

Souls of man and nature

Now the belief in a soul is, like the incest tabu, universal in human culture: man has an inner self, the real he, which can even go abroad in dreams when he is yet alive. Above all, it does not disintegrate at death like the body, but escapes and survives, perhaps forever, perhaps awhile (but at least as long as the living people vividly remember the aliveness and personality of the one who has died). Thus, once more, do people find a symbolic way of rejecting the fear of the end of life, and indeed the impermanence of society itself.

Souls may become gods, then, and in ancestor worship that is just what they do. The Bakongo are those same Congo people who recognize Nzambi Mpungu, benign maker of the world, and who fear the attacks of a ndoki, a witch; they are great magic workers, partly through fetishes; and they have a major secret society with long and terrifying rites of death and resurrection for initiation. But their real religion is a humble and homely worship of their own dead, the people in the ancestor village, nearby but underground, who are the true owners of the land, animals and palm trees. Only the good, who lead blameless lives and do not die by violence, go to this village; others become malevolent wandering spirits. And these good dead are the ancestors who earnestly wish to see the living people continue and prosper, as long as the living also walk in the paths of righteousness. The living go to the cemetery to speak and make offerings to the dead, the Bakulu, to assure them that the people are doing their best, asking the ancestors not to forget them, but to send game and crops and keep sickness away.

The people, speaking through their own elders, are familiar but respectful, as they address the souls of men who a few years back were elders of the village themselves. If departmental gods are like the Executive Branch of our government, then the ancestors would be like the Senate, made up of older men who do no wrong and are carefully chosen to be wise, just, dignified, merciful, heedful of the true good of their supplicant younger brothers. Like this imaginary Senate, the Bakongo imagine another village, living by Bakongo culture, but purged of the bad side of life. To that perfect village they try to draw near themselves. This may idealize their point of view. But we see nonetheless a cult that, much more than shamanism or magic working, is a social conception.

Nor is a cult of this nature absent among the hunting peoples, though it is hardly common. Look back at the totemism of the Australians, who link their own souls and those of nature through totem ancestors. This shows us one more important thing about culture: it is really all one, and not carved neatly up into compartments of "economics," "society" and "religion," as we do to it when we look at it. It has these several natures, but they flow into one another over such boundaries as we make.

We think by the logic of Aristotle and the geometry of Euclid. But the Australians think by totemism. They themselves are totem souls incarnate. Their societies—their clans and marriage groups—are ordered and kept in mind by the totems they belong to. The past is the story of the totem ancestors, the present is the knowledge of the totem places of the country, and the future is the bringing forward of the past in the ceremonies that re-enact the totem time of the myths, ensuring that the world will go on in the totemic way it was made to go. This is no childish matter, and the natives are not children: the myths are extensive, and it might take a man years to learn a large body of them; the songs and ceremonies are intensely sacred; and the whole provides a philosophy to which the natives give much thought and from which they take much comfort. For the present is joined to the past, and man is joined to nature, and there is unity in life because of the totems.

16. Inventions and Changes

Culture is all one. And a given culture—that of any particular people—hangs together also. If the culture of the Australian natives gives them a unity in life, it is because their culture has a unity in itself.

I do not mean the unity flowing from the stage of the culture, or its background. Hunters all tend to be nomadic, to have few material possessions, to lack temples and priests, and to depend considerably on magic. Naturally they do: their way of life demands most of this, and they cannot support a full-time priest, free of the duties of getting his own food, as a farming people might. And pastoralists living in the Asiatic steppe, and depending on livestock, do not surprise you when you see that their houses are portable and that their culture has rather a milk-and-wool note to it.

Apart from such obvious influences, however, any culture, of whatever level or region, is apt to have a certain consistency and internal harmony. At any rate, no culture is ever a hodgepodge of possible things, as though we used wooden forks, copper knives and silver spoons, or as though the art of a given moment were strongly religious in painting but abstract in sculpture. Ruth Benedict put forth the view that a culture may almost have a personality of its own, meaning that its institutions and its sense of values will pick one possible kind of temperament, out of those which are present everywhere (violent and excitable, or reserved and careful, or aggressive and boastful); and by making this the admired, rewarded type of person, will thus have marked effect on the social behavior of the whole.

The people of Dobu, an island group within the kula ring in Melanesia, are, for example, especially mean, and suspicious to a degree almost paranoid, compared to most Melanesians. A Dobuan will behave in shyster fashion in the kula, receiving a prized necklace and then allowing more than one of his trading partners on the other side to understand that this necklace is coming to them when they visit. Thus he manages to get presents of several major bracelets from the opposite direction which he may not be able to requite in the expected time, but which add to his own prestige all the same. The Dobuan put trust only in their clan mates, which does not include their own husbands and wives. They cannot believe that one spouse will be faithful out of sight of the other, and marital discord is merrily fostered by their unusual rule of having newlyweds change yearly from living with her clan to his, so that one of them is always at home in family secrets and gossip, and the other is held at arm's length and spends the year thinking how to get even when the places are reversed. This disposition is reflected in one aspect of the culture after another, and fear of black magic is rife.

Such interpretations of culture have been pushed a step further, to suggestions with a Freudian basis that all the individuals of a society are molded (not merely persuaded by cultural example) toward one kind of personality or another. Here the cause of the ruling personality type is sought in childhood and infant experiences dictated by the culture, such as the severity with which children are housebroken, and other practices which make them feel secure or insecure in general. From this have emerged attempts to paint whole modern nations in a single color, giving us the secret of "the" Russian or "the" American with his alleged mother-fixation and father-rejection. Most students feel that this step is a little headlong.

But at the same time it would be wrong to throw out the baby with the bath water and fail to see the great and inescapable force of culture in showing the way for people to act. I do not mean, of course, the simple rules it makes for marriage or its other outright institutions; I mean the tone it sets. There is no question that our own culture endlessly suggests to us that we should all "succeed" and "get ahead" and admire the hard competitor. Now it seems certain that, as card-carrying Primates, we have a degree of natural competitiveness in us anyhow, yet not all human cultures require one to "succeed" in order to be content, but only require one to conform.

Furthermore, there is a degree of conflict in our cultural ideals. Our powerful philosophy of competition certainly acts to release a tremendous amount of human energy, and has put us where we are. At the same time we bridle it with another powerful philosophy, the ideal of meekness, restraint and turning of the other cheek, which is so honored that it is the essence of Christianity. Thus our culture has stresses and strains. No matter how hard we vie against one another, we must be all moderation and good will when we are face to face. (Automobiles have put us in a position to vie with other people without having to meet them face to face, and we have not yet worked out an etiquette to control things. One of the prominent automobile manufacturers can advertise that its latest is "Designed & Engineered to stay ahead of other cars," not merely speedy, comfortable or safe. Once behind the wheel, the hobnailed side of our culture finds a clear field. The baboon in us decides to have some fun, tears up the New Testament, and sets off down the highway, hogging the left-hand lane, to see how nearly he can miss an accident.)

In spite of such contradictions, our culture does argue the existence of important themes. Other cultures do the same, and usually have a greater harmony in their themes. Not only that, but different parts and institutions in a culture fit together and take on a common coloration. The lobola is one institution, itself formed from others. So is the kula, as Bronislaw Malinowski clearly reported: it is a complex integrated institution embodying social position, magic ritual, ordinary trade, and relations between islands, even though the natives themselves do not see it as a single whole, but only as various bits of known behavior affecting them as individuals. This is the kind of coherence toward which an entire culture trends, though achieving it only partially, and to a greater or less degree at different times in its history.

This brings us to the process, the question of how this may come about. Obviously, to fit its parts together, a culture must have some choice of parts—it must be able to select, among the possible ways of meeting a problem, the way that best goes with its other culture traits—and it must be able to modify any such part to fit the other parts. And this brings us in turn to the whole matter of how culture changes and progresses.

Now it should be realized that change and progress are not the same thing. Some change is mere change. Fashions shift, and clothes may get less comfortable rather than more so—look back at the wasp waist. Pottery styles, the archaeologists know, have changed constantly over long periods. We think very well of change and progress in America—in material things—but others do not share this love. Independence of thought and action is looked on with suspicion among the native Australians, who prefer to decide things jointly and to be guided always by the past. And there are other forces hostile to change in every culture, meaning mental and physical habit. People depend on their own culture, the one they grew up in, which showed them how to act and how to do things. Naturally they rely on this as *the* way things should be done, and are apt to be upset if they are forced to change.

But culture, remember, is the mental patterns of a whole society, not something that is found in a book or as the property of one individual. And this fact cuts both ways. One generation teaches the next, but there is many a slip 'twixt cup and lip, and the learning may not come out quite as the teaching intended. Culture could stay exactly the same only if everyone copied everyone else perfectly, and nobody ever forgot anything, got bored, got curious, or had a new idea. And that is impossible. Little novelties slip in, for no two people are just alike, and the novelties may be liked, tolerated, or simply not noticed. Thus accents and fashions continually creep in some direction or other. And, since human beings are really far from stupid, more important new ideas are bound to come along. Change and progress do take place. A new idea comes to a group in one of two ways: either they think it up themselves, or they borrow it from people who already have it. These two things are called invention and diffusion.

Invention, or something old, something new

When we think of invention, we think of Thomas A. Edison, or some other man whose face is on a stamp. We are apt to believe that we struggled along without some vital thing until such a genius gave it to us. But it will not detract from the inventor to say that culture itself should get more credit, because almost all inventions depend absolutely on what exists already. They are apt to become vital after they are invented, but they cannot arrive until the culture is ready for them. Quite apart from having the necessary knowledge, people must be able to receive and use them, or they will fail. On the other hand, if there is a place and a need for them along with the proper resources, they will almost invent themselves. This would not be easy to show for primitive cultures, although such a thing as the appearance of weaving with settled life is suggestive. But our own history illustrates the point well. We know Leonardo da Vinci sketched several flying machines but could go no further, lacking the necessary motive power; and doubtless flying could have been nothing but a stunt in his day anyhow, without the navigation or the commercial uses of today. Much of the humor in Mark Twain's *A Connecticut Yankee at King Arthur's Court* turns on this very idea.

On the other hand, it has often happened that two men have made the same invention at the same time, simply because it was in the air. Professor Alfred L. Kroeber[1] has written at length about the whole business of invention and culture, and assembled a striking list of simultaneous discoveries, including the telephone, the telescope, photography and the planet Neptune, in each case produced by two or even three men within a single year. The classic example is that of Gregor Mendel and his laws describing the non-blending nature of inheritance. His was no accidental find, or even a bathtub inspiration like Archimedes'. He knew the problem he wanted to study. He chose his plants for crossbreeding with care, and he kept a statistical account of his results that gave him his answer: it was the model of a scientific experiment, and he announced the result in 1865, publishing it a year later. Modern biology and agriculture are unthinkable without his findings (except for the unfathomable aberrations of Russian political genetics), and yet in that day his work, duly published, had no effect at all. In spite of the interest in Darwin, and of biological advances in general, the naturalists were somehow unready to use Mendel's find. Then, after he was forgotten, biology at last began to catch up with him, and in 1900 three men, working in different countries, all reported having rediscovered Mendel's laws for themselves. While experimenting, each had come across Mendel's old work and acknowledged him as the pioneer. And genetics, which was established in this way, has ever since moved steadily to the center of biology. "The stone which the builders rejected has become the chief cornerstone."

There are, then, the inventions for which the time is ripe, and the inventions for which the time is not ripe, to say nothing of the inventions for which the time will never be ripe, like the top hat out of which pops an umbrella at the press of a button. Good cases are known of native inventors producing the right thing at the right time, such as the now popular black-on-black (actually matte-on-

[1] *Anthropology*, p. 342. See also Ralph Linton, *The Study of Man* (New York: D. Appleton-Century Company, 1936).

glossy) pottery invented by Julian and Maria Martinez of San Ildefonso Pueblo, New Mexico. It is better to use examples from our own civilization simply because the complexity of the simultaneous inventions, and the distance between the inventors, dramatizes the importance of the cultural background. (The first person who says "telepathy" goes to the foot of the class.)

Inventions follow the bent of a culture, as all the foregoing implies. Any idea that did not have meaning in the existing state of affairs would be like a bird laying an egg in a nest that is not there. And people are apt to invent significant things by improving on what they are already doing, rather than by sitting down to plan how to get to the moon. Thus most inventions are minor. And a major invention may need a number of minor improving inventions before it is satisfactory. I have already shown how pottery actually called for a number of technical discoveries.

Finally, a minor invention may turn out to be a major one. Suppose—and it is entirely possible, since the gadget exists—that the original bow was a small thing really used for making music, by holding one end in the teeth like a jew's harp while the string was twanged. The first man who decided to make a weapon of it—not the first man who ever propelled a stick or a pebble with it, but the first who saw what this meant—was certainly one of the great men of the end of the Paleolithic.

Some forward steps can hardly be looked on as single "inventions" at all. Thus domestication of plants was probably a long, unconscious process and not an isolated discovery. And who invented the automobile? What does an automobile consist of? The motor? The coach part? Or the gasoline, or the rubber tires, or the smooth roads? All of these are necessary, as was found to their sorrow by those who tried to make automobiles a hundred and fifty years ago: they were forced to give up, put their automobiles on rails and call them railroads. And yet we now look on the automobile and on domestication as unitary things, and we understand that they are two of the greatest contributors to change that man has ever seen.

The appearance of material inventions can be traced, in history and even in archaeology: if the Martinez family had lived before the last century or so, the first signs of their pottery style in prehistoric sites would have been spotted as a new invention by archaeologists. But other kinds of invention are harder to study. Religions, we know, have sprung up and succeeded time and again, always providing they had some kind of fertile ground to grow on. And of course they tend to follow older, acceptable patterns. The ancient Near East and India especially have been kind to them, but we ourselves are surprisingly tolerant. The California kind of extreme oddity, worshiping Aphrodite or wearing lion skins, does not get far with us, but any cult that calls itself Christian may do well, even if it rolls on the floor and shouts. But socially and economically we are terrible old maids. Say "planner" about an engineer or a businessman, and you mean he is forward-looking; say it about a politician and you mean he is just plain visionary, and dangerous.

This tendency to dive under the bed at new economic and social proposals, or to try to exorcise them with magical phrases like "creeping socialism," may be especially strong in our culture, recognizing the proven worth of our present institutions. And yet it is really not in the least odd, because social institutions are nowhere "invented" like material things. Social changes take place largely without conscious direction, by an unrealized process of joint consent. Our institutions made our laws and our Constitution, more than the other way round. There is no sign that social forms arise by any other methods among primitive peoples. Of course the people may say that the gods, or the totem ancestors, ordered things to be the way they are: that is one of the duties of religion.

If the workings of inventions in the social side of life remain obscure, it is worth noticing that we ourselves have gone to the other extreme in the scientific and material side. We have taken invention into our own hands and away from chance as far as possible, for the first time in history. The universities and the great industrial laboratories have concentrated the men and the means for invention and discovery; and in our own lifetime the day of the lonely genius in his garret workshop, or even of the Fords and the Edisons, seems to have gone for good. There will be men as great as those of before, but they will not be lonely. Edison invented the electric light, but color television was invented several ways, by whole teams, to order. And what about the atomic bomb? We have, also recently, seen the same kind of change in diffusion. We have made a business out of something that once took care of itself, and we call it advertising.

Diffusion, or something borrowed

By the nature of things, there is less honor for people who diffuse ideas than for those who invent them, for diffusion is typically a more social process. But it would not do to give too little notice to this second main source of culture growth. Comparing it with invention would be like the futile comparison of heredity and environment, but its importance is enormous. An invention would be of little use if it were not spread around, and much of its significance depends on the degree of its diffusion. We may never know whether the Levalloisian flake-making technique was invented in the Lower Paleolithic more than once, but we do know it covered a great part of the Old World. We are pretty sure that domestication of grains took place in the Near East, and we have seen the spread of this. And we need only reflect that our own religion, writing and mathematics all came from the Near East in order to understand the meaning of diffusion to our present civilization.

Theoretically, something invented once may at last, by diffusion, become available to the whole world. Actually, this very question is one of the constant problems in studying unwritten history. Two things that are much alike are found thousands of miles apart in different cultures. Is it diffusion? The importance of trying to decide whether there was some actual contact or trade between the peoples involved, or whether each developed the same thing for themselves, is obvious. But so is the importance of being reasonable about it. There have been far too many authors who have got the diffusion bee in their bonnets, been carried away by a few likenesses, interpreted all other facts in the light of their own conclusions, and decided that there was not only diffusion but migration. Such imaginings have transported American Indians to Polynesia, Polynesians to America, Harappas to Easter Island, Egyptians to Asia to the Pacific to the Ohio Valley, and people from the lost Atlantis to every place that ever showed a sign of civilization at all.

The anthropologists have usually been so busy fending off the most unrestrained of these romancings that they have had difficulty in taking a serene attitude toward the problem themselves, and have usually been most suspicious about possible long-range diffusions. Certainly the only thing to do is to judge each instance on its own merits, and not in support of some conviction that the American Indians are the Ten Lost Tribes of Israel. It is an interesting fact that the hot-eyed authors who trace connections between the ends of the earth are usually writing about moldering temples and legends of White Gods, rather than about humbler, more matter-of-fact and sounder evidence from the daily life of people.

Take blowguns. A blowgun is a fine weapon for hunting in the forest where the air is still. You must have a strong poison, for your dart is small. But it can be shot accurately (disturbing game as little as possible) and with a good deal of force, if the gun itself is long enough and can be kept from bending too much. Blowguns are very popular in Southeast Asia, among the Semang, the Sakai and the Malays of the Malay Peninsula, and in various parts of Indonesia, especially Borneo (although Sherlock Holmes made a wrong deduction in thinking they are used in the Andaman Islands). And they are also popular in the forests of South America. In both places they are as long as ten feet, and occur as simple hollow lengths of bamboo, or as inner tubes strengthened against bending by an outer tube, or as a wooden pipe made from two halves that have been split, grooved and put together again. They shoot light darts, fitted to the tube with a wadding of cotton or pith, and tipped with poison (especially ipoh sap in Asia, and curare in South America, both strychnines). And they are shot the same way, holding them close to the mouth, and shooting on the drop.

Such things are found nowhere else. Is this not a strong argument that some enterprising Borneans, let us say, loaded up a canoe and set out across the Pacific to America? Or, if you prefer, some of the Amazonian Indians went in the other direction? But is this really likely? Borneans are quite unequipped to cross the whole Pacific. Blowguns would have had to move east by stages, and to appear in Polynesia, if they were useful enough to be taken along at all. But it is too windy for the darts in Polynesia, and there is no poison, and nothing to shoot. Suppose the gun nevertheless arrives in South America, on the west coast. Here and in the highlands it is too windy, and there is no poison, and nothing that cannot be shot better with bows. So, unless you can imagine some people like the Borneans, simple in culture (those of higher level do not use blowguns), getting to the Amazon Basin in one generation, before they could have forgotten just how blowguns are made and used, then you can only suppose people had the wit to invent them separately in the two parts of the world.

But how does that explain the many likenesses in making and use? The answer is that these likenesses are natural features of a blowgun, and the natural best ways to use it. And poison happens to be available in both places. In fact the use of a blowpipe has spread well outward from both its centers (as far as the Iroquois in America) but, although it can kill a tiger in Malaya, it turns into a toy beanshooter or an unimportant dart shooter of little effect when it is away from poisons and forests.

The case of the blowgun has long been argued, but no conclusion seems plausible except two independent inventions. And if the blowgun traveled across the Pacific Ocean why did it not travel along the Indian Ocean to the Congo forest?

On the other hand, such things as tobacco or the alphabet are known to have spread from one source: we have their history, and their distribution is what you might expect. And therefore when a group of similarities is found between the Paleo-Siberians and some of the northwestern Indians (just across the Bering Sea from one another), including such things as a series of myths in which the Raven is a major figure, the argument for diffusion is irresistible.

But most of the puzzles are not so clear-cut. So diffusion suggests certain rules. Obviously, the closer two tribes having the same thing, the more likely they got it from the same place, or one from the other. Obviously, the more things they have in common, the more likely it is that they have had contact through diffusion. But the more a group of details exist together because they are tied together by necessity (the blowgun being no good without poison, wadding for the dart, etc.), the less the argument for diffusion; contrariwise, the less natural connection among the different details of a thing (like the events in a story or designs in art), the less the chance of the whole having been invented separately twice.

In Rudyard Kipling's "Namgay Doola," when the teller of the tale finds the obstreperous villager in the Himalayas, whose hair is red and who sings, as a hymn his father taught him, a chant that is almost the same in words and music as "The Wearing of the Green," his suspicions as to where that father must have come from are overwhelming. He hardly needs to see the brass crucifix and the ancient regimental badge as well. But in the hidden history of human contact and migration, one cannot be too careful.

One must also consider the nature of the culture traits under consideration. Material things diffuse easily enough where contact is possible, but with limits: blowguns do not travel in the plains, and heavy fur clothing does not migrate to the tropics. Religious notions spread with ease, and stories and myths, which are light luggage, with the greatest facility. Traits of social organization, on the other hand, seem to be the poorest travelers of all.

Cultures pick and choose

Diffusion and history are interesting, but let us get back to diffusion and culture generally. Diffusion is the faster way of building cultures, because if three men each make an invention and all exchange, each has got two of the new ideas by diffusion and one by invention. And, theoretically, one invention could travel everywhere. But diffusion is not like sound waves, going in all directions at the same speed. It is really a complicated business: the mechanical side of it, which I have just been considering, is of less consequence than the social and cultural sides.

Acceptability of something new is an important factor, in diffusion as in invention. And an important factor in this, in turn, may be the status of the people who have the new thing, as against those who are being exposed to it.

Paris has a well-deserved reputation in fashion and, as a result, people are automatically receptive to what Paris has to say every year: that is the direction from which they expect diffusion to come. The primitive world has the same feelings: in northern New Guinea the Arapesh-speaking people who live in the mountains have come to consider themselves very much as hillbillies compared to their tribesmen on the coast, who are in the stream of traffic, which is also the stream of diffusion. The mountain people go down to the coast to learn new, complicated costume dances for which they humbly pay the coastal slickers a pretty penny, and then bring them proudly back to the mountains. To make up a dance themselves and try to sell it on the shore would never enter their minds. Testimonial advertising is hardly different: a movie star whose taste buds are about the same as yours nevertheless carries a lot more weight when he states, on the back of a magazine, how much better is the taste of the cigarette that bought his testimonial.

But acceptability in the main rests with the accepting

culture. For example, the Ghost Dance of 1890, which started up among the Paiute in Nevada, was carried by Indian missionaries to a great number of different tribes all over the West. In northern California, where the Ghost Dance of 1870 had been popular, it was therefore not a new thing in 1890, and had no success. It was taken to the Hopi in Arizona, but to their sedate culture, tuned to a complicated, priestly, highly ritualistic religion, this new cult, rather vehement and shamanistic, seemed like rubbish and was without effect. The Sioux of the Plains, however, were feeling the doom of their free buffalo-hunting life, and the aftermath of the Custer affair, as well as disease and poverty on the new reservations. The Ghost Dance, promising return of the dead Indians and the disappearance of the Whites, and sharing with traditional Sioux religion a strongly emotional quality, was accepted feverishly; and this was a factor in the disturbance that brought about the death of Sitting Bull and the Battle of Wounded Knee. Thus the diffusion of the Ghost Dance was rapid, all in about a year, affecting or skipping large areas, and it struck its greatest spark far from its point of origin.

We are now back where we started, at the internal harmony of a culture. Invention, but particularly diffusion, provides the culture with new ideas to choose from, and it will choose those that do not violate the general nature of the culture itself, and will reject those that might. By picking and choosing it has the chance to maintain its integrity. Furthermore, a trait that is handed over by one people to another (in any of a dozen ways, war included) may even look different to the giver and the taker, because of their backgrounds. A harpoon is a harpoon, let us say, but a five-gallon gasoline can may also make a good raft float to people who have no gasoline. This would be particularly true of religious ideas, which would be nearly impossible to convey in their exact meaning between different people, so that even Christianity has undergone some strange modifications among its wilder converts. And when a new idea has made its way in, then it is almost certain to be squeezed into a different shape, as much as is needed to suit it to all the old ideas already present. Again, it is like Paris fashions: what finally appears on the streets of Peoria is not what was first unveiled by St. Laurent, but only the degree of it that seems just right for the streets of Peoria. And the original Bikini bathing suit is an example of something that was not acceptable on this side of the water at all, except in newspaper pictures.

Integration, and what happened to the Tanala

So a diffused idea, in so far as it is accepted in the first place, must be integrated with the accepting culture so as to be consistent with it. But this is only the second-best proof of the consistency of culture. For the integration of the culture itself is such that a new trait, in finding its place, may in turn send waves of change throughout the culture, as the existing traits in turn become adjusted to the new one. What happens will depend on the importance of the new trait, of course. A fine illustration of this has been given by Ralph Linton.[2]

The scene is Madagascar, the island neighbor of Africa, which has nevertheless been strongly affected by Indonesia, all the way across the Indian Ocean. The tribe is the Tanala, studied at firsthand by Dr. Linton himself, who was able to piece together some interesting happenings of the last two centuries. This tribe was living by a simple pattern I have already described for Indonesia: isolated villages growing dry rice by slash-and-burn methods, and moving approximately once a generation when they had used up the nearby jungle soil. Like the simpler Indonesians, the Tanala knew their tribal affiliation, but there was no tribal organization, and even the village head man was only a sort of moderator, with the elders deciding affairs.

So rustic was this culture that there existed neither slavery nor the social classes visible in Southeast Asia, nor yet the differences in wealth and property that go with social class. On the contrary, they were particularly democratic

[2] The Study of Man.

and simple: they had ideas of private property but not as applied to land. For on establishing a new site, the village elders simply parceled out jungle to the several joint families making up the village, each of which thus ran its own farm. If one family turned out to have poor land, the elders would adjust things the next year, so ordinarily all joint families were equal in resources.

Along came one new trait: wet rice. This must grow in damp ground, but it yields better than dry rice, and through more of the year. But there would be only a little valley bottom in the plot of each joint family, not enough to keep all its members busy, so the typical joint family simply detailed one household to see to the wet rice. Shortly there arrived the idea of terracing, the general Eastern practice, to increase and maintain the plots of wet rice. So the wet-rice households built terraces and repaired them. Insensibly this tended to detach these particular households from the joint families to which they belonged and with which they had always worked co-operatively. Thus, when the dry land gave out, the main body of the joint family would say, "Let's move," and the household that had gone to such trouble over the terraces would say, "Thanks, we'll stay." For the terraces and the wet rice would go on yielding indefinitely.

So when the village moved, following custom, it was split in two. Not only that, but it did not simply leave some of its joint families behind and take others, which would merely have resulted in two independent daughter villages, each like the mother. Instead, the joint families themselves—the basic units—split apart, some households going to a new village and some remaining.

What now of village isolation? Households thus began to have important close relatives in other villages, with whom to gather for ancestor worship; and the marriage pattern also, especially with some preference for cross-cousin mating, brought marriages between villages that had once been endogamous. Villages became permanent, not transitory, and instead of a simple stockade they began to have a kind of heavy fortification copied from another tribe. This changed the war pattern from general attacks for cattle and women to seizing of stragglers for slaves. Slavery came in; wet rice would support it as dry rice had not. So did social classes; for terraced land, the end of so much labor, became private property, not something to be called in and redistributed by the elders, and land thus became wealth, to work with slaves. The joint family was no longer the main unit; clans, also present before, grew in importance. Finally the head of a leading clan declared himself king, now ruler of most of a recognized tribe, of socially related, strong villages. King, classes, wealth, slavery, tribe, village, and social organization all came in or changed in nature, after wet rice knocked at the door and was welcomed.

This chain of cause and effect is not at all unfamiliar to students of our own society. The automobile alone, for example, has not yet stopped doing to us whatever it is that it is doing, and it has done a great deal. It is just that the Tanala, a small society in a single place, will let us see much better the whole history of such a process; we can, so to speak, take it into the laboratory and study it. It shows admirably the integrity and the fluidity of a culture in the way it responds to change, so that the life and nature of the culture maintain themselves. This only begins to be strongly evident among the larger societies of a Neolithic level, for among hunters there was obviously little new and little change.

Finally, it is because a culture hangs together that it sometimes falls apart. That is the key to what Europeans have done to native peoples. With muskets and money they have forced on other cultures things that these cultures could neither reject nor assimilate, and so have destroyed the integrity of such a culture and the self-reliance of the people. With the best will in the world, the Europeans have knocked over the idols that were the carefully fashioned props of those societies, and have tried to substitute Christianity, the prop of ours. Without the coherence of their old way of life, such people have often lost direction and become dependent, giving a totally false impression of lazy and shiftless savages. It is nobody's fault and everybody's misfortune.

THE NEW WORLD

17. The Oldest Americans

One time, while the late Ice Age hunters of France waited for big game by the caves in the Vézère Valley, a similar band of hunters was moving eastward in the far corner of Siberia. They too were looking for game, and in the search or in the chase they continued to the east across a low-lying plain. They did not know that this plain would be covered by the Bering Sea, much later, when the glaciers melted. They did not know they were entering a whole new world, splendid with game animals: mastodons, mammoths, horses, camels, long-horned bison, musk-oxen and such oddities as the giant sloth, to say nothing of elk, moose, caribou and deer. They did not know they were the first Americans.

They could not have felt particularly prosperous. They fought the cold, while the ice of the Fourth Glaciation covered much of Asia and North America (though not all of the Bering Strait region or the coast of Alaska), leaving them only certain passages by which they could move into the open continent below. They were doubtless one isolated horde out of the scattered hunters of the Far East, and belonged to the Mongoloid branch that had not been remodeled in face forms, either because they came over too early or because the unknown area where this remodeling took place was not adjacent to America. But they were the first of a series of such parties, no doubt differing in detail but alike in general culture, which wandered sporadically into America for a good many thousand years, until the water at last rose and Bering Strait could no longer be crossed by accident. They cut themselves off from the Old World and populated the New. And that is a favor they have done to the study of human history. For they went to work and duplicated, in the Americas, the same general steps of culture advance as were being gone through in the Old World.

The new Americans would probably have gone along the arctic shore of Alaska at first, and then found their way south between the glaciated mountains of the west and the great Laurentide ice sheet of eastern Canada. Gradually they occupied all of the hemisphere. It was no constant trek: hunters are nomadic, to be sure, but they move around in the land they know and to which their style of hunting is suited, and only slowly do they venture into new kinds of country calling for any change in their way of life or in the food they rely on. And this itself argues great antiquity for the first Indian immigrants. For some of the hunters had already reached the bottom end of South America, and were eating horses, sloths and guanacos, in the year 6689 B.C. (plus or minus about four hundred and fifty years). This is the estimated date determined by radiocarbon from the very meat bones they left, in a fireplace in the Palli Aike cave. And these are not the earliest remains in that cave.

Even before this, one day about 10,000 B.C., an Indian was hunting mammoths around the swampy edge of the lake that then filled much of the Valley of Mexico. (It was the end-glacial parent of the lake where the Aztecs lived, and of which only a remnant now exists.) This Indian somehow became mired, or drowned, and fell on his face, and was evidently partly eaten by vultures. Here at Tepexpan, northeast of Mexico City, his skeleton was found still lying on its face, under the now-dusty bed of the lake's edge, and in the same late glacial layer as two nearby mammoths, which had met a similar fate. It has been suggested as possible that the human skeleton might have been artificially intruded into this layer by burial (though there were no signs of it), but any doubts that men and mammoths were here at the same time have been

FIG. 28. *Some of the ancient sites and cultures of man in America.*

dispelled by finding still other mammoths at nearby places, obviously butchered by man and with stone knives and points lying among the bones.

Other probably Pleistocene skeletons and skulls have come to light, in the gravels of a glacial lake in Minnesota, in a layer of volcanic ash containing Pleistocene animals in Ecuador, and a few other places. The best of all cases is a shattered skull from Midland, Texas, which quite certainly came to rest, in the sands of a now dried-up lake, before the time of the Folsom hunters, and probably between 12,000 and 18,000 B.C. What do all these people look like? They look like Indians, and one may only remark that most of them were of one general type, with long heads, not large brains, slightly projecting teeth and no particularly strong racial stamp; perhaps a little less Mongoloid than most Indians of today.

When did the first comers arrive? Before the end of the Ice Age, that is certain. By the latest evidence, they had arrived before 26,000 B.C. (at Tule Springs, Nevada, they were killing and cooking the native American camel). Weaker testimony of man goes back before 35,000 B.C. The time of first arrival thus remains vague and is likely to remain so for some time. During recent decades, it has come about that dates that were previously dubious have been buttressed by more solid evidence and so the time when the Indians were actually known to have been in America has been constantly pushed back and it may go further. At the moment, it is clear that the early Upper Paleolithic men of Europe had American contemporaries.

From all appearances, the stone culture of these first comers was rather simple: not as primitive as in the Old World Lower Paleolithic, but not developed like the European Upper Paleolithic or later American work.[1] It contained crude scrapers and other vaguely shaped tools, with dependence on percussion striking. The whole thing is rather characterless, and was apparently the property of unspecialized hunters and gatherers.

There is a good possibility that, in areas like Nevada, such a simple way of life came down unchanged to the present. But in most of North America, the Indians developed a highly successful dependence on big game animals of the late Ice Age, with particular attention to the mammoth and the large, extinct bison, *Bison antiquus*. Their important weapon was a javelin, tipped with a well-made point whose usual hallmark was a channel running up each side made by a long flake struck off at the base. Styles of these points changed during the long period of

[1] See Gordon R. Willey, "New World Prehistory," Smithsonian Report for 1960, pp. 551–575, for a review of American culture development.

specialized big game hunting: Sandia about 15,000 B.C., Clovis from perhaps 15,000 B.C. to 9000 B.C. and Folsom from 9000 B.C. to 7000 B.C. as the main stages, and several local styles following as the large animals petered out.

FIG. 29. *Left, a "Clovis fluted" point. Right, a Folsom point.*

The "Mesolithic" in America

The ice was receding now, and the climate which had supported the great game animals was undergoing various changes in different places. Many of the animals themselves were disappearing, perhaps because of these changes, but certainly hustled into extinction by the Indians themselves as well. (Both the ice and the animals lingered longer in North America than in Europe.) And it seems clear that the effect on the hunting cultures was like that in Mesolithic Europe: localization. Game became rarer and smaller, and the Indians must have studied the resources of their different regions attentively, learning what there was to be gathered, how to find it, how to prepare it for eating.

There is evidence for this sort of thing in the still-spotty record: the Cochise Indians of southern Arizona and New Mexico had a continuous culture of several thousand years which evidently depended strongly on the gathering of vegetables and seeds, which they ground on stone slabs. This is the process that must have produced a great many local and special cultures of hunters and gatherers all over the Americas, such as that of our own recent Great Basin Indians, between the Rockies and the Sierras, who made staple foods of piñon seeds, grass seeds and grasshoppers, or that of the people of Tierra del Fuego which I have already mentioned, where the Ona and the Yahgan had two quite different hunting systems (shore and shellfish versus upland hunting) in the same general area. The Yahgan probably invented canoes independently. Elsewhere, also, all kinds of little discoveries and adaptations were made. So there is indeed a suggestion of the Mesolithic of Europe, and "Mesolithic" is what we might best call these later American hunters.

There may have been various contacts in this time with the peoples of Asia, almost certainly in the case of pottery. The first inhabitants of America walked into their new domain dry-shod, of course, and this kind of immigration continued for an unknown length of time. But by the end of the Pleistocene the rising waters of the Bering Sea covered the old bridge. This does not mean that nobody ever crossed again, but only that boats were now necessary, and that the people crossing would probably be skilled boatmen. And this in turn suggests that the pattern changed from migration to contact: that landsmen coming over in the course of the hunt, and marching off into the interior, gave place to people accustomed to shore and water, crossing back and forth but not going into interior America for the very reason that they were shore people by culture. The last people, the Eskimos, demonstrate this well, occupying the straits and hugging the arctic shore. From such considerations it seems likely that the bulk of the American population descends from the early comers. Another fact argues the same thing: the absence of tribes, other than the Eskimos, who uniformly show the strongly Mongoloid racial form of the peoples of present-day Siberia.

Aside from any Asiatic contacts and introductions, the important thing was local culture development. The Americas had entered into a long period, following the Pleistocene, of enforced local specialization. Out of this, on the one hand, there eventually rose the American Neolithic. On the other, there developed some highly successful Mesolithic patterns. Let us consider three, all of which were apparently touched in one way or another by Asiatic influences. They are Pacific, Arctic and Woodland, and they are very different.

The fortunate gatherers of the west coast

The people of the Pacific shore, to begin with, take the rule about hunter-gatherers being nomadic and break it into little pieces. Even farmers using slash-and-burn agriculture usually must move their villages periodically, but along the Pacific the sources of food were so dependable that the people could build villages of Neolithic size and stay in the same place continuously. And this, naturally, allowed a Neolithic kind of social organization.

In California a main staple was the acorn. Since nuts flourish in California this food was plentiful and easily kept, only requiring its meat ground and soaked to take the tannic acid out in order to be made into bread. Salmon, rabbits and deer were other main foods. So satisfactory were their natural foods that the Californians practiced no agriculture, though it must have been available to them by diffusion, and they actually did grow some tobacco. They may have been almost completely resistant to pottery for a similar reason: they were the world's best basketeers, producing finely woven baskets which would hold water, fancy baskets with feathers and beading worked in, and even making some examples the size of a pea, just to show what they could do. The women wore basketry skullcaps for hats, but otherwise dress was informal, of skin; and

weaving, along with other arts (except for some remarkably fine chipped obsidian blades), was lacking. They used
the sinew-backed bow in hunting, and made ceremonial
earth lodges partly underground; this kind of house is
very ancient, and both things run over into Siberia. They
had shamans, brothers to those in Siberia. Religion otherwise consisted largely of a long series of dramas and dances
enacting their mythology. These and games kept the people
busy during the winter after the nut harvest, and strengthened social contacts, in the same way as feasts or the kula
in Melanesia.

North of California, up the Northwest coast to Alaska,
there is a complicated shore of inlets, sounds and islands
bearing a growth of magnificent timber, especially cedar
and spruce. From the Salishes in the south through such
people as the Kwakiutl and the Haida, to the Tlingit in
the north, the people have a striking culture and a vigorous
art, both notable for their work in wood. They live in
villages along the shore in large gabled houses of plank-
ing, with totem poles either forming a corner post or standing out in front. They use dugout canoes which, for war,
may hold up to fifty paddlers.

Nowadays they work in canneries, but they used to
support themselves on the bounty of the sea, especially on
salmon, but also on halibut, herring and cod, all taken in
a variety of ways, and on clams and oysters. Drying and
smoking allowed them to stock these foods for the whole
year, the key to a settled existence. Seals, porpoises and
whales were also killed; berries and roots were the main
land foods; oil was made by putting quantities of eulachon,
a small fish, into an old canoe in which water was boiled
with hot stones.

The culture has its oddities, compared to other American Indian cultures. It has the Raven myths, composite
bows, and body armor made of rods, things also found
among the Paleo-Siberians. It lacks (or nearly) a list of
things common in the rest of America, such as moccasins,
chipped stonework or shields (as well as agriculture except
for tobacco, and pottery which is here replaced by

basketry, as in California, and by excellent wooden containers). It has its own peculiarities, including woven hats with spindle tops, and cloth made from shredded cedar bark. This all suggests an isolated development, even more than in California, in this naturally rich region, and also points to some recent contact with the Old World, conceivably through the Aleutian Islands. At the same time, excavation has not shown the culture to be a very old one.

The Northwest coast people were somewhat peculiar in their social life as well. We find a strong class system and an almost feudal organization, with titled families who showed their "crests" on totem poles ("totem" is not a good name for them). The heads of such families were nobles, rather than chiefs, and headed their own families as well as attendant families of commoners and slaves. And the workings of this social system took place through the famous potlatch (particularly in the center of the area), which should put you in mind of the far Pacific. A potlatch is a ceremonial gift-giving, held to celebrate any event of social importance (among the socially important). Like the taking of a head in Southeast Asia, a potlatch served to recognize and validate such an event, and not leave it, let us say, in the status of a common-law marriage.

A man held a feast and gave away blankets at the birth of a child, at the naming of a child, on assuming a title, on taking a new name, or at a funeral. A title would lapse if no potlatch were held for it. And the gift had a sting, because in many cases it had to be returned with interest. Boys when still young might get a loan of blankets at a low rate of interest (say a hundred percent) and would be allowed to lend them out for a short term at a higher rate, and thus start building capital. Wives were "bought" by a potlatch for the father-in-law, who repaid the payment; to keep your wife you had to keep your father-in-law in your debt. No books were needed, for the potlatch, like the kula, was the great interest in people's lives, and everyone was on the watch to see that the accounts were settled.

The climax of the whole system was potlatching between nobles. If, in the Melanesian kula, giving gave glamor, it was done with good will, in friendship between two men. In the potlatch a rich noble backed by his retainers gave to a rival in the hope that his rival could not meet the challenge and would go down in dreaded disgrace. The feasts were nothing less than battles with gifts, ending in a gulf between pride and shame such as we can scarcely imagine. Piles of blankets were given, and furs. Much more valuable were coppers, T-shaped and decorated slabs of the beaten raw metal, which had names and great traditional value, like the kula necklaces and armlets.

These might be given as gifts; or they might be disdainfully destroyed or cast into the water before the eyes of the rival noble, to see how he would respond. He might answer by burning a canoe or killing slaves, or with coppers of his own. If the response again were the burning of more canoes, and of oil, and even of the house itself, what matter? The man under attack and his group should try not to be impressed with this small blaze, even as it singed their robes. Such an affray went down in song and tale, to the everlasting glory of the winner, while the loser might be forced into suicide.

So here is a society without domesticated food but having nonetheless a class structure as well as a clan structure, and with a complex general institution in the potlatch that was something like the lobola or the kula, putting family effort and wealth to the service of the prestige of the family through its head. In religion the shaman was the dominant figure, but secret societies were important, presided over by totemlike animal spirits, with a novice being taken in after a period of fasting in solitude in the forest, during which he supposedly visited the spirit home. A dramatic dance was held to lure him back, with masked figures to represent his kind of animal spirit, something that may also be represented on totem poles as well as the crests of the nobility. It was in the masks for these ceremonies that the Northwest coast Indians best developed the force and boldness of their art.

The admirable Eskimos

The Eskimos make a second great "Mesolithic" hunting culture. Speaking a single language, they reach all the way from the south coast of Alaska around the American Arctic to Greenland and Labrador. Small groups of them live on the Siberian shore as well and so, with the near-Eskimo Aleuts of the Aleutian chain, they now occupy the region through which the Indians came from Asia, and have occupied it for some time. They are not settled like the Pacific coast Indians; they are strictly hunters and must move seasonally, sometimes in very small groups. There have been, it is true, a few heavily settled places like the ancient town of Ipiutak near Point Hope, Alaska, where the game was plentiful; here there were six hundred houses.

They may hunt caribou in the summer, and deer and ducks and geese, while fox, wolf and polar bear are always present. But their true dependence is on the mammals of the sea: whale, walrus and above all seal. And the true stamp of their culture is that it lets them survive through the winter. Mesolithic though it is, it stands head and shoulders above that of any other hunter-gatherers in the ingenuity and intelligence it exhibits and in the way it has adapted man to a most forbidding environment through a wealth of inventions. The Eskimos have faced, in addition to all the cold, the handicap of having almost no wood to use except driftwood.

They live, in different places, in earth-covered houses of stone or whalebone, or wood where possible, and use tents in summer. And no school child breathes who does not know about the igloo, the snow house of the central Arctic. This is really a better shelter than it might seem to be. The entrance is protected by a special corridor to keep the wind out, and the house itself may be lined with skin, hung from thongs through the snow wall, so that it is practically a tent within a shell, and well insulated. The air within may be close but not very cold. They have no fires which might melt the whole thing down, for they have no wood anyhow, and they get what they need for light, warmth and cooking by burning oil with a moss wick in a soapstone dish. One hazard is the humidity: if you wear your outdoor clothes indoors they are apt to take up so much moisture from the humid air as to freeze stiff when you go out again.

Clothes are of skin and fur, of course, and for cold weather the Eskimos wear two suits, the inside one with the fur side inside and the outside one with the fur side outside. There is nothing primitive about these garments. The Eskimos are tailors and fitters extraordinary, and decorate their clothes with inset panels of furs of varying colors. They can also sew a watertight seam, and do so in making seal-gut waterproofs, like a seaman's oilskins, for rain and for protection against shipping water in a kayak. For the usual caribou or sealskin outfit they wear long boots, and the parka (a Paleolithic inheritance?) with a hood, detachable or not, for covering the head or carrying the baby, as you wish. Only the face goes without good protection, and even here they use wooden slit goggles against snow blindness.

They hunt with bows and spear throwers, and catch birds with a thrown bola (see Chapter 6). But their vital weapon is their harpoon, which is made of several parts. The main shaft is of precious driftwood, with a joint and then a foreshaft of bone; and on the end of this is the harpoon head itself. Thongs hold the whole thing rigid until it is thrust into an animal. Then the joint in the shaft loosens, which keeps the wooden shaft from breaking as the animal shakes it, and also frees the long rawhide line which is attached to the harpoon head. The point itself thus comes off: it has a barb on one side only, so that it turns crosswise in the flesh of the prey when the line is taut, and there is the animal securely hooked.

In winter the hunter goes out on the ice, searching with his dog for the holes in the ice (usually covered with a blanket of snow) through which a seal must come every so often to breathe. If he finds one, he knows a seal must be near beneath the ice, for the hole would soon freeze if the seal did not constantly use it. All he need do is wait, harpoon the poor seal, and pull it in when it has tired itself out trying to swim free. In summer the harpooning of seal and walrus has to be done from a kayak. After being harpooned, the prey is prevented from escaping, and quickly exhausted, by floats of inflated sealskins and by tambourine-like drags, attached to the harpoon line.

The kayak itself is a beautiful piece of construction, with a light frame of wood and bone, covered with a watertight skin except for a hole the size of the paddler's waist, so that an Eskimo can overturn and right himself in the water with his paddle without filling up. This is no stunt; it is simple lifesaving practice and he must be able to do it. The Eskimo sledge, the dog harness and tackle, and the driving of dogs are all further examples of Eskimo skill and ingenuity, especially in making out with little choice of material. Add to this their traps, some of which are no less than fiendish in their simplicity. Let us note only the wolf coil, a strip of whalebone sharpened at both ends, coiled up and implanted in a piece of meat, which is allowed to freeze, and then left out. The greedy wolf comes by and swallows it down without chewing and —serve him right—the meat softens, the whalebone uncoils and he is stabbed to death from within.

The Eskimos have their troubles, and their shamans, but they are impressively self-reliant and adjusted. Hunters though they may be, they certainly could not carry their possessions on their heads like the Bushmen, and in fact have advanced about as far in culture as would be possible in their environment. The only progressive invention they might make now would be to go south, and their very way of life would make them reject the idea.

Eskimo origins are still unknown. However, the Eskimos are not really old in America. The culture is traceable back in time, in its same general form though with changes in emphasis, for about two thousand years, to the beginning of the Christian Era, but no more. And in its early days it already had an art style, which seems to reflect classical

Chinese influence, and to demand trade iron from China for the cutting of ivory (recent Eskimos have used native copper and meteoric iron, both worked raw). Alone among the Americans, the facial type of the Eskimos belongs with the highly modified, flat-faced Mongoloid peoples of Siberia, and this argues powerfully that the Eskimos are a recent immigration, quite distinct from those that had come before, even though they may have culturally influenced some of the Indians, particularly on the Northwest coast.

Now some of the features of Eskimo culture also occur along the north shore of Siberia, and the present best explanation of the whole Eskimo phenomenon is that it crystallized, as a successful shore culture, from late Mesolithic elements on the arctic coast of eastern Asia, where it was isolated from the advancing cultures of Central Asia and the Far East; and that it blossomed in the Bering Sea region and flourished in America.

The woodlands, heart of North American culture

So no great antiquity can be assigned to the life recently lived by the Eskimos or by the Indians of the Pacific Northwest. The Californian pattern, however, may be very old; ancient remains are abundant, probably of a seed-gathering culture like the Cochise of the Southwest. Whatever the history of these western and northern fringes of the continent, a third sort of Mesolithic culture made its appearance in the interior woodlands of North America at a very early date, about 7000 B.C., overlapping with the latest of the big game hunters to the west. This is termed the "Archaic" by specialists in American archaeology, and it was marked by improving and varied stonework and by efficient general hunting, fishing and collecting—in many ways the natural forerunner of the recent Indian life of the eastern United States and Canada. By 3000 B.C. it was making striking polished stone tools of various kinds: adzes and gouges for working wood, fancy "banner stones" and other strange shapes (plummets and bayonets), some of them used as balancing weights for the spear thrower.

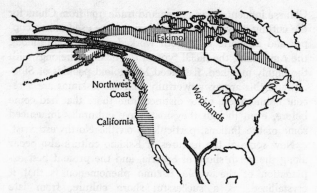

FIG. 30. *Suggested Mesolithic influences from Asia on North America, and later counterinfluences from native American Neolithic culture in the south.*

They had ground stone axes with grooves around the middle for hafting, and a variety of stone knives, scrapers and points; also hooks, needles and awls of bone. They worked skin for tailored clothes, and ate much wild vegetable food, grinding acorns and seeds such as ragweed, pigweed and sunflower, on grinding stones. And they were users of shore food particularly, for they have left great shell heaps on the coasts and rivers all the way down to Florida and Louisiana. Sometime before 2000 B.C. such Indians built an astonishing system of weirs for trapping fish in the tidewater of the Charles River; the remains still exist deep in the silt under the Back Bay section of Boston, in the form of several banks containing some 65,000 stakes in a space of two acres.

This general culture, known in its later phases as the Woodland, continued to flourish and improve, rising to a climax before the beginning of the Christian era. It had the benefit of specific additions, some domestic, some foreign. Its excellent stonework was a development of its own, but the appearance of pottery, by 2500 B.C., seems to be an introduction from Asia. In shape—with a conical or lemon-ended base and a generally vertical form—and also in decoration—coarse finish with markings usually made by the impression of a cord or a cord-wrapped implement—it strongly resembles Siberian pottery and contrasts with that which was apparently developing independently at this time in Central America. Considering the early date of Asiatic pottery, and its very wide spread among people of a Mesolithic culture type, this derivation is hard to doubt. Here, then, as in some other late Mesolithic settlements in the world, we have pottery in the hands of people who were not yet true agriculturalists, but who would have found it useful in cooking wild vegetables and seeds.

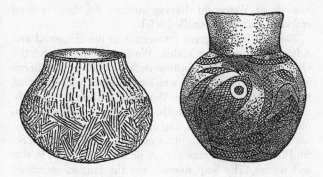

FIG. 31. *Pot of the Woodland type, left, coarse-surfaced, compared with pot of the Mississippi type, right, smooth-surfaced and engraved with the head of a mythological bird (see next chapter).*

Before long, however, the Archaic Woodland peoples may actually have begun to cultivate some of these seeds and plants, either as their own invention or as the result of ideas coming from the south. Following this, in the last centuries before Christ, actual corn arrived. But already a particularly vigorous phase of the culture had been under way, from about 800 B.C.

Another new trait that had recently appeared was the making of earth mounds for burials. Interest in the dead was old in this Woodland culture. Goods had long been buried with the corpse, and there was a strange love of including red ochre, either along with the other materials or sprinkled over the whole contents of the grave.

But now, whether as an idea introduced from the outside or as one arising locally in the eastern United States, the dead began to get very special treatment, having the bones stripped of flesh and buried alone, or being cremated, and being buried in any case under a mound. Here we have the once mysterious Mound Builders, supposed by some of the romancers to have been here "before the Indians." Simple conical mounds were the early form, leading later to various kinds of earthworks, such as the effigy mounds of Wisconsin, having outlines like large animal crackers, with their bundle burials.

The cult had its great florescence in the Hopewell and Adena cultures of the Middle West, and especially of the Ohio Valley, which constitute such an outburst of energy and artistic ability that it was long difficult to believe that they rose out of the general Woodland pattern. They made rich and artistic grave goods, using copper, silver, mica, obsidian and river pearls, and carving some stone statuettes and ornamental tobacco pipes of the highest artistic merit. And the mounds themselves are no less impressive, in size and nature. The Seip mound, not the largest, contained some twenty thousand wagonloads of earth, brought by men using baskets. And the mound floors were evidently the scene of special rites, as remains of wooden structures and burning pits for cremations indicate. Burials were of every sort: plain, cremated or secondary (the clean bones alone). Some were in log crypts, and some were very strange: the Kiefer mound had twelve bodies laid out like swimmers making a star, and three of these had their heads between their legs.

The riches (great wealth for such a culture), the work of building, the wide spread of the culture itself, and the trade necessary to bring river pearls, gulf shells, Great Lakes copper and Rocky Mountain obsidian together, all bespeak a period of tranquillity and stable political organization in the eastern United States. This disappeared, and the area had a temporary subsidence.

In the Great Plains, where simple argicultural villages succeeded Hopewell influence, some of the tribes found buffalo hunting and a seminomadic life more prosperous than crude farming, and so took a partial step into the past. When they got horses and the art of riding from the Spaniards, the hunters flourished and became the rulers of the Plains, living on the buffalo and casting agriculture aside, assuming some of the warlikeness of the nomadic Bedouins or of the central Asiatics, and becoming a fiery chapter in our own history.

But in the woodlands to the east a kind of restoration was taking place. More and more of a new kind of culture was pressing upward from the south, mixing with or replacing the older pattern, up to the region of the Great Lakes especially. It was flowing out of the tropical regions where progress native to the Americas had been taking place, and its origin and spread are a different story from the one we have been pursuing.

18. The Rise of American Indian Civilization

Far less is known of the antiquity of man in South America than in our own country. But it is clear that the hunters came there in the course of the peopling of the Americas generally, and that they explored the possibilities. In southernmost Chile, the Palli Aike cave shows a long series of occupations by hunters alone, from the earliest ones about nine thousand years ago down to the Ona of today. And in certain other southern parts and in south-central Brazil the hunters remained nomadic and primitive, without benefit of Mesolithic suggestions from Asia or of the natural bounty of California and the Pacific Northwest.

But elsewhere examination of the possibilities brought its reward. For plants began to be domesticated, in the American version of the Neolithic discovery, and before the Spanish came something like a hundred different kinds of food were being grown. If the Europeans have been generously diffusing their ideas to the rest of the world lately, think what they in turn got by diffusion from the Indians: corn, potatoes, sweet potatoes, beans, tomatoes, tobacco, chocolate, vanilla, peanuts, pineapples and rubber. Never mind things for the gourmet, like avocados, papayas, Jerusalem artichokes, cassava, chiles and chewing gum, or a number of drugs including coca, ipecac, curare and cascara (quinine also is American, but the Indians were ignorant of it, having no use for it until we diffused malaria to them). These are only the things that have become important to us, for they had a host of others that we have not taken up.

Such a long list shows how many were the kinds of plants available for domestication, particularly in South America, and it also shows that the idea of domestication must have been a pervasive one over a long period. For some of the types, notably corn, were not simply taken and planted, but underwent a long process of improvement toward the things we have today. A great deal of scientific study has gone into the background of these various plants, and the picture is steadily taking shape, but it is still dim; where domestication first took place is not clear.

Indeed, the main fact emerging is the difference from the Old World, where farming of grain can be seen appearing in the Near East, clearly within certain dates. In the Americas, the process of domesticating plants took longer, and Dr. Gordon Willey is prepared to say there may have been as many as four different centers in each of which domestication took place independently of the others. Certainly the known facts are very much against its having happened in one only. Dr. Willey's suggestions are Mexico (corn), Peru (gourds, beans), the Amazon basin (manioc and other root crops) and eastern North America, just described, which had sunflower seeds and pumpkins.

A key plant in this is doubtless corn. Other plants such as beans or squash can be traced back to 5000 B.C. in probably domesticated form, and perhaps to 7000 B.C.—in other words, to a date almost as early as the first domestication in the Near East. But these alone would not allow solidly based farming and large villages; this was provided by fully developed corn, with its high yield, good protection against birds because of its husks, and good ability to be stored. However, it appears that development of corn from its wild state was a slow process compared with that of Old World grains. In the Near East, wheat took some lucky forward jumps by accidental changes in the numbers of its chromosomes, allowing the gardeners to select suddenly vastly-improved strains. This kind of change did not occur in corn. So in a way, the New World was held back to the pace of corn, which first appeared from almost 5000

B.C. onward, in primitive small-eared form, in Mexico and New Mexico. Gradually it became suitable for a basic crop during the next three thousand years, after which it spread through South America and into the Woodlands of the north.

Finally, it has been shown with varying force that at least cotton, gourds, sweet potatoes and coconuts were being grown both in the Americas and in different localities in the Old World (anywhere from Polynesia to India), before Columbus—i.e., they had traveled from one hemisphere to another in earlier times. This is a most interesting business, and a very controversial one. But it does not argue with any strength that the invention of domestication itself was brought to the Indians from outside, considering the solidity and the native look of the whole thing, and the fact that the plants in question, if they crossed the Pacific, most likely went from America in the direction of Asia, not vice versa. But let us leave this discussion and note only that the Indians performed a great series of botanical feats, whatever the details may later turn out to be.

The American Neolithic takes shape

Thus there was a long period, from the first tinkering with natural plants, perhaps as early as 7000 B.C., down to the period 1500 B.C. to 500 B.C., by which time agriculture was well developed in the center and corn, at least, was reaching the most distant areas. It was a period in which exchange and diffusion allowed each region to build up its eventual stock of domesticated foods to the point where reliance on farming, without hunting or collecting, would take care of the food supply. For example, corn must have been no more than a curious supplement to the menu of the people using Bat Cave, New Mexico, well before 2500 B.C.; in other ways they were like the Cochise collectors. On the other hand, people at Huaca Prieta, on the coast of Peru, were sedentary enough to accumulate a large mound of rubbish beginning about 2500 B.C. They ate gourds, squash, beans and cattail roots, and grew cotton;

they were evidently used to settled growing, since the mound contains fish bones but no animal bones or hunting weapons. Corn arrived here very late, about 700 B.C., in a developed state.

Pottery appeared in Huaca Prieta about 1250 B.C., apparently having come down from northern South America. This was American, not Asiatic pottery, invented here about 2500 B.C. Now the pace was quickening, both by invention and by diffusion. It had added as animals the llama and the guinea pig (the inevitable dog was present, apparently brought from Asia); rich in plants, the Americas were poor in domesticable animals. Then, following 1000 B.C., culture took important strides. Pottery was not only present, it was excellent, being represented, for example, in Peru by fine effigy jars, some with masks, some

FIG. 32. *Examples of Peruvian pottery. A black sculptured pot from one of the earlier periods (Chavín) with cat mask motif.*

with vegetable shapes and some having the cat form that was a strikingly widespread art motif on Peru's north coast. Weaving was done on the loom, though it was not yet the craft it later became; and various arts, including working in gold, were present. And at Chavín some major religious buildings suggest cults attracting a large population, and a complicated social structure.

The people, no longer depending partly on fishing or hunting, were now advanced and efficient farmers. And various kinds of evidence indicate that, in addition to the basic arts and a temple-and-priest religion, there were social classes, major public works, organized war, human sacrifice, trophy-taking, and well-defined gods known over large areas. Clearly this kind of culture, of a well-advanced Neolithic type, had its home from the central Andean region up through Colombia and on into Mexico, and that it was a sort of common base in this whole territory from which the later civilizations developed.

Farmers on the Amazon, the Rio Grande and the Mississippi

It also acted as the wellspring out of which corn and various aspects of higher culture flowed into other areas, resulting in the spread of well-established village life. One direction of flow was along the north shore of South America and up into the islands of the Caribbean, giving rise to a heavy population in these parts and adding them to the general area of high culture in America. Beyond, these ideas continued along the Atlantic coast of South America, turned back and went up the Amazon, and so penetrated the equatorial jungle heart of the continent; that is to say, they went the long way around instead of simply coming down the eastern side of the Andes.

This was an area where apparently some foods had already been domesticated. Adding the new elements produced the simple farming culture that survives today. The Amazon Indians live in good-sized villages, traveling by canoe. They grow corn, yams and sweet potatoes among other things, but their great crop is the poison manioc (or cassava). This root has hydrocyanic acid in it, and you must remove it or it will remove you; grate the root and squeeze the juice out in a tubular basket which you stretch by using the limb of a tree and a lever, and you have cassava meal. Cultivation is by slash-and-burn, with the usual consequence of moving the village every now and then; and the men do a good deal of hunting with bows and blowguns, not because they must but because it is the thing for a man to do. The Indians make pottery, and weave cloth and sleeping hammocks. But they wear more ornaments and paint than clothing, which is mostly striking in its absence. They tattoo and paint lavishly, and wear buttons or plugs in nose, lip or cheek; they bind their arms in tight basketry ligatures; and they are great users of feathers and iridescent beetle wings for personal decoration. The Jivaro use these wings in strands on their shrunken heads, which are their particular expression of the general taking of heads as trophies. War is constant, and villages are isolated and fortified.

Socially and religiously, the complexity of the central area is missing. The Amazonians are known especially for the spartan initiation rites for boys, such as contests of whipping with long cane lashes, putting stinging ants inside a basketwork binding on the arm, where they cannot be scratched, and so on, things which are also used as magic for good health (to wake up a sluggish system). Noting this whole jungle culture to be a trimmed-down version of that of the great central area, you might compare it thus with Melanesia's relation to Southeast Asia. You might also note a sort of general resemblance in nature and a number of strong likenesses between the Amazon and Malaysia as well (e.g., head-taking, blowgun), without jumping to conclusions about contacts.

The basic central culture apparently had some fringe influences, rather than direct colonies, in North America. In our own Southwest, we have seen, the arrival of corn goes far back but this does not at once mark the beginning of a general farming population. That came later, about the beginning of the Christian Era, with farming of developed corn and a simple village life coming from Mexico.

Two parallel developments took place. One was the

Hohokam of the Arizona Desert, which continued to have influence from Mexico but finally went downhill into the Pima and Papago peoples of our day. The other was the Pueblo tradition, with the simple Basket Makers being transformed into the people of the stone and adobe hamlets of Pueblo times, which grew for a period into the large one-house cities (probably for protection against the Navaho and Apache, warlike hunters and raiders who came down from northwest Canada), and then spread farther out again in the self-contained towns, still of good size, of recent times. The Pueblos make, and always have made, fair to good pottery and textiles, and their religion is a well-developed priestly one. But their culture is a homespun thing compared to that which gave it birth, to say nothing of what was flourishing later on in Mexico.

Another set of influences, and less direct ones, came into the southeastern United States, perhaps both by Mexico and the Gulf Coast, and across the Caribbean itself, from South America. Corn, of course, arrived well back in the pre-Christian period, but an actual new cultural tradition formed itself in the Southeast, commonly called the Mississippi pattern, and it was this that thrust itself northward, into and through the old Woodland area. These people were builders of mounds, but used them to put temples on and not primarily for burial; and the mounds were rectangular and flat-topped rather than dome-shaped. In late times (as the Spaniards were arriving) the mounds became very large indeed, like the Cahokia mound in East St. Louis.

The Southeasterners made pottery of a great many different styles, less coarse than the Woodland and quite distinct from it, normally using shell as a tempering material, and running to broad, flat-bottomed shapes, with some external features like handles. Effigy forms were made as well. They went in far less for stonework than the native Woodland culture, but what they made was good. In other art they rivaled the earlier Hopewell people in the making of bodily ornaments such as shell necklaces, gorgets, armlets, beaded leg bands and belts, using copper, pearls and broad shells. They were also able weavers and feather workers; and in late centuries their art was to a great extent employed in the service of some kind of ceremonial cult, probably of Mexican derivation. The remains, and carvings on shell, show men handsomely accoutered with insignia featuring animal-human motifs, a death's-head, and a hand with an eye in the palm.

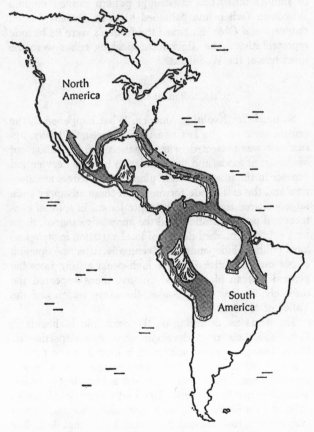

FIG. 33. *The rise and spread of higher culture in America, and its peaks of development.*

This was the culmination of the Mississippi culture. General disruption and disease on the arrival of Europeans kept the latter from seeing much of it in action. Nevertheless, the French and Spanish were impressed with the relative prosperity of the towns along the southern seaboard, and with the elegance of their chiefs. The Gulf and the Mississippi Valley were the scenes of its best days, but in earlier or simpler forms this Mississippi pattern pushed up into Wisconsin (where the palisaded town at Aztalan was an outpost) and Ohio. Eastward the Iroquois were its historic representatives. The Algonquian-speaking tribes were the inheritors of the Woodland.

Civilization in the Andes

So much for Neolithic America. What happened in the central region in the last two thousand years? Briefly, agriculture was perfected, with irrigation and the filling out of the list of foods, and the population became heavier and heavier in the most favorable places. Knowledge, architecture and the arts strode forward, and these advances were largely shared throughout the central area. In spite of contacts and communication, and the knowledge shared, there long existed a marked degree of local variation in style and local political independence. Eventually, after the opening of our own Christian Era, like high peaks arising from the general plateau of advanced culture, there appeared the three civilizations of the Andes, the Maya region and the Valley of Mexico.

The Andeans, centering on the coast and highlands of Peru, had their great development in two departments: the craftsman arts and politics. It is hard in a short space to say anything that will convey the nature of their artistic achievements. Pottery early reached a high level and remained varied and lively. The north coast produced a striking naturalistic style, with pots taking animal, human and other forms, including human heads that look like actual portraits. The southern part used simpler shapes but with lavish color painting. Both kinds of ceramics depict

FIG. 34. *A portrait jar of later Peruvian period* (*Mochica*).

much of the life of the people themselves, and pottery as a whole shows us the boundaries of different groups at different times, as well as the spreading influence and control of successive larger states.

Textiles need a book of their own, for the Andeans invented and used more different techniques of weaving than any other people on earth, having the basic weaves as well as a multitude of tricks that we do not take advantage of today because they can be done only on a hand loom. Much of their fanciest work was made for mummy coverings rather than for everyday clothes. Not having been exposed, like the Europeans, to the Siberian-Eskimo idea of tailoring by cutting and sewing, their clothing ran to rather squared-off shapes like the face cards in *Alice's Adventures in Wonderland* (which it has also done elsewhere, as among the traditional dress of the Pueblos), a defect that they counteracted to some extent by shaping the piece of cloth *in the weave*. They made some extremely fine yarns; they started with cotton but went on to wool and maguey fiber. One wonders what they might have done with silk. Fortunately quantities of woven material have survived in graves because of the dry climate, and I can only repeat that they are as impressive as this description is short.

Finally, metalworking at the time of the Spanish Conquest had reached the point of using bronze for a number of everyday implements like chisels and points for digging sticks. Copper had already been used, and decorative work in gold and silver was old, and the Ecuadorians were even working platinum and making gold filigree.

The last major art, that of building, seems connected with social developments. One important religious center, Chavín, had existed before the Christian Era. Then, following some very localized developments, the last centuries before A.D. 1000 apparently saw some larger unities or political communities, culminating in the general dominion of the Tiahuanaco culture sometime after that date. This is visible in a variety of traits of pottery style and textile design, which were present all over the central Andean region, and it is named for the abandoned religious center of Tiahuanaco itself, high up near Lake Titicaca, and just over the Peruvian border into Bolivia. This city is extraordinary not only for its altitude but also for its size and apparent importance, and such features as the gateway carved from a single stone.

The indications are that it was one major ceremonial center in a cult that managed to command the worship (and the labor) of all the area for a while. But the Tiahuanaco influence, religious or otherwise, evaporated, giving way to various large or small strongly organized, well-defined states. These were building major cities, and the form of the cities (laid out in wards or barrios, with reservoirs, regular streets, cemeteries, etc.) indicates that city life was now a true feature of the culture, and that political arrangements were certainly complex. There was evidently a good deal of fighting, to establish authority and to defend it. Finally, not a century before Francisco Pizarro came, the Incas carried the whole trend to its logical conclusion. They came out of their particular region around the city of Cuzco and subjugated not only the central Andes but Ecuador and half of Chile as well.

The Inca people were actually rather inconspicuous among the states of previous times, though their own development must have been about like that of others. They had a record of twelve sun-descended rulers, but it was under the last four that the Inca Empire rose and fell. In 1445 they began, deliberately and with great determination, to bring under their sway by diplomacy and war all the states and tribes of the region. This they did, unifying a territory the size of the Atlantic states of the U.S.A. and holding it successfully until the Spanish, with horses, armor and superior ruthlessness, murdered the last ruler, Atahualpa, and so destroyed the structure. It is a pity, and not only for Atahualpa, because the Incas had just taken certain potentialities in the Andean culture and applied them with a new energy, and it would be interesting to see what would have followed.

The Incas had no secret weapons, but only the old ones, even though the use of bronze was fairly new. But they exercised the draft and had a well-drilled standing army officered from the noble class. When they went to war it was a true military operation and no raid: conquests were planned, sieges laid, roads were built and kept in condition, communications were maintained by runners, forts (like the astonishing mountaintop site of Machu Picchu) were built, especially where defense was necessary, as against unconquered forest barbarians. And if a subdued population gave trouble, they uprooted segments of it, transplanted them, and replaced them with well-domesticated people from elsewhere.

It was therefore not weapons that made the Inca conquest possible. It was: such a thing as a perfected agriculture, which, giving a large surplus of food, had long before allowed the arts of peace to develop and now allowed the arts of war by enabling the feeding of an army (a fixed proportion of the food grown by farmers went to support of church and state); such a thing as the development of a class-ranked society and the idea of broad political control by a ruling class; such a thing as advanced stone building for forts and cities. In the end, it was the ability to take large quantities of human labor and dispose of it according to the plans of those in control.

This was probably the motive, conscious or unconscious, of the Inca conquest itself, to which they modified still other ideas of Andean culture. Slavery, for example, was a very old idea, but what the Incas were doing was not capturing slaves for the service of a few nobles or owners, but capturing whole communities of ordinary farmers and workers, simply to incorporate them into the economy, as going concerns. This can probably be defined simply as imperialism.

And they also invented true totalitarianism as well: they put laborers together in groups of ten under a foreman (this might correspond to a village or ward), grouped ten such groups into a "tribe," and so on up to the four great divisions of the empire. Insofar as there were still remnants of an older joint family or possibly a clan organization of

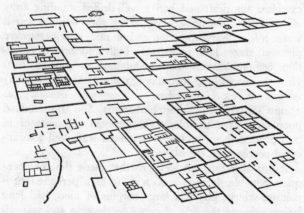

FIG. 35. *Air view of a portion of the ruins of Chanchán. The grouping of buildings into wards, within walls, in a highly formal arrangement, suggests a strongly organized political control.*

society, this later political or economic arrangement replaced it as the order of things (and it may have existed before the Incas, judging by the plan of such a non-Inca city as Chanchán). And all life was stiffly regimented for commoners, who had to work on what they were put at, and could neither make nor own any luxury materials for themselves. The nobles were either relatives of the ruler or else the surviving rulers of other conquered states.

Thus the entire empire could respond to the orders of one man. It was a system as efficient as it is horrifying, and it was indubitably successful. You have probably seen pictures of the massive masonry work of the Incas, of closely fitted large blocks of stone. One of its striking examples, the fort of Sacsahuaman, is reported to have been built by a force of 30,000 men, and it is also said that the rulers sometimes had difficulty keeping their supply of labor busy. Certainly the population was heavy, with Cuzco and its environs having 100,000 souls. Even so, the system had its weakness. It had lines running only up and down, and it was too antlike; and so when the Spaniards seized the person of Atahualpa the empire as a whole was paralyzed. The time of the Incas was one of the great episodes of human history, and it is our sad loss that we know too little about it. We must depend on the patient labors of the archaeologists, for the Andeans did not write, and they had only the simplest forms of keeping number records.

The Mayas: architects and astronomers

In these things they were mastered by the Mayas of Guatemala and Yucatán, the second pinnacle of American achievement. This is a little strange on the face of it. For the Peruvians could have made good use of such knowledge in commerce and in political administration. But the Mayas used their mathematics, astronomy and "writing" for religion. And their building art, supreme in the New World, served the same end.

Now you have seen how, in the Andes, religious centers

occasionally had widespread importance (particularly
Tiahuanaco) in the days before politics became the engine
of control of the whole region. It was this side of culture
that prevailed among the Mayas. Here was clearly a peaceful area during most of the centuries, made up of city-
states presided over by one general religion and by priest-
hoods, not by rival secular rulers. This is not to say that
they lacked warfare or human sacrifice, for they have left
us paintings of these things. And the states sometimes
formed alliances for defense. But their cities are actually
centers for temples and other religious structures, quite
without fortification, and serving as the ceremonial hubs of
suburbs and of districts of humble farming villages.

The Mayas occupied the core of Central America, and
during the period of their civilization the center of gravity
or of development shifted from the highlands of Guatemala in the south, northward through lowland Guatemala
and finally up into Honduras, Yucatán and southern
Mexico. Their stone cities first appear in the lowlands, the
Petén, sometime after A.D. 300, reaching an imposing climax during the Dark Ages of Europe. Then they underwent some kind of disruption which is not yet understood,
followed by a final phase preceding the arrival of the
Spanish, after A.D. 1000, centering in Yucatán.

Chichén Itzá is the city you always see in photographs,
with its simple and pleasing great pyramid, El Castillo, its
Ball Court, its Observatory, and the Temple of the Warriors, surrounded by the once-roofed Court of a Thousand
Columns. But Chichén is late, represents a mixture of
influences, including Mexican, and was built apparently in
hodgepodge fashion over a long time with little planning.
Such an early city as Tikal, deep in the jungle and until
recently inaccessible, is at least as interesting. It has a
highly formal orientation of temples around a central
acropolis, with a marked uniformity of style and an insistence on height of both pyramids and temples. Another
city, Copán, is famous for its inscribed stelae (columns)
and its stairway. And Palenque, in a region of hard stone,
made much use of plaster and had a freer sculpture style,

making it highly individual; most Maya buildings were of limestone, worked with stone tools.

The Mayas were architects where the Peruvians were merely contractors. The latter used some decoration by carving or by arabesques in the mud surface of walls, but they were only making structures for certain purposes, however well. The Mayas, like the Greeks, meant their buildings to be viewed as wholes, and they knew the meaning of proportions, symmetry, zones of decoration, light and shade, and so on. Typical temples (not the galleries called nunneries) were on pyramids, with lavish carving of panels into serpent masks. Buildings and pyramids were stone-faced, and probably mostly plastered and painted.

But the Mayas for all their artistry shared a general American ignorance of certain principles of building. Their stone walls were not structural (like the Incas') but only facing filled with rubble. And walls were the weaker because the stonework was not properly bonded, or offset from tier to tier, like good brickwork. And worst, the Americans never discovered the meaning of the true self-supporting arch (though they made a few by accident), and relied on the false or corbeled overstepping (cantilevered) arch instead. This made their walls heavy, their rooms small and their structures weak; and the jungle's roots have seized the opportunity to wreak havoc in the dead cities.

Maya mathematics is if anything more impressive than the architecture. For one thing, they invented zero, or something for nothing, which is the key to the principle of "numeration by position," and so to the writing and handling of large numbers with ease. Even the Romans lacked this. You have doubtless ground your teeth at seeing Roman numerals for dates. Write 1948, for example: MDCCCCXLVIII. We have renounced this bestial system except, for some reason, on public buildings.

The mental process of unraveling this Roman date is as follows: "One thousand; one five-hundred; four hundreds; ten short of fifty; one five; three ones." In our own Arabic decimal system we simply let the *order* of the digits say

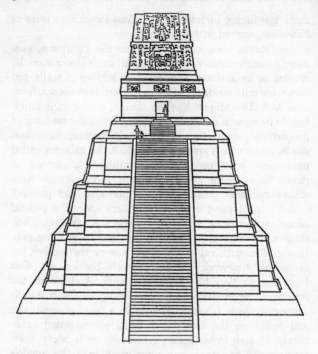

Fig. 36. *A temple at Tikal, restored. This is one of the earlier Maya cities, and the largest. It is characterized by steep pyramids and temples with high decorative roof combs.*

how large they are, instead of spelling this out (i.e., writing "M" for "one thousand"). Thus we read 1948 mentally as "One thousand, nine hundreds, four tens, eight ones." And we recognize how far away a digit stands from the vital decimal point, though we do not always write the decimal point. The necessity of zero for this system is to *hold* a digit *away* from this unwritten decimal point whenever it is required. So we can write exactly 1000, "one thousand," the zeros saying to us "*no* hundreds, *no* tens, *no* ones, decimal point."

Accordingly we write everything, very easily, in powers of ten. The Mayas used different basic amounts, running up to twenty, which would have been as clear-cut as our system except for the use of eighteen at one point. This was for their day count, and it went like this: 20 kins (days) made 1 uinal; 18 uinals made 1 tun; 20 tuns made 1 katun, and 20 katuns made a cycle (of 144,000 days, about 400 years). So the date on Stela D at Copán, which reads "9.15.5.0.0—10 Ahau 8 Chen," means 9 cycles, 15 katuns, 5 tuns, or a total of 1,405,800 days.

This is only part of the meaning of the inscription, and is purely a count of days, and periods of days, not of true years. They knew the length of the true solar year very accurately—more accurately than that followed by our own calendar up to two hundred years ago—but they did not use it in quite the same way. Instead, they had a month and day count, something like our day names; and also another kind of cycle, of 13 numbers and 20 named days, both in sequence, so that the same day name did not have the same number for 260 days. Further, the year (of months) did not begin on the same named day except once in 52 years. Now look at the date I have just cited: this reads "the day 10 Ahau, the 8th day of (month) Chen." This combination likewise could only recur in 52 years, that is, any given pairing of a named day with a day of the year.

Now all days of the Maya calendar are dated from a day which was 4 Ahau 8 Cumhu, about a million and a half days in the past, whose long-count date was 0.0.0.0.0. The typical date simply states the number of days that have elapsed since that fixed day, and then gives the correct day name for the day arrived at—a great help in confirming the accuracy of inscriptions. In the case above, for example, the date 9.15.5.0.0, or 1,405,800 days, will indeed give a day 10 Ahau 8 Chen (although this would turn up every 18,980 days anyhow). The original starting date, "0.0.0.0.0—4 Ahau 8 Cumhu," would be about 3000 B.C., but that does not certify that the Mayas founded their calendar then. Instead, something about their system, once they established it, probably made them choose this mythical date as one when various cycles *would* all have worked out together. In fact all the clear dates of Maya remains are from the late seventh to the tenth cycles.

These dates make up about a third of the inscriptions. The rest apparently have to do with other checks on dates, not yet fully made out. They do not, alas, contain the history of the Mayas, or directions to buried gold; they concern the same kind of matter, whatever it may be, much of it apparently relating to the place of the moon in all this.

The day counts are perfectly clear. Why then do we not

FIG. 37. A Maya inscription from Naranjo (Stela 24). The glyphs are read from left to right and down. The first (top left) is the introducing glyph, signifying that what follows is an "Initial Series" or full day count (there are extra decorative elements in the numbers), along with standard glyphs for the periods involved, i.e., 9 baktuns, 12 katuns, 10 tuns, 5 uinals, 12 kins (or 9.12.10.5.12, a total day count of 1,386,112). The next two glyphs give the proper day name for this date, 4 Eb 9 Yax. The remainder of the inscription is supplementary material, not fully understood. In numbers, a bar is "5," a dot "1."

know the exact Christian date for each and every inscription? Because in the times of Chichén Itzá, when the Spanish came, the Mayas had become careless, and wrote only the smaller divisions of the count (like '97—is this 1897 or 1797?). And in their hot zeal to destroy this illustrious paganism the newcomers never ascertained which cycle, or part of that cycle (thought most likely to be 11.3.0.0.0), the Mayas were at that moment counting. Bishop de Landa wrote the best chronicle on the Mayas, and yet he himself burned twenty-seven Maya manuscripts (written on their own paper).

How many others the priests destroyed nobody knows. Three remain and one of these, the Dresden Codex, alone contains a mine of Maya calculation and records of the moon, and of the movements of Venus, probably of Mars, and possibly of Jupiter and Saturn. It also contains a saving note for the Spaniards, in the supernatural beings associated with all the pure astronomy, indicating the heathen divinatory nature of the work.

Aztecs, avarice and aggression

The third region of highest culture centered on the Valley of Mexico, with the Lake of Texcoco in the middle of it. It shows once more the potentialities of the American social and political inventions. It was the scene best described by the Spanish, and it is the one American civilization that lives on vigorously in the traditions of a modern nation, Mexico.

It grew from a farming-town base similar to what we see in Peru, and it followed a somewhat similar course. This early or formative culture was more advanced than our own Pueblos of today. It produced the first of the little pottery figures found in such volume in Mexico, and later, still before the beginning of the Christian Era, was already beginning to develop the ceremonial traits (a calendar simpler than the Maya, pyramids, the rain god Tlaloc, etc.) of historic times.

This culminated in the Teotihuacán period (of the Toltecs). The culture is named for the great religious city northeast of Mexico City, with the long avenue ending at the Pyramid of the Moon, and the huge Pyramid of the Sun at its center, flanked by many smaller temple mounds and by the Citadel, which is a whole court of such mounds, one of the oldest of them having the famous frieze of the Feathered Serpent and the Obsidian Butterfly. Characteristic Mexican civilization had now developed, before A.D. 1000. Later gods such as Quetzalcoatl (the Feathered Serpent himself) and others were in evidence. Pyramid building used stone and mortar. The simple picture writing was present, in which Chapultepec, for instance, might be written by drawing a grasshopper (*chapul*) on a hill (*tepetl*), which is just what the name means. The arts of working in jade, metal and feathers were developed. This seems to have been a long, prosperous classical age in Mexico, and a peaceful one in which religious centers served a large area; nonetheless, Mexican warriors invaded Maya Chichén, and the war is recorded in the carved columns of that city.

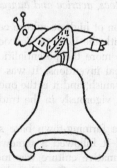

FIG. 38. *Aztec picture writing for "Chapultepec."*

Then this state of affairs suffered collapse. It sounds rather like the fall of Rome. Barbarian peoples, the Chichimec, came into the valley, like the Goths and Vandals, attracted by the higher culture, overthrowing it (traditionally in 1122), but finally picking up the pieces themselves. Several of these tribes set up city-states around Lake Texcoco. One of them, the Tenochca or Méxicas, had a long legend of their wanderings, taking their god Huitzilopochtli with them, looking for a place to settle. By prophecy, they were to know the spot when they saw an eagle perched on a cactus and holding a serpent in its beak (see the national flag of Mexico). This at last they did, causing them to found Tenochtitlán (the center of modern Mexico City) on the island in the lake.

Histories preserved from other tribes tell it a little differently: the Tenochca—the Aztecs—arrived on the shore of the lake in the region of modern Chapultepec about 1250, and suffered some defeats from rival peoples, particularly the Colhuas. They aided the latter on one occasion, however, and were given a chief's daughter by them in order to found a royal line of their own. But the Aztecs indiscreetly sacrificed her instead, and had to take refuge in the lake from Colhua fury, which they did in 1325. Now they prospered, and in two hundred years became the dominant city, through aggressive war and the making of alliances. They did not, like the Incas, incorporate other peoples into a single nation; they simply kept tribes under tribute by war and the threat of war, over much of Mexico, even though they were by no means in absolute control of powerful neighbor cities on the lake itself. It was into this sea of suppression, hatred, treachery and fragile alliances that Hernán Cortés and his tiny band waded in 1519, so that the extraordinary Spaniard was able, in his campaign against the Aztecs, to make allies out of many of the tribes he defeated along his route.

He and his men were deeply impressed with the city of Mexico, with the arts and crafts of the Aztecs, and with the luxury and elegance of Montezuma's court and the deference with which he was treated, even as they were appalled by the quantities of human sacrifice, and of course by the heathen temples that dominated the city from their pyramids in the *zócalo*. The Spaniards found a well-organized trade, with markets in all the main cities, and roads maintained by the government. They found not only

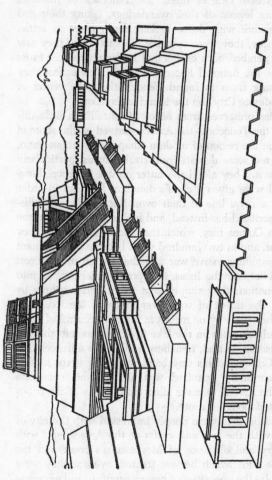

FIG. 39. An artist's reconstruction of the central portion of the ceremonial plaza of Tenochtitlán (Mexico City) as it probably appeared to Cortés in 1519. Dominating the scene is the great pyramid, topped by the twin sanctuaries of Huitzilopochtli, the god of war, and Tlaloc, the rain god. The low-lying building just beyond the pyramid is the palace of Montezuma, while just this side of the pyramid is the palace of Axayacatl, where the Spaniards were besieged during the unsuccessful phase of their conquest of Mexico. (Based on a recent large-scale model by Ignacio Marquina.)

certain goods (textiles, corn, cocoa beans) serving as currency, but also other goods being brought in as constant tribute from submitted tribes, according to a fixed tribute roll kept in picture writing. Such tribute included feathers, fancy garments, gold and incense. Merchants were in fact a professional and privileged class, who actually acted as intelligence agents for the government, gathering information both as to what could be had in tribute and as to how a given tribe might be attacked. And to add insult to injury, these commissars were assured diplomatic immunity by the Aztecs, who would punish any injury to them.

The government itself consisted of a full court of officials, and there was an extensive law and system of justice. Life was not as completely dictated as in the Inca Empire, but ideas were strict nonetheless. Pulque could be drunk by none but old men, and chewing gum was chewed only by little girls and women of the street. So political life was well developed, even though there remained vestiges of the old tribal structure of society. The military organization was built on the old clans, which were still of importance. The "emperor" himself was actually a war captain elected from the clan war chiefs, and he was still in process of changing rapidly into a powerful ruler in his own right when the Spanish arrived.

This is the last of the high cultures that were just burgeoning in America when the Europeans ended their development. Did these people or their forerunners in Central and South America have contacts with the Old World, especially across the Pacific, before Columbus? It is a perennial question. There are many strange parallels in simple culture; the blowgun is only one. For example, two early plants, gourds and cotton, occur together on the west coast of South America soon after 3000 B.C., and these are two of the small group of plants that seem to have been grown long ago in Asia as well as in America. But the Polynesian islands—the necessary stepping-stones—give no evidence of having seen human beings before 300 B.C. Some of the suggested connections are simply fantastic. Some are baffling, but must be looked at seriously, like the series of likenesses in temple art motifs between the Hindus and the Mexican-Mayan area.

There are nevertheless certain considerations that are usually jumped over by those who prefer the romantic to the probable. First is the fact that the American sequences found in archaeology look like long, native, natural developments without signs of sudden intrusions from elsewhere bringing marked changes. Second is the fact that what has been invented once can be invented again in another place. Third, do primitive adventurers undertake voyages of the utmost danger in order to carry their own culture to others? And do those others behave with proper gratitude when the boatload arrives? (Accidental voyages seem far less likely to have any effect, though perhaps are more likely to occur.) Finally, do most of those people who look at a map and imagine such voyages really consider what it means to cross thousands of miles of turbulent salt water in any kind of boat at all, let alone a still-primitive one? The voyage of the *Kon-Tiki* is by no means the whole answer.

Such things may have happened. But what is their meaning to the Americas? The weight of evidence gathered by those who make it their business is this: the eastern Pacific Ocean was too great a barrier for man until the Polynesians penetrated it first; and the American Indians themselves built up the culture that made possible the Aztecs, the Mayas and the Incas.

CITIES AND BRONZE—THE
THIRD STEP

19. *The Cradles of Civilization in Asia*

Digging in America is likely one day to give us a full record of culture rising from a hunting level. Already this much is clear: domestication of plants by the Indians allowed steady progress from simple beginnings to a highly efficient food production using irrigation. And the ability to raise all the food with something like half the labor at last permitted an actual new stage of society, that of civilization.

Now you might get various definitions of civilization, but let us here use simply "having cities," with all it implies. It implies food in quantity from the surrounding country, on which a city can live. It implies transport, to bring the food in, and also markets, and so trade generally, and so trade goods, and so full-time artisans, the makers of anything except food. It implies new political inventions, with a kind of formal government to rule not only the city but also the country that pertains to the city; and these new institutions bring the erosion of the older kind of local social organization, where kinship is strong and politics weak. And it usually means an expanded religion, with major gods becoming general instead of tribal, a thing that was in the process of happening among the Aztecs.

In other words, emerging civilization means that the countryside grows itself a head. Civilization does not signify cities alone, with the farm villages remaining "Neolithic," no matter how simple these villages may be. Rather, it means cities as the focus of a peasantry, and includes the villages, which are no longer isolated and self-sufficient, like those of the Melanesians or the Indonesians in which each man is a farmer, whatever else he may do in his spare time. It means not tribes but states.

Dahomey, in West Africa, produced a simple civilization, as we saw. The American Indians of at least three regions reached a higher point. The Indians suffered certain handicaps, and had failed to make certain inventions, which shows their achievement all the more remarkable. In the first place, their best excuse for a beast of burden was the llama, a humpless, weak-backed, cranky, undersized camel, which is better than nothing, but which in any case was known only in South America. Perhaps this was a reason why the Indians did not use wheels for carts, another handicap in transport. They were forced to depend on human carrying, and they made special efforts to cope with their limitations: they established roads, had systems of runners for communication, and trained the armies to live off the land as much as possible. They had also only just begun to use metals in the proper sense, and the writing of the Mayas and the Mexicans was still rudimentary.

Nevertheless, the great social change had been made, and the Inca Empire, writing or no writing, was a fact. The same change was made in the Old World, and here, with important technical advantages which the Indians did not have, and with no powerful outsiders to strangle its development in mid-career, civilization and urban life carried through to make the connection between the Neolithic and the life we live today.

The scene of this was the same as the old Neolithic center of Southwest Asia, the Middle East. The location is perhaps not even as precise as in the New World but, as in the New World, there seems to have been a general base of high Neolithic culture which flowered into civilization in certain spots, in this case the river valleys of Mesopotamia (Iraq), Egypt and India.

The basis of the Bronze Age

People are known to have been living, in the Neolithic, on the fringes of the Tigris-Euphrates and Nile valleys. They began settling the actual valley bottoms at a time when these were swampy, overgrown, difficult to work, but nevertheless well watered and supremely productive for farming, especially by irrigation. In the Copper Age, a sort of late, improved Neolithic with some copper tools, we see settlers arriving in the floor of the Tigris-Euphrates Valley in Mesopotamia. More important, we see, between 4000 and 3000 B.C., some inventions of great importance being put to use, and in fact forming the base for the new society.

This Near Eastern civilization was in full flower before 3000 B.C., to take a round date that will serve as a turning point. We can also call this the opening of the Bronze Age. This is an old term originally attaching to the use of metal, but one which is now employed for the civilization that had been hatching in the Copper Age, just as we can use Neolithic, meaning New Stone, to better purpose as the name for food-growing village life. From 3000 B.C. on, the Old World had passed the high-water mark reached by the New, and civilization was being established from Egypt to India. Let us see what had been happening just before.

The floor of the valley in Mesopotamia, at the head of the Persian Gulf, had only recently risen above sea level when the first people came down from the Persian highlands, about 4000 B.C., with the culture known as the Ubaid, and began draining the swamps and founding towns. Cities rose, their mud walls washed down and were repaired, and mounds grew higher, as Babylonia was populated by the Sumerians in the south and the Akkadians in the north.

Before long the first great invention appeared: the use of beasts for power, to replace human muscles alone. It was applied in two main ways, for plowing and for transport.

Neolithic agriculture is done with a digging stick or a hoe, in America, Africa, Melanesia or Neolithic Europe. If you can get an ox to draw a big hoe, you can not only cultivate far more ground in the same time, you can cultivate it deeper and more effectively, and so enormously increase the food one worker can produce.

And if you can get an ox to draw a cart, you can carry all this extra food from farm to city, and otherwise take advantage of easy transport, which was made possible by the discovery of the wheel. Oxen were in fact first used to

FIG. 40. *The great centers of early civilization in the Old World, and some of the cities, including the Neolithic sites of Jarmo, Jericho, and the Fayum.*

drag dry-land sledges before wheels were invented, and they continued to be used later for ceremonial purposes such as royal funerals. But carts and war chariots, drawn by oxen or by donkeys (horses were not used yet and there was no riding), had both appeared before 3000 B.C. The wheel was also promptly employed to speed up pottery making, by turning it as it was shaped, but this was hardly a world-shaking innovation. One other use of non-human power was made: sailing ships, which were certainly present in the Mediterranean and the Red Sea before 3000 B.C.

A second great advance lay in metalworking. As in America, the first use of metal was doubtless cold-worked copper (as found in predynastic Egyptian graves). For the earliest Mesopotamians copper was scarce, but they soon began casting it in molds by melting it. Later on they were using the lost-wax method of casting, by making the desired object in wax, enclosing it in clay, and baking it, which hardens the clay and melts out the wax at the same time, leaving a hollow mold for the metal, to be broken off after the molten metal has been poured in. Also, still before 3000 B.C., they had come into possession of the knowledge that adding ten to fifteen percent of tin to the copper makes bronze, an alloy that is not only easier to cast than copper (which is apt to develop oxygen bubbles in a hollow mold) but tougher when it is finished. That is why bronze, rather than copper alone, became the industrial metal of a whole period of man's history.

Like pottery, this is a fairly complicated craft. It means not only knowing where the ores can be found, and how to smelt them, but also having some method, like bellows, to get a heat of almost 1200° centigrade, so as to cast the metal, and having various molds and tools for working it. And the discovery had some complicated effects. Now perhaps metal for tools, and the plow and the wheel, are not all necessary for an emergent civilization, for the Mexicans managed without them. But here in the Near East the plow and wheel opened the paths of trade, and metal enforced trade. There was no raw metal at all in the mud of the valley and so it had to come from outside, just as had stone in the earliest period. At the same time metal had taken on the greatest importance. It makes much more deadly and dependable weapons than stone: a stone knife might break in a fight, but metal is more rugged, can take a sharper edge, and can be resharpened or, if need be, recast. And it can be made into new shapes, such as a sword or body armor, not possible in stone. It is true that the Aztecs had a fearsome non-metallic sword of their own, a cricket bat edged with obsidian blades, but the advantage that Cortés' armored men had can be imagined. The same advantage can be seen in the hands of bronze-armed men facing stone weapons that were not even as good as those of the Aztecs.

Thus, in contrast to Neolithic people, the pre-Bronze and Bronze Age Mesopotamians became absolutely dependent on trade to bring them copper and above all tin, ores that occur in only a few parts of the world. Now history makes it clear that such a people will use force if necessary to maintain a vital trade. The Mesopotamians did exactly that, and you may surmise what this may have meant in the expanding city society. Metal was not only important, it was expensive, and so it was primarily held in the hands of the ruling classes for military ends, and not put to everyday purposes, which increased the effect of class distinctions.

Sumer and Babylon, temples and empires

Making use of these things, the early Mesopotamian cities grew up, among them Kish, Ur and Erech. Building changed from wattle and daub to mud brick, and the use of the true arch appears in some early tombs at Ur. Before long, temples became conspicuous parts of the city. About halfway through the formative period, Erech had a temple measuring 100 by 245 feet. This and other cities also had ziggurats (we know the ziggurat of Babylon as the Tower of Babel). They were pyramids or mounds with setbacks, like boxes set one on the other, with a small god-house on the top, which had a stair leading right through the roof, so that the city's god could step down out of a cloud if he so desired. The temples, still early in time, began to show a marked richness, in precious objects and gold, and in ornamentation with imported woods and glazed bricks.

And this reflects the fact that they had become the focus of society. The gods ruled the people, through the priests, and the gods owned property as well. For the temples were a sort of corporation, which owned and rented out much of the land, loaned seed to farmers, and collected taxes, acting generally as the state. So the priesthood and

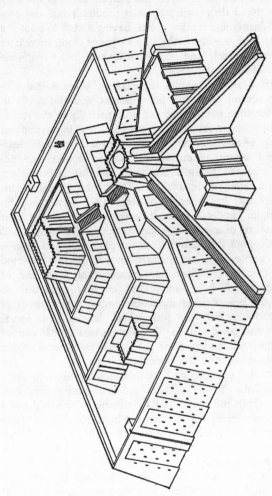

FIG. 41. *The ziggurat of Ur, as it probably appeared.*

the gods were the nerve center around which city life formed. Thus Sumer recalls the Mayas. Temples not only administered their own properties profitably but also produced luxury and market goods, having a staff to farm the temple land, tend its flocks, and to weave cloth, brew beer and make bread (one temple in Lagash had twenty-one bakers of its own).

Thus were the temples in religious, political and economic control. This was big business, and the needs of administration led, as they did only partially in the Americas, to a second set of inventions important to civilization: the arts of measurement, mathematics and writing. Measurement means, of course, proceeding from rough-and-ready means to the use of standards, and this the Sumerians did in a variety of departments. Their cubit (which means the forearm) had a length of about 19½ inches, and included 30 "fingers," which reveals where they got their first notions of measuring short distances. This may sound primitive; but they also divided the circle into 360 degrees of 60 minutes each, and we have never to this day departed from that usage. They had measures of area, and of weight, in which a mina (16⅛ ounces) contained 60 shekels. These various numbers suggest their system of numeration, which was sexagesimal, having signs for 1, 10, 60 and powers of 60. This system was a little clumsy to begin with, and in some cases used the Roman device of subtraction, as in "IV," meaning 5 less 1, or 4.

Their first accounts go back to something like 3300 B.C., dealing with all sorts of loans, rentals of land, estimates of labor supply and so on. Their mathematics was addressed to practical problems of the same kind, such as estimates of volume, but it advanced markedly in what it could handle as time went on, with tables and formulas. They arrived long afterward at the use of fractions; in the beginning the Sumerians had avoided the problem by creating a large number of subdivisions of their standards of weight and length. (The Mayas avoided fractions by using equations, which were suitable to their astronomical purposes; i.e., as though you said, "He walks 2 yards in 3 steps,"

FIG. 42. *Examples of Sumerian writing. Left, early pictographs. Right, cuneiform of the later Sumerian period. The more familiar cuneiform usually illustrated is Babylonian, and later still.*

instead of saying that he walked two thirds of a yard at a step.)

As to writing, this began as it did elsewhere by using pictures, and went on to have signs standing for given things (ideographs), becoming symbolic rather than pictorial. At first these were drawn on wet clay, and later pressed into the clay with a stick having a wedge-shaped end, so that the symbols were a combination of little wedges, as Chinese is a combination of strokes of a brush (for a while they also used round impressions, but gave it up). It is the wedge shape that gives this famous script its name: cuneiform. Now if there was one thing Mesopotamia had plenty of, it was mud and clay, and fortunately for us they used this in the form of biscuitlike tablets to write on, often baking them afterward. Therefore there are copious remains of their writing, including methods of teaching the script itself, with schoolboy work—very helpful—and even, in later times, collections of ancient writings preserved by *their own museums.* After all, by 1500 or 1000 B.C. the Mesopotamians could regard tablets of 3000 B.C. or earlier as something ancient, and quite comparable to our own antiquarian study of Rome.

But we are discussing the earliest writing. Still before 3000 B.C. the signs of the script had come to have sounds,

instead of meanings only. That is to say, they were phonetic, and so could be used to stand for syllables in writing
new words, just as you might write "before" by making a
picture of a bee and using the numeral 4. One reason for
this was that the Sumerian script began to be used to write
Akkadian names. The language of Akkad was a Semitic
one, but Sumerian was not (nobody knows what it actually
was). And so signs that might have both sense and sound
in Sumerian lost their specific sense when they were used
to write the sounds of a foreign language. At any rate, by
this time the script had grown to have some two thousand
signs.

Now we stand at a major gateway to the present. By
about 3000 B.C. the heavy work had been done. Full city
life, resting on a plentiful agricultural base, and with a government capable of handling national affairs with the administrative tools of writing and mathematics, had reached
fruition. And bronze tools, and chariots with donkeys, supplied the force both to defend the city and to rule it. This
was the Bronze Age, and mankind was now equipped to
go right on to life as we know it, and to form societies of
unlimited size.

History began, if you will blink at some of the remaining
uncertainty about exact dates. Mesopotamia, in any case,
began to have a history. The cities started with temple
governments: the god of a city was looked on as king, ruling through an *ishakku*, who was both high priest of the
god and his executive governor. These governors eventually
became royal in their own right, and not seldom made
themselves divine as well. And so after 3000 B.C. the cities
of Sumer and Akkad had actual dynasties. The early Royal
Tombs of Ur, with their opulence (human sacrifices; gob-
lets, bowls and helmets of gold; the ornaments and harp
of Queen Shub-Ad, and the gold and lapis-lazuli ram and
thicket), attest the power of the dynasts.

These early kings are hard to date, for the records give
them reigns of impossible length. Not only that, but the
royal houses at once invented still more improbable ancestors who were supposed to date from before the flood

(which is recorded as a great catastrophe in the land just prior to the dynastic period, and which might well have been an actual inundation of this whole valley due to unusual rain, wind and high water in the Persian Gulf). The lives of those heroic begetters in the fifth chapter of Genesis seem short in comparison, for two versions of the list of the eight (or ten) antediluvian kings in Sumer add up to total 241,200 and 456,000 years respectively.

Whatever this may signify, succeeding personages were real enough. At first the little city-states fought among themselves, exerting occasional dominion one over the others. Then Sargon, of Semitic Akkad to the north, ruling from his still undiscovered capital city, came down, overthrew the prevailing Sumerian tyrant, Lugalziggisi of Erech, and destroyed Erech's walls. He reduced the rest of Sumer and came to the shores of the Persian Gulf, where he washed his hands ceremonially in the waters of the sea, as the ruler of all Sumer and Akkad.

This little empire held together for a while, and under Naram-Sin extended its conquests westward as well. But then it disintegrated in the face of various attacks; and into the anarchy that ensued there poured down out of the eastern mountains the barbarians of Gutium, who seized power for more than a hundred years. Here we see the first signs of a process that repeated itself over and over in history: a civilized center rises, diffusing culture over a wider and wider area, and finally attracting the barbarians on the fringes, who come in with nothing to lose, use the weapons of the civilized to conquer them, and end by becoming part of the civilized realm themselves. It happened in Mexico with the Chichimeca; it probably happened in Peru; and it is certainly a major note in Chinese history.

Then several of the Sumerian cities recovered their own rule, and rebuilt temples and palaces. Lagash, Ur and Erech flourished again, with Ur briefly re-establishing an empire. But now a new barbarian threat arose from the Amorites, up the Euphrates to the northwest, and the Elamites from the eastern hills, who came down and overturned the last dynasty of Ur, setting up two others at the cities of Isin and Larsa, each claiming the rule of Sumer and Akkad. Finally, after 2000 B.C., another Amorite dynasty was founded at Babylon which, in a hundred years, at last firmly established the supremacy of the Babylonian Empire, running all the way to Nineveh in the north; and ancient Sumer and Akkad were no more. Even the Sumerian language went out of use and was lost. The famous ruler of this time was Hammurabi, who among other things brought together and codified the ancient laws of Sumer in the great Code which bears his name, and established them for the whole of his dominion. He also enlarged his territories, developed trade, made changes in religion (raising up Marduk, the god of Babylon) and planned the future of the city.

But this did not mean the lasting or serene rule of Mesopotamia by Babylon. After three hundred years invasions were renewed. First the Hittites from the west (speaking an early Indo-European language) pillaged the city, leaving a broken empire. Then an apparently similar people, the Kassites, took the dynasty and lasted for over five hundred years; they were probably responsible for the introduction of horses. During these centuries Assyria had grown up to the northwest, and beyond this the Hittite state, which in turn was neighbor to Egypt's territory in Palestine. Assyria came more and more often to hold sway over Babylon, though sometimes it was the other way. So empires grew in size. Just before 600 B.C. the Assyrian Empire was destroyed for good by its enemies, and Babylon had a brief resurgence, until the Medes and Persians at last conquered everything from Greece to India.

Iron Age improving inventions

This is a history full of the smoke of war, but it is also one that saw some notable steps in the arts of peace. In the first place a new metal, iron, was discovered. A few objects of meteoric iron had been made much earlier, but these should be looked on as oddities and not as a real knowledge of iron. This knowledge was practically a brand-new invention, for the primitive smelting of iron is quite different from that of copper, and so it did not come about naturally from copper and bronze working. Instead of running out as a bright liquid ready for casting, iron appears, from the proper mixture of ore, at somewhat lower temperatures, as a dirty spongy mass with slag in it, which can then be beaten into the desired shape. (The actual melting and casting of iron at higher temperatures was first done in China, long after the beginning of the Christian Era.)

Ironworking seems to have been achieved far to the north of Mesopotamia, in Armenia, possibly as early as 1400 B.C., but the knowledge spread rapidly in the next two hundred years. For one thing, metal was now something thoroughly appreciated and iron is better in many ways than bronze (if not as handsome). For another, iron ores are much more plentiful than ores of copper or tin, and they are more widely found. The spread ushered in the Iron Age, although this was by no means the opening of a great new era in the sense that the Bronze Age was.

Other improving, polishing-up inventions also had arrived by this time, or soon after. Just as early city life was accompanied by the use of copper, leading in the Bronze Age to bronze, so it was also accompanied by simple numeration, measurement and writing, all of which had reached important development by 3000 B.C. The Sumerians had numeration by position, or making the position of a digit say whether it stood for 60 or 1 or a fraction; but the finishing touch to this, the invention of zero, was not applied until after 1000 B.C., a few centuries before the Maya (and India invented the same thing again probably a few centuries after the Maya).

Measurements had been becoming more standard, especially with the idea of payments in trade. Silver was used as a medium of exchange, values of other goods being given in shekels of silver, and this in turn led to the temples turning out silver bars, stamped with their weight and the certification of the temple. This eliminated the necessity of weighing out silver for every transaction, but it left the bars of silver as objects of high value—not what anyone could carry in his pocket but something for the business of the merchant class—and also varying in the value they carried. Finally in far western Turkey a wonderful idea was hit upon: make the silver into very small coins, all just alike, so that they could be spent in small amounts and any man could have them.

Writing also underwent a blessed simplification. The Sumerians had done a splendid thing in constructing their system, but even after their signs had changed from pure ideographs to stand for sounds as well, they continued to use many hundreds of them. They never went any further, but stopped at the same stage as Chinese. And their scribes were a privileged class, somewhat mysterious and requiring a long training, like doctors of today. The writing did spread, however, and finally, on the shores of the Mediterranean, a pair of brilliant advances were made. About 1500 B.C. somebody at Ras Shamra in Syria took twenty-nine of the Sumerian signs, made these stand for basic simple sounds alone—not even syllables—and threw away the hundreds of others still surviving with all their ideographic sense. This was a true alphabet, which could spell anything. It was not our alphabet, but by about 1200 B.C., somewhere in Phoenicia, a completely new set of twenty-two signs was put to use for the same purpose, and this is the alphabet from which came all those of history: ours, Hebrew, Arabic, Hindu and others.

So the Iron Age of the Near East may be looked on as a culmination of some of the fundamentals of the Bronze Age, in which these fundamentals were rendered into the form we use today: ordinary objects into a cheap metal, money into coins, and writing into an alphabet that any child can learn. These simplifications took away the monopolies of the captains and the kings, the merchants and the scribes, and opened much of civilization to the common people, greatly reducing the class distinctions that had been the rule in the Bronze Age.

The Harappa people of western India

But we have now moved along into historic times. Let us retrace our steps and look at other sproutings of civilization in Asia. One was a great and unremembered empire all up and down the Indus Valley, in westernmost India. It lasted perhaps a thousand years, from 2500 B.C. or earlier, and then it was somehow banished from history for over thirty centuries, coming to the light of knowledge again hardly more than a generation ago.

Before this empire there appeared, from the Indus westward into Baluchistan, copper- and bronze-using villages.[1] This was evidently at the time of the early towns and cities of Sumer, for there are some faint pottery style connections. (The region must have been far less arid than now, and it is likely that the limit of the monsoon rains has since shifted eastward, away from it.) When these village cultures had existed for some centuries, there sprang up a uniform civilization, evidently a single realm, including a number of towns along the Indus and dominated by two very similar cities, Harappa in the Punjab, in the north, and Mohenjodaro three hundred and fifty miles away in the south. This Harappa civilization must have had its roots among the simpler village people, but it must also have owed some major impulse to another source, doubtless Mesopotamia or Persia. Just how all this fused into the new civilization, and just why it appeared full-fledged in so great an area, are mysteries. However, the deepest levels of Mohenjodaro have never been dug because, in spite of a drier climate, the subsoil water level has risen.

The people grew wheat, barley, cotton and dates, and had both humped and shorthorn cattle, buffalo, sheep, elephants, camels, pigs and chickens, a list that shows their connections with the rest of India were good, and that the climate was indeed wetter (rhinos and tigers were also

[1] See Stuart Piggott, *Prehistoric India to 1000 B.C.* (Harmondsworth, England: 1950), for an excellent account of this and what follows.

present). Like the Sumerians, they worked bronze, as well as copper, lead, gold and silver. But where the Sumerians built their early cities of mud brick, with the streets laid out higgledy-piggledy and with later walls showing no reverence for older walls, the two Indus cities followed a strict street plan over the centuries and built with fired brick, which leaves the details of the bases of buildings in clear form for modern inspection. The better houses were of good size, with brick stairs to the second story, and timber-supported roofs, and with indoor baths emptying down ducts inside the walls to major drains running through or under the street itself. The outer walls were more or less unrelieved faces of brick, without windows, on narrow streets, indicating love of privacy. You might say the houses had no front doors but only back ones, since the entrances are unobtrusive. Much of the interior wall was apparently plastered.

Some houses of this kind were near-palaces, with smaller rooms that might have been for watchmen or servants. But another kind of house, of which there were a great many, was a two-room affair built in rows and evidently for workmen. If there were temples, they have not been recognized or discovered (possibly one is still hidden under a modern Buddhist temple at Mohenjodaro). The prominent buildings visible are granaries, and a great bathhouse with washing alcoves and a central bathing tank, which may be the parent of the ritual bath tank of later Hindu temples.

Oddly, there were no royal treasures or masses of luxury goods, but only hoards of personal jewelry, of gold and semiprecious stones. Small statuettes and many clay figurines found are probably religious, and these and seals may suggest both animal attributes of gods and early representations of some of the Hindu gods themselves, like Shiva. But these things are not impressive, or reminiscent of the treasures of the temples or royal tombs of Mesopotamia. There is only the impressiveness of the cities themselves.

The Sumerians, of course, speak to us through their tablets and inscriptions. The Harappa people also had a fully developed script, totally unlike the Sumerian but probably inspired by it in the first place, being certainly a good deal later in time. They must have written it on various substances, and it is well developed when it first appears, but they used it on clay only when they stamped jars with their stamping seals. These fragments of writing are all that have survived, and the script itself is still a mystery intact. So we learn nothing that we cannot see with our own eyes from the ruins.

FIG. 43. *A seal impression from Mohenjodaro, with an example of the Indus Valley script.*

The surprising thing about this whole culture is its uniformity, and a certain dry and boring quality. There is no significant variation in styles or type, even in brick size, throughout the settlements. This uniformity, together with the persistent street plans and the housing of workers in rows of quarters obviously not of their own building, argues some powerful, practical political control centered perhaps on a priest-king like those of Sumer, directing building, the organization of labor, and the collection, threshing and storage of grain. Perhaps even more surprising is the uniformity in time: the lack of change and the fidelity of building to the original plan of streets. So great a stability is unexpected in a long culture sequence.

At last the whole civilization collapsed, and the latest remains found are crude huts built over the ruins of Harappa itself. Various signs point to growing raids and incursions of barbarians from the west, culminating with the Aryans in about 1500 B.C. They, and their Indo-European language, were probably part of a general spread of Indo-European-speaking tribes who had already burst into Babylonia farther west. At any rate it was their history and their gods which were celebrated in the Vedic hymns, and not the history of the Harappa people, who were thus excluded from memory by the conquerors.

This can hardly mean, of course, that the culture of the great Indus cities was blotted out, or that the Harappa culture did not affect Aryan life and religion, and perhaps the very nature of the Aryan gods, as all these were finally handed on to later Hindu culture. Surely Harappa left some kind of a legacy, and the ruins themselves even suggest other Hindu ideas: intense conservatism and ritual purity. For the last, note the baths, and the quantities of broken clay cups around the wells, apparently meant, as in modern India, to be drunk from only once.

The dynasties begin in China

Whatever the influences that spurred civilization in Mesopotamia and India, they also reached China a number of centuries later, and a parallel civilization arose there. Such influences must have followed the same path as the Neolithic connections, to North China in the bend of the Yellow River. Here the core of China passed quickly into a bronze age with the Shang Dynasty, which dates itself from 1766 B.C. but is thought to have begun about two hundred years later. The use of the wheel in making pottery had already arrived, and so had copper; and Shang bronzes, large vessels with simple, strong ornamentation, were not only technically good but are also one of the world's great arts.

Already preceded by the legendary Hsia Dynasty, which

is supposed to have established a time count and to have charged the priest-emperor with reading the will of heaven through the study of astronomy, the Shang rulers were now presiding over an urban civilization, a well-organized army and a luxurious court, and were having themselves buried in sumptuous tombs with human and animal sacrifices, altogether reminding one of Sumer and Egypt. And writing appeared, possibly as a native creation based on a foreign idea. It is first known on oracle bones, shoulder blades of cattle or turtle shells, heated to produce a pattern of cracks to be read like tea leaves (this shoulder-blade reading is called scapulimancy and is an old Far Eastern device for soothsaying, applied by the Siberians to reindeer shoulder blades). These bones were inscribed, and the characters used can be recognized as the ancestors of modern Chinese writing. It is plain that they started even earlier as pictures, and gradually became the mass of Chinese "letters" or characters (not an alphabet) representing, like the Sumerian cuneiform, a mixture of ideas and sounds.

FIG. 44. A Shang Dynasty bronze vase.

Sun   Moon   High   Elephant

FIG. 45. *Chinese characters of the fourteenth century B.C. (top) compared with their modern equivalents (below). The idea of "high" was first expressed by a tower on a hill, and the same picture is now "written" in a series of rapid brush strokes.*

The Shang emperors at last lost the favor of heaven, and were replaced by the line of Chou (1122 B.C. or later), then rulers of a small state in the west. Under them Chinese government advanced, and the empire spread down the Yellow River to the sea, and on southward, the beginning of the expansion that centuries later had carried to the present borders of the country. The emperors had their ups and downs of power, and faced dynastic replacements, usually from the semibarbaric western states, but they managed always to supply a center of authority to which China as a whole returned.

As in earliest times, China was so far away from the West that she could have received only stimuli and basic ideas rather than full cultural forms, even though her Bronze Age civilization had a similar outline. Once started, Chinese culture followed its own paths, even when further influences (like iron) arrived. Chinese culture is distinctive, and Chinese inventions, such as paper and printing, have put the West in debt to China in turn.

A great Chinese interest has always been devoted to the techniques of government; and the fall of Shang and the rise of Chou is cast in legend as a story of imperial oppression and immorality replaced by liberality, morality and a decent feudalism. When you remember that Confucius, the good Machiavelli, had government as his first love, and that ancient Chinese education led through long study and examinations to positions in government, then it is less surprising to find that the Han emperors (206 B.C. to A.D. 220) were already trying out many modern-sounding solutions to farm relief, tax problems and money panics.

Japan deserves a word, not as a cradle of civilization but as a receiver of it. She has in fact been something of a specialist at this. Enjoying an insularity like Britain's, she has been a picker and chooser, consciously adopting or rejecting at will, from the time of her founding as a nation to her first taste of conquest in 1945. Japanese prehistory, unfortunately, is still much beclouded and its origins are like those of culture in the Americas: indefinite. Until recently it was thought to cover only a brief period, but here and there signs of early man are coming to light, including an arm bone diagnosed as Middle Pleistocene.

Nevertheless the past as it is now known is largely covered by the Jomon culture. This was the culture of hunters and fishers who made cord-marked, "rope"-decorated pottery, and, if the radiocarbon dates are right, they began doing so before 7000 B.C.—possibly the earliest pottery in the world. They lived in pit houses and used bonework, both of them signs of northern Siberian influences. Only late in this long period, a few centuries before the Christian Era, did agriculture and cattle appear, probably from Korea. Then a later Neolithic culture bringing rice, the Yayoi, appeared in the south and spread north. The White Ainu must have been a part of the Jomon population, but probably only a part; they once extended farther south, but perhaps not far. We cannot tell who the other Jomon people were just now. And other peculiarities of Japanese life are not explained: tattooing, lightly-built houses in a cold climate and certain other things, which look like intrusions from Indonesia.

Chinese bronze was imported in the Yayoi culture, but Japan never had a bronze age. Instead, the Yamato people, with iron and horses (some of the latter were already present), arrived about A.D. 200 and founded the Japanese nation, and the only dynasty Japan has ever had. Out of their clan organization grew a powerful military feudal system. Japan continued to get ideas from the mainland, such as rice, the plow and Buddhism. Indeed, in the seventh century A.D. the Japanese sent a committee to China in quest of good ideas and took over such as pleased them; and they did the same thing in the last century, with visits to England, Germany and the United States, after having resisted European contact for a while, until they saw the realities of the situation. This move to meet diffusion more than halfway, by a whole culture, is something practically unique.

20. Egypt, Crete and
the Beginnings of Europe

Our own prehistory, that of Europe, drew to a close as
civilization spread slowly into the West. Here, in the Mediterranean, its early home was Egypt. Classical Greece and
Rome, indeed, tended to look on Egypt as the mother of
civilization, but they certainly gave her too great a share
of the credit, for she drew on older sources in common
with Sumer, and continuously thereafter on the Near East
and Mesopotamia. Nevertheless, she had her individuality,
and there is no indication that her writing and her pharaoh
system were not her own developments, even if the basic
notion of writing might possibly have come from Sumer.
Lying in the corner of Africa, mostly in a narrow valley
flanked by the desert, she was more isolated than Mesopotamia from uninvited intruders.

Egypt had a rich Neolithic culture, about 4500 B.C. in
the Fayum Basin. This was succeeded by a sort of Copper
Age culture, the Predynastic, appearing in the Nile Valley
itself, known not from its villages but from its cemeteries.
In these, the dead were outfitted each with some household goods and ornaments, and buried in a crouching position in a simple pit in the ground. There was plenty of well-
made pottery. Men had a few weapons and women a
dressing-table kit of sorts, particularly a comb, some green
earth for painting the eyelids, and a small stone palette
to grind this paint on. Copper tools appeared, and later on
they were being made by a regular casting process.

These villages must have been growing up all along the
Nile and in the Delta, doubtless with more complicated

culture and social life than we can discern. Then about 3100 B.C. the dynasties begin, and civilization almost jumps into being. Actually the simple farming life, with no new frills, went on for ordinary people; the new thing was the pharaoh—and the growing arts and sciences which surrounded him and his court—imposed on the top. If you might represent early Sumerian society by a ziggurat, with the temple corporation or the king as the small top block, the privileged and noble classes as the next block down, and the common people as the biggest block at the base, then you might almost represent early Egyptian society by an obelisk, one central spire for the pharaoh and his governors rising high out of the dead level of the population.

There may have been some knitting together of towns or villages already, but the first pharaoh, Menes, conquered all of Egypt and gave it a unity that it almost never abandoned. He and his successors established the fixed administrative districts of Egypt, the nomes, and imposed a new ritual in which, from Menes on, the pharaoh was not only the descendant of Osiris and of Horus the falcon god, but also their divine reincarnation, and the living embodiment of Menes, the uniter of Egypt, as well. The pharaohs' gift to Egypt was not only unity but administration: keeping the peace internally and defending the valley from the outside, undertaking public works, exercising control of irrigation, and studying the flooding of the Nile. The result was to make the land highly productive.

But most of this came back to the benefit of the pharaoh rather than the people, since he took it into the next world with him. The simple pit grave of Predynastic times turned into a deeper one and then into an underground chamber; and in the very first dynasties the royal tombs of Abydos had become small buried apartments. Food, toilet kits and copper tools accompanied the dead as before, but now also gold, turquoise, lapis lazuli and other precious things. As preoccupation with the dead grew, the Egyptians tried to preserve the body (the mummy was the "new," imperishable body, Osiris revived). More and more wealth was buried with the king, including slain servants and eventually whole miniature households in model form, with orchards, houses, cattle and so on, along with quantities of the actual goods.

Above the underground tomb there shortly began to be a mastaba, a flat mound of moderate size, made of mud or stone, and having chambers within itself. Finally, still in the Third and Fourth dynasties, about 2600 B.C., the pyramids were built. These great works were not made again, but the underground tombs and all the riches ran right on down through Egypt's history.

Now this, and particularly pyramid building, is a major business, done during the pharaoh's lifetime over many years, not thrown together by an undertaker on the king's demise. Of the food grown in Egypt, the farmers took their livelihood, and the government took the rest. Much of it was converted into work, making it possible to take 100,000 men off the land and feed them, while they cut and transported stone blocks. More of it was concentrated or refined in this way: expeditions went out for trade to get the wood, the gold, the copper, and various kinds of riches that were not to be had in the valley of the Nile, and these materials were made into ornaments and luxuries by corps of craftsmen. And then this distillation of so much of the country's wealth was put in the grave with the dead king. Thus, while an ordinary farmer was part of a civilized nation, with tax collectors and governors, his daily life was much like that of Neolithic times, since his lot had not changed and he was still—and for a long time after—using stone tools.

Nevertheless, Egypt had the forms of civilization from the beginning. Even if bronze did not become truly general until the Eighteenth Dynasty, after 1580 B.C., work in copper showed a real knowledge of metal during the Predynastic. And the presence in Egypt of the same arts and the same kind of advanced government and cities as in Mesopotamia and the Indus Valley means that we should look on the Bronze Age as beginning at the same time, before 3000 B.C. as a rough date, when the dynasties commence.

Their mathematics, which had to deal with land areas, with problems of pyramid size, and with amounts of labor and material needed, was good. The Rhind Papyrus of 1700 B.C., eighteen feet long, shows how to do a variety of practical problems, by methods of reckoning harder than ours today but effective all the same. Writing appeared, clearly developed, in the First Dynasty, in the famous hieroglyphic script using little pictures, and was already by this time partly phonetic, or a mixture of sounds and symbols. The hieroglyphics continued in use, and there shortly appeared a simplified version of the same signs, the hieratic script, for easy writing. The Egyptians also early devised an alphabet of twenty-four letters for simple sounds alone, but they made the sad error of simply adding these to the rest of the mass and so not actually "inventing" the alphabet.

FIG. 46. *An example of Egyptian writing shown both in the hieroglyphic (above) and the simplified hieratic scripts. (Translation: "What is the number being referred to?")*

They did better when they came to the calendar. Now there are several obvious ways of adding up time. You may readily observe that every twenty-four hours there is an alternation of light and darkness, called a day. Also, about every twenty-nine days the moon goes through all its phases and appears as a new crescent in the evening again. Finally, and this has no such obvious marking points, there is a succession of seasons lasting 365 days and a fraction. Now these various fractions of days cause trouble: they keep the moon "months" from being neat divisions of the year, and the days from being neat divisions of either. Yet the new moon is something so obvious to anyone that it has almost always been seized on, formally or informally, to divide up the year. Even the Mayas, who understood the discrepancies fully, and who made an arbitrary year of twelve months of thirty days plus one month of five, all at the same time that they were using a pure day count to write dates with, nevertheless seem to have felt that they must keep track of the moon as well.

But the Egyptians were less concerned with long-time dates, and in fact began counting years all over again with the reign of every pharaoh (something which is responsible for our being uncertain about the older dates). Instead, they were interested first and foremost in the exact measure of the year itself, so as to know when to expect the flooding of the Nile; and they achieved this by bypassing the moon and using the stars. They began the year with the day on which Sirius, the Dog Star, has passed the sun so far that it may be seen rising in the east just before dawn, on the fifteenth of June, close to the time of the flood. So they threw out the moon, divided the 365-day year into arbitrary months, as did the Mayas, keeping track of the error from the true year at the same time (instead of correcting every four years with leap years as we do), and so gave us the kind of yearly calendar we use ourselves.

The Old Kingdom, the first six dynasties, was a glorious time for Egypt, seeing the unification of the land, the new rulership and religion, the broadening of writing and science (which may have gone back into Predynastic beginnings yet unknown), and the raising of the pyramids. Then, about 2500 B.C., the government came apart at the top, with the priests and the princely governors renouncing the king's authority and setting up local dynasties.

As the royal power foundered there ended the time when the pharaoh alone owned everything and governed through officials and viceroys who were of the royal family themselves. Actual technical progress slowed down, but the poor people rose in real revolts, and themselves began to enjoy some of the good things of the world, and to aspire to learning and office, while the patricians were humbled. When Egypt was once more united in 2160 B.C. in the Middle Kingdom, under the Theban pharaohs of the Eleventh and Twelfth dynasties, the commoners under the "just laws" enjoyed their new rights and the richer life. Bronze was at last introduced, and the cult of Osiris, judge of the dead, became the national religion, replacing the narrower old cult of Horus.

From 1788 B.C. on there was a second interruption, this time an invasion from Asia by the Shepherd Kings. These, the Hyksos, brought in horses and chariots for the first time. Finally, after 1580, the native kings of the Eighteenth Dynasty drove the Hyksos out and established the New Kingdom; not only that, but they then went across into Palestine and Syria and conquered those areas, in Egypt's greatest expansion, which put her in close touch with the later Mesopotamians and with the eastern Mediterranean generally.

At home this dynasty had tombs of great magnificence. Toward its end, the young Ikhnaton, whose wife was Nefertiti, overthrew the worship of Amon, who had become the principal god, and of all other gods, Osiris included; he decreed the worship of Aton, another manifestation of Ra the sun, with himself as first priest. Thus he beat down and expropriated the powerful priesthood, and took the religious reins in his own hands to enhance the power of the kingship. This was not popular. His son-in-law and heir Tutankhamen felt forced to reform the reform and to restore the old gods; even after this concession he had to have Ikhnaton buried secretly, and was buried in a secret place himself, while his own successor defaced all records of him. In this way little news of Tutankhamen came down through history, and his tomb survived the robbers almost completely and became the richest find of Egyptian archaeologists in our times.

Already, in 1350 B.C., Egypt's great days were over. From the Nineteenth Dynasty on, the kingship again became shaky and the priesthood powerful, until native control gave way to outsiders from Libya, Nubia, Ethiopia and at last from Assyria and Persia, Greece and Rome, with only occasional home rule. As in the case of Sumer, the period when Egypt was one of three small incubators of Bronze Age civilization was a thing long past, lost in the spreading wars and empires of the Near East.

The Aegean: Minoans and Mycenaeans

Nevertheless, Egypt had had her effect for Europe. She did not leave us a great deal directly. But she did serve as a focus in the West of commerce and knowledge, which drew civilization westward, and joined with Mesopotamia in stimulating the eastern shore and the islands of the Mediterranean. Cyprus, off Syria, was so rich in copper that its name has given us our word for the metal, and Cyprus soon began to profit from its export. The Cyclades, in the Aegean Sea, with no Neolithic remains—they are not a good place for farmers—found themselves thickly populated in the Copper and Bronze ages with a clearly prosperous people producing copper, marble, obsidian and other materials; this is a rich culture rising out of nothing in response to the trade of the civilized lands, right at the beginning of Mediterranean commerce. But later the importance of the Cyclades subsided. It was two other centers, the island of Crete and the southern Greek mainland, which saw the first of European civilization.

Certainly Crete was well situated to be important at this moment. It lies between Egypt, Greece and Turkey, or Africa, Europe and Asia, on the great routes of the time; on the routes, moreover, by which tin would come southward from Europe by western Greece and copper westward from Cyprus, so as to make Crete a center of the bronze trade. She had an old Neolithic occupation, by stock breeders, until sometime after 3000 B.C., when there opened the copper-using phase of her long Minoan civilization. Here we are not talking about one of the cradles of civilization but about one of its schools: this was not a

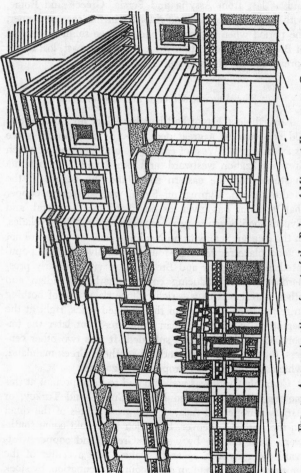

FIG. 47. *A reconstruction of part of the Palace of Minos at Knossos, on Crete.*

valley-bottom development but a maritime one, fed by trade. The cities were numerous, and faced on harbors rather than farmlands for their nourishment. They sent out olives and wine, cloth, bronzework and jewels, in exchange for grain and metal, and prospered by trade, bringing back ideas that they remodeled for themselves.

Cretans of the first phase made use of gold and silver as well as copper, and built good-sized houses, probably of two or three stories. Bronze came in about 2400 B.C. or later. Trade expanded, and so did the cities, and by approximately 2000 B.C. such buildings as the great walled palace at Knossos were coming into being. The towns themselves were not walled for defense, perhaps because Crete was a naval power. But the palaces in the great towns were suddenly destroyed about 1800 B.C. Was it invasion, of which there is no sign, or was it earthquake, of which there have been many signs, from that time until this? The palaces were rebuilt and enlarged, and between 1700 and 1400 B.C., Crete had her most magnificent period. Egypt, under the Hyksos, was less of a rival or of a trade partner than before, and Crete was trading particularly with the Near East and with Greece until, about 1400 B.C., the mainland Greeks overthrew her cities for the last time, and brought about the abandonment of the palaces.

We cannot tell much about Minoan politics and society, except to see that there were princely palaces, suggesting rulers of some grandeur, while at the same time other re-

FIG. 48. *Minoan scripts. Signs in the top row are in the hieroglyphic script, showing their pictorial nature. Those below are in the Linear A script, showing how they are simplifications of the hieroglyphic.*

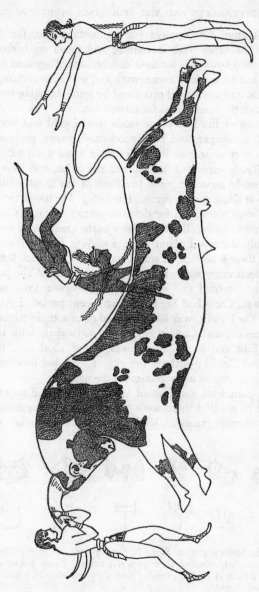

FIG. 49. A Minoan fresco showing the bull-leaping game.

mains seem to show that the common people were not paupers subject to a despot, but prosperous merchants and workers, townspeople sharing fully in the country's wealth, and probably the most fortunate people in the world during their time. Written texts mention their occupations: king, herald, armorer, bowmaker, bondsman, property owner, tenant, shipbuilder, longshoreman, merchant, bath attendant (female) and a host of others.

More of the tale is told by the copious seals and sealing impressions, and by fresco paintings and other objects of art. We know the stylishness of women's dress—highly developed fashion, not at all barbaric—with full flounced skirts and wasp waists, and bodices that not only did not cover the bosom but went out of the way to expose it. Men wore only a waistcloth. We know about their games, especially their almost incredible kind of bullfight, or rather bull-leap, in which the toreador apparently hooked his arms over the horns of the charging bull and allowed himself to be flipped onto the bull's back, perhaps ending with a somersault off the animal's hindquarters.

But the most striking thing about the art is the style of the art itself. It is free, fresh, bright and lively, with a spirit quite different from the kings and phalanxes of Mesopotamia or the staid religious and funerary paintings of Egypt. It shows some ideas about deities, like the Snake Goddess, but it does not devote itself to royal personages; instead it portrays every kind of human and animal scene, naturally and vigorously, and yet with a style of its own. This art may have drawn on Egypt far back in its beginnings, but where painted Egyptians stand still, painted Cretans move; it was the forerunner and source of the first art of Greece, and that is what it suggests. More than anything else, it bespeaks the independence of the Minoans from Asia and Egypt, and sets off theirs as a truly European civilization.

Partner, rival, and eventual inheritor of all this was Mycenaean Greece. Southern Greece had a Mediterranean, Copper Age culture and population similar to that of the nearby Cyclades, and later began using bronze. About 2000 B.C., at the start of the Middle Bronze Age, a new people came with a distinctive kind of gray pottery having connections with Asia Minor, and it is thought that both they and the Minoans of Crete may have been speaking an Indo-European language akin to Hittite. But the Late Bronze Age, which is called the Mycenaean, saw the rise of the cities of Homer: Agamemnon's Mycenae, Nestor's Pylos, and others. The graves of their kings were rich in gold, gaudy jewelry and long bronze swords. And these people, by 1500 B.C. at least, were speaking Greek.

For the palaces, both on the mainland and in Crete, have also yielded quantities of inscribed clay tablets, mostly preserved by being baked in the burning of the palaces themselves. From their first finding it was clear that the script of the tablets started as pictorial hieroglyphs, became simplified into a linear script, known as Linear A, and later changed somewhat, with new signs, into still another, Linear B. Although quantities of the latter writing were known, it resisted decipherment until 1952, and even now the tablets do not tell history, but only give inventory records of people and of property: they list servants, sailors, chariots, jars of oil, bronze valuables, and so on.

FIG. 50. *A tablet inscribed in the Linear B script, found at Knossos. It is an inventory item concerning a chariot. The probable translation, lower line first (and including a broken-off end piece), reads: "[Horse-vehicle] painted red, with bodywork fitted, supplied with reins; the rail of wild fig wood with jointing of horn; and the pte-no is missing" (whatever the "pte-no" may be).*

The earlier script, Linear A, was found only on Crete, and was used to write the unknown Minoan tongue, which was probably Luvian (the Hittite relative, from Asia Minor). Linear B was evidently taken from Linear A, but remodeled for a different language, and the decipherment revealed this to be Greek—pushing knowledge of Greek back centuries at a stroke. Linear B was found on Crete only at Knossos, but was used widely on mainland Greece, going on after the end of the Cretan palaces. The latest tablets, from Pylos, seem to reflect careful planning against an attack from the sea: the placing of coast watchers, naval units, and armorers; and the disposition of rations of supplies. Nothing further.

Cretan culture, the Minoan, rose during the Middle Minoan, and developed a script, Linear A, for the use of trade and palace scribes. On the mainland, the Mycenaean Greeks, however they arrived, built up a parallel culture, somewhat more barbaric, but vigorous and rich. They traded with Crete, and so Minoan influences among them were strong; they even borrowed the Cretan script for their own purposes. Before the final fall of Crete, in fact, there were already Mycenaean rulers at Knossos, using Linear B. Thus the final war at Knossos may have been Greek against Greek, with Mycenaeans from the mainland overthrowing Greek dynasts on Crete, and burning the palace of Minos about 1400 B.C. Minoan culture degenerated, but the Mycenaeans went through the Homeric period, and then were toppled themselves by new invaders from the north.

Western Europe, a road-show Bronze Age

What about all the rest of Europe? We left her, in Chapter 9, in the late Neolithic, as the Megalithic culture of big stone monuments was spreading up the Atlantic coast. This Megalithic was probably associated with a Copper Age culture in Spain, which did not reach much of Europe at all. For, along with such influences coming out through the Mediterranean, bronze-users like the Mycenaeans themselves were also coming up into Europe from the southeast. Just such a people established themselves in Italy, in the Terramare, which were fortified villages of pile dwellings. But in the north and west of Europe there was less turbulence, and the use of bronze spread slowly during several centuries.

Here it produced little change. The villagers adopted it, but they simply began using bronze objects without significant modification of the Neolithic culture. Europe in fact had to be pried open by southern trade demanding tin, from Cornwall and Brittany, and amber, from the Baltic coast. England celebrated the advent of the Bronze Age by changing burial mounds from oval to round, when an addition to the population arrived from the region of the Rhine with a particular kind of pottery beaker, and perhaps bearing the religious notion that resulted in the building of Stonehenge and a few other monuments of this peculiar kind.

Now Stonehenge has been dated by two different methods to about 1840 B.C., and even this may be rather early for the beginning of the British Bronze Age. In any case, Europe continued to be highly provincial, to say the least. Mesopotamia and Egypt had reared civilizations without the knowledge of bronze, before 3000 B.C., and Egypt lacked bronze much longer. When the metal crossed the English Channel a thousand years and more later, empires had risen and fallen in Mesopotamia several times over; yet Western Europe clung to tribal life and went uncivilized for many centuries more, down to the end of the Iron Age. Nothing remotely like a city-state appeared. Only gradually did the population thicken up, react to trade, and finally, quite late, begin to live a rude town life of its own.

Nor was there a high variety in culture. Bronze objects themselves changed and improved as people learned the manufacture of the metal. Battle axes, swords and daggers were the important things, but bronze was also used for other objects and adornment, especially in the form of bracelets, pins and safety pins. The Europeans were beguiled for centuries by this last invention, making safety pins plain and safety pins fancy, doubtless for the purpose of holding a cloak in place.

Things of bronze are found far less in the usual living

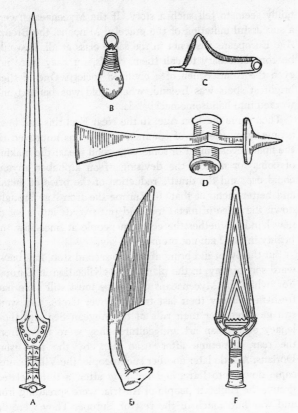

FIG. 51. *Objects from the Bronze Age of Europe:* (A) *sword,* (B) *bell,* (C) *pin,* (D) *battle axe,* (E) *razor,* (F) *dagger.*

sites or dumps than in burials, and above all in hoards, probably belonging to rich men or merchants. Some of these latter collections have numbered thousands of pieces. Such finds suggest that, as in Mesopotamia, bronze was expensive and not for common people, and instead acted to arm the rich and the noble, and so to increase their power in society generally. Burials that include whole chariots certainly seem to tell such a story. If the Mycenaeans were a successful imitation of the graceful Minoans, the Bronze Age Europeans were not in the same class at all. It would be complimentary to call them yokels, for they were not even the frontiersmen of a civilized society. One of their brightest spots was Ireland, where gold was panned and worked into handsome neckbands.

Then came the Iron Age. In the Near East this had been a time when the life of common people was improved by the final development of some very good ideas: the making of coins for money, the devising of an alphabet anyone could use, and the drastic reduction of the price of metal, and better metal at that. In Europe the Iron Age brought down the price of metal too, and put swords into a lot of new hands. Whether the common people at once saw the beauty in this I am not prepared to say.

But the event did bring about the second step, in a backward sort of way, in the planting of civilization in Europe. For, while the Mycenaeans of Greece must still have had fresh in memory their last triumph over Crete, and were still gloating over their rule of the Aegean Sea and their legacy of Minoan art and culture, they were taken from the rear, sometime after 1200 B.C., by the iron-using Dorians. A little later another such people, the Villanovans, came down into Italy; and not long after, a third related group, the Hallstatt people of Austria, were spreading iron and war into much of the rest of Europe. They were no noticeable improvement culturewise over the Bronze Age inhabitants. They had iron, and they were on the march, but those are the main differences. They were entirely uncivilized, making only villages and a few forts, and carrying over some of the tools, particularly swords, into iron, while still making most of their ornamental objects in bronze.

It is not clear just how iron arrived in Central Europe and the Balkans—whether it came with new invasions or whether it evolved simply as a technique. But the Dorians came down into Greece from the north and fiercely attacked the Mycenaeans. The latter had built up their Mycenaean culture partly from Minoan sources, and carried on from the civilization they themselves had destroyed. The Dorians robbed and pillaged and pulled down the existing Mycenaean culture, and put an end to it and its remnants of the Minoan, and a dark age overtook Greece. But this did not mean the end, only a darkness. If the Mycenaean record was closed, it was like the Toltec, for of course culture did not vanish. As usual, the barbarians ravished the higher culture and then married it. And so, in spite of their uncouth approach to civilization, the Dorians in effect attached Greece to Europe, and thus accomplished the final step. Greek influence began to appear in the rest of Europe. Fresh Eastern influences also appeared in Greece. And when the air cleared, Greece was embarked on her own great civilization, with that of Rome to follow, built by the natives of Bronze and Iron Age origin.

This is the end of the chronicle of man before books. For Europe, particularly the part that makes our own heritage, there was still some cleaning up to be done. While Greece was flourishing and Rome was building, the west was occupied by Keltic-speaking peoples of the later, La Tène Iron Age, with its richer art, its complicated safety pins, its growing town life, and its crannogs in Poland and Ireland.

But these Gauls were still tribes, pure and simple. As the Roman Empire spread, they were conquered and weaned away from their tribal ideas, changed from the ancient pattern in which the tribe is the limit of society and it is not murder to kill anyone outside it, to come under the single law and state of Rome, for all men. So the Romans brought an end to the simple European Iron Age. A few tribes resisted both Caesar and the orderly process of progress: defeated by the Romans in France, they fled across the channel into England as the bringers of some phases of the final Iron Age there; and so they stepped from history back into prehistory. You can study their archaeology. Or you can read about them in Caesar's own best seller. But that is another book, and if you are going to turn to a Johnny-come-lately like Caesar, then you must say farewell to me and my story.

Epilogue

Historians claim that it is actually possible to learn something useful from the past. At this suggestion, however, the ordinary person goes into his arsenal of reasons for avoiding mental exertion and comes out again with "History never repeats." He has found this item next to its idiot brother, "Lightning never strikes twice in the same place," and the two are certainly akin for truth. Lightning may not strike many things twice, but lightning knows what it likes, and it strikes the Empire State Building every time a thunderstorm comes by. If history never plays precisely the same scene over again, it is because changing culture changes the scenery. But this has not prevented a historian-statesman like Churchill from knowing what England will do by what England has done before.

Can we then peek into the life of our descendants, by projecting the past on beyond ourselves? Well, what have been the trends, in the last thirty or forty thousand years since modern man took over the planet? After foraging for his meals for most of this time, he put himself through two great changes in his affairs. In the first, he captured control of his food and settled down to tribal life in villages, inventing certain ways to make it easier to string people together socially. This was the Neolithic. In the second, which was Bronze Age civilization, large populations were brought under the dominion of cities, to form states. This happened through a sort of perfection of farming and the supply of food. This in turn was secondarily helped by other inventions, particularly by using the muscles of beasts for power and not for nourishment alone.

Has any other such major turn in history been taken since? Or are we still improving on the basic state of affairs that the Bronze Age brought into the Middle East about 3000 B.C.? For certainly there was a period, thousands of years long, when invention simply cut and polished away at the rough diamond of beginning civilization. This not only produced money, writing and the nascent sciences. It also produced Greece and Rome, and at about the same time it produced the great religions. Christianity above all called any who could hear to join in one society, at least as far as beliefs and ethics go, and so, in addition to everything else it has meant, it should be looked on as another of the perfecting developments of civilization, as civilization itself progressed. Christianity indeed did much more than this, acting as a sort of safe international bank of culture, when civilization itself was having something of a depression in the Middle Ages.

Very likely we have already seen the advent of another age, though I reserve the right to wait two or three thousand years to be sure of it. It would be hard to say just what its key features are, and we have no very good name for it, though most think of it as the Industrial Revolution. It had its seeds in the founding of modern science, from the seventeenth century on, by which nature began to be understood broadly for the first time.

It was as though, earlier, people had looked at jigsaw pieces, seeing a little something on each, without realizing that they went together to make a big picture. When the first two pieces had been fitted, and as the finished part grew ever larger, science had been born. The secrets of nature were cracking open; men could discover and invent deliberately, and stop their hit-or-miss fumbling in the darkness of alchemy.

And one great result was the finding of new kinds of power, not from muscles but from molecular reactions: steam, petroleum and gunpowder. We read in school about the machines that were invented: cotton gins and reapers, spinning jennies and locomotives, some of which could run by hand or by simple water power. But the real essence of this age is the enormous energy drawn from nature, in the form of coal, oil or rivers. For, even if machines had taken effect before the use of steam, they were like the wheel and the plow of the ancient Middle East, which needed an ox to give them their true meaning.

So it may turn out that Atomic Age is a pretty good name, and not just a journalist's invention. For we might easily look on ourselves as still living in the formative period, like the Copper Age of Mesopotamia, wherein the experiments and inventions that were being made established civilization in its full form in the Bronze Age proper. We have made the experiments and we know the physics and the chemistry. We have the alloys, and the machines to make machines, and the understanding of how to bring power to what we want to do, whether to run a dentist's drill or a battleship. Is this just about to usher in the true, persisting stage, built on atomic, not molecular, power, and on machines that run other machines as well as make them? These things are now visible on the horizon: we have electronic computers with memories that are the beginnings of mechanical brains, and anyone with the money can at least have a machine in the kitchen that will tell itself to stop washing and start drying.

And anyhow we have already given ourselves up mentally to such a future. Some years ago, bad children shot the insulators off Cape Cod's power line, and life on the Cape well-nigh went down in confusion to the grave. Few had water; water pumps stopped. None could get gasoline (no pumps); it was just as well, for those who still drove had no traffic lights to keep them from destroying each other. No light in the streets; no light in churches, theaters or restaurants. Food was eaten raw in houses with electric ranges, and babies got the colic unless their mothers warmed the milk at the police stations, which had generators. The police also saved the population from Neolithic perils to health by storing serums and vaccines when the drugstore refrigerators stopped. But near Hyannis the cows went all the way back to the Paleolithic: the mechanical milkers could not work and the cows, nearing the bursting point, lowed piteously while the neighborhood sorrowfully stood around in total ignorance of how to milk a cow by hand.

Such is the tomorrow that is taking shape. One prediction about society looks safe: there will be a world government. It will have a difficult birth, with all the cultures whose differences have to be reconciled; and both the One Worlders and the King Canutes of the present may be wrong in their hopes and fears. But if ever there were a visible trend in culture, here it is. If, in Peru and Mesopotamia, larger and larger states followed one another, and if nations in Europe could proceed even temporarily to empires like those of Rome, Austria-Hungary and Great Britain, then the collapse of distance and the growth of giant economies, and communication that can spread news around the world faster than it can travel around a Neolithic village, certainly are doing everything to push that trend along.

But do not ask when, or what kind of world government. I can only assure you that our social problems are going to be harder than our mechanical problems. Our culture passionately loves an engineer, and will push on fiercely to turn the dream of the future into the kitchen of the present, though I think that the great discoveries to come will be in biology, not in engineering. But how can we really predict much? If less than five thousand years intervened between the first farming and the first civilization, in the Near East and the Americas, and if the same space fell between the first civilization and the recent revolution in science and industry, then how can we possibly imagine life ahead of us except as a glorification of what we already have, entailing a few thousand years more?

For we cannot guess what new departure might be the key to the age after the Atomic Age. Could hunters have looked ahead to the life of farmers? Could the farmers have foreseen the cities of the Bronze Age? Could the Sumerians have imagined electricity? You can help yourself to any brave new world you want, for culture is a very changeable thing from one thousand years to the next, and you cannot foretell its distant shape any more than that of the next cloud.

The proper study

This kind of forecasting is not the main business of history. Forgetting about man himself, and trying to peer into a future of gadgets, is picayune stuff compared to the understanding of the present that we might achieve by looking at men and their institutions together, not separately. Culture is a merry-go-round, but no matter how gaudy it may be, the real thing is not the machine but the sensations of the people riding on it, as it goes faster and faster. And man is the more constant, because he changes biologically at a very slow rate, not like mercurial culture.

Consider this: the very same kind of man lived thousands of years as a hunter and then, when farming suddenly presented him with the brand-new social problem of living in larger groups, he turned out to be entirely capable of meeting it and forming new kinds of social organization. And, as culture then shot up, ordinary men, surprisingly, were able to keep pace with some of the most intricate inventions. Who would have thought it, ten thousand years ago? In fact, when we finally understand how it happens that human beings had seemingly become much too intelligent for the life they were leading, we will know an important secret of the evolution of mankind in the first place. And yet even this is not something unique. Chimpanzees, also, seem to be unnecessarily intelligent for the life *they* lead. And why should higher Primates have so much better color vision than most animals anyhow? Because they have a poorer sense of smell? Here we are up against some of the more devious workings of evolution, in which there seems to have been a certain amount of luck.

But if we do not yet know everything about evolution, we are not thereby relieved from trying to understand human nature through evolution. There are still people—in diminishing number, it is true—who feel it is wicked to believe that men evolved out of simpler animals and who, at any rate, are greatly distressed at the idea themselves. Doubtless they think that man cannot be an animal without being a beast. Certainly we will all be much happier when evolution has ceased entirely to cause qualms, and is quietly accepted like the idea that the earth goes around the sun, another opinion that was once good for a visit by the Inquisition.

For there is every nobility to animal life, and—do not laugh—man is a noble animal. He is a creature who got where he is through the fire of evolutionary trial, which made him ever and ever fitter for his world and for the possibilities toward which his kind of body and brain (that of Primates) had pointed. His animal background is a billion or two years long, and it is a good background to have. He has a sound physique, intricate as it is, and sound kinds of natural behavior, unless he is actually the joker in the animal kingdom, which hardly stands to reason. He comes by his title of the highest form of life by legitimate descent. His existence is no cockleshell upon the deep, for he is healthy, long-lived, adaptable and well adapted; and he has moved into a cultural world that puts the rest of nature at his disposal.

This existence is not entirely an untroubled one, it must be granted. Humanity has had severe cultural indigestion on occasion, as we seem to be having now. Cultures are clashing, spoiling the harmony that any might maintain by itself. Europeans ban Indonesian headhunting, and Indonesian culture rocks. Westerners offer the Middle East an oil economy, and the Middle East, the provider of farming and of civilization, now has a culture so backward that it cannot cope with this offer except by surrendering to it. Inside a rapidly changing culture, like our own, brash new parts buffet crusty old parts until the latter crack and fall or, more usually, change in nature without changing in name.

And what about ourselves? How civilized are we? Are we all civilized or only some of us? You can call a culture civilized when it has cities and a broad trading economy, and when some of its citizens are similarly cosmopolitan as individuals, meaning that their loyalty and responsibility are toward the culture as a whole. But it may have in it a great class of people who could be called Neolithic, not because they are farmers but because their loyalty is to their own little tribe, the we-people, and not to society as a whole, and who take very poorly to being transplanted. Then, of course, there are those social gibbons and baboons whose loyalty is to themselves alone.

But all this is doubtless largely due to degrees of education and upbringing. Perhaps we could actually have a civilization all of civilized men. There are other differences among men—between brothers—coming from the chance combination of the multitudinous genes a man receives, and this kind of difference must always be present, from its biological nature. Hence, inevitably, some men must be more teachable and more inventive than others can be.

Does this mean that, starting from the rock-knocking of which Pekin Man was capable, the demands of human living have begun to move up along the scale of human intelligence and ability, until they are putting severe pressure on people at the lower end? It is true that kitchen apparatus is beginning to look as though it needed a female engineer to run it, but otherwise daily life is nearing the push-button stage and putting a mechanical strain on nobody at all. In fact, it doubtless encourages simpletons to sneer at Navaho and Zulu, who could certainly push a button with the best of them if they had buttons to push.

No, if our culture is putting a strain on the least able end of our population, it is doubtless in the hidden intricacies of social and political life, at which every man is his own expert no matter how pithecanthropine his ethics or his approach to his own large society. For human affairs today demand both brains and responsibility. These are things that the baboons among us despise and deride, as the marks of an egghead and a do-gooder. But the simple fact is that, after a million years, culture has begun to rush forward and overtake natural human mental and social capacity, and it is not going to ease up on us. We are probably going to need all the brains we have while we are waiting—and it will be a long wait—to evolve some better ones.

Here we are probably at the central point of the relations between culture and the animal out of whom it grows. Does it mean we are racing to chaos? Are we going to fall into the gears of the thing we ourselves have made? Not likely. For we have two bulwarks that seem pretty sound.

One is the tremendous power of man to learn and to use his culture. There are, of course, individuals of limited or defective mentality, but we have no real evidence that most men are near the limit of what they might do—near the end of their capacity to react to culture—with the right teaching and exertion. It is true that one may be more impressed by the extraordinary skill of hand that a man or woman may achieve than by the degree of actual, articulate thought human beings generally use (as distinguished from making conversation by opening a mental closet of clichés and prejudices). It might make you think of chimpanzees, so quick and active and alert in most ways, but so deeply reluctant to speak the simplest words. But the horror of true thinking may be more a matter of culture and teaching than of the final boundaries of ability.

The other thing is the great potentiality of culture, the many possible choices still to be made, which we have not even approached. The hundreds of tribes and states have tried many solutions to any problem, and there are many others, still waiting in the wings like unborn children, which may do better if they can find a way to be admitted to a trial.

Let us look on some of our own greatest institutions in this light. As Europe moved from its barbaric Iron Age into civilization, it was faced with the problem of finding new parts of culture by which to put a large society together. Rome contributed common law and common citizenship. Christianity gave Europe a common set of ideals and a freemasonry of knowledge. Later, the northern peoples brought forth representative and constitutional government. Our American Constitution and the system flowing out of it is a giant piece of social and political machinery. It is no accident. It is a crystallization of a whole heritage of self-government by a free, literate society, which was put together by a group of men thoroughly educated in their own history, practical idealists who knew their culture well.

And look how it works, in cultural terms. It encourages different groups to co-operate and interact fruitfully so as to form a massive society like ours: it does not spell out leadership or triumph for any man or group of men, nor guarantee a workers' paradise, but instead calls forth the efforts of all to make an equilibrium that is generally right for its time, and will change when it is not right.

It recognizes that some of the basic facts of culture change as well, in the interplay of liberal and conservative. Our Constitution does not even mention the two-party system! And yet it so works that the forces of invention and liberalism are always active, while the forces of stability and conservatism also never sleep. In the latter there lies a resistance to change that sometimes seems purblind but always is necessary, to ensure that the one change of culture is not revolution but evolution. Thus the introduction of the new is prevented from making damaging cracks in what is old; while the crust of the old is prevented from keeping out the addition of the new, when the new is needed to arrive at a fresh equilibrium.

So our ancient institutions, revised from time to time, have enabled us to construct a very large society, while still giving freedom and economic ease to the individual. This is a marvelous thing. Our constitutional forms are so complicated that it is wonderful they are also so rugged. Forming large societies is a difficult achievement. Although their states were far smaller, neither the Bronze Age peoples nor the Greeks had such freedom as we have. Nor, of course, have many modern states. It is hardly necessary to point out how primitive by comparison is a dictatorship of any kind. Such a borrowing from the Incas belongs to the first chapter of civilization, not the latest, and it lacks the recognition of the nature of culture change that democratic government has.

The lesson? Only that we should be loyal to our culture, understanding what it does for us, and that we and it must stand or fall together. Culture must evolve or it must die; but, because culture hangs together like parquetry, the only healthy change is a slow one. We have no choice but to be a partner in all this, and the most successful society is that whose culture calls forth the best from its citizens and responds to the best in them in turn. Man, society and culture are all one, Siamese triplets who must die together, not separately. "Know thyself" means knowing all of these. Says Lord Tweedsmuir, in his essay "The Other Side of the Hill":

> *An open and flexible mind, which recognises the need of transformation and faithfully sets itself to apprehend new conditions, is a prerequisite of man's usefulness. But those who take my point of view will try to bring all change into harmony with the fundamentals drawn from the past. If the past to a man is nothing but a dead hand, then in common honesty he must be an advocate of revolution. But if it is regarded as the matrix of present and future, whose potency takes many forms but is not diminished, then he will cherish it scrupulously and labour to read its lessons, and shun the heady short-cuts which end only in blank walls.*

Author's Note

In this book I have tried to make a single story of the human background. I have not attempted simply to make a preface to history by telling about ancient man, nor to describe certain primitive institutions merely for purposes of discussion. I have wanted to bring together fossil skulls and island trade, so as to make something understandable out of our past for anyone who might like to know about it in a general way.

Trying to make as much sense and as little mystery as our knowledge will allow does not mean parading all the knowledge. It means choosing this and that, trying quite deliberately to create for the reader an impression that, though it cannot be complete, is not an untruth. I deal with the importance of classical clans in Melanesia and parts of Malaysia. I contrast them with fiercely complicated Australian kinship systems. If I neglect to say that kinship systems almost as awesome are indeed found also in a part of Melanesia, and suggested even in Southeast Asia, it is to protect my picture not from being damaged but from being obscured, which is sometimes worse. The exceptions, the irregularities, the inconsistencies are endless, and they are necessary elements of culture and the study of it. Of course to ignore the exceptions consciously would be intolerable in professional writing. But, in carrying the fruits of all the work out of the profession and into the hands of a public who is kind enough to want to know what the anthropologists have been doing, digestive interpretation and condensation—call it "processing" if you like—is a task and a responsibility which cannot be avoided.

In reconstructing history I have used what seem to me the most conservative interpretations. I have sometimes, though not always, suggested reasonable alternatives, but I believe the ideas I have set forth are generally near the center of gravity of my colleagues' present opinion. Such interpretations are apt to be less instantly exciting than those of the occasional Don Quixote who finds his very own explanation of the origins of civilization, let us say, and writes a book in its behalf, as his way of tilting against the professionals, with their allegedly moss-grown prejudices. But you will find that the professionals are usually forced into the conservative position—to defend the classical music against the jazz—more by the weight of all the knowledge, and in fact by awareness of all those exceptions I have left out of this book, than by any will to conspire against clairvoyant amateurs.

I hope that this may help explain why many things are not mentioned, and also why footnotes are rare, whether to indicate "ifs" or "buts," or to acknowledge sources of information. I am grateful to the host of writers whose ideas and materials I have used, and I hope they will recognize them and accept my thanks. Some of my colleagues have read parts of the book and given me much appreciated advice. This does not necessarily mean they approve of everything I have written, but I acknowledge their kindness warmly. They are Drs. D. W. Ames, D. A. Baerreis, M. L. Barnett, M. Fowler, C. W. M. Hart, G. Herzog, E. A. Hooton, P. MacKendrick and H. L. Movius, Jr. In addition, my own wife, mother, daughter and son have severally acted as the most helpful guinea pigs imaginable; all have survived, and I thank them with my love.

Index